HARD sho

HAR

D
shoulder

PETER WOODS

NEW
ISLAND

HARD shoulder
First published October 2003
by New Island
2 Brookside
Dundrum Road
Dublin 14

www.newisland.ie

ISBN 1 904301 23 1

British Library Cataloguing in Publication Data.
A CIP catalogue record for this book is available
from the British Library.

Typeset by New Island
Cover design by New Island
Printed by CPD, Ebbw Vale, Wales

New Island received financial assistance from The Arts Council
(An Chomhairle Ealaíon), Dublin, Ireland.

10 9 8 7 6 5 4 3 2 1

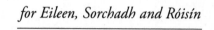

for Eileen, Sorchadh and Róisín

I WAS TRYING TO PUT A NAME TO THE COLOUR OF THE morning. The skies were leaden with rain and the glow of the streetlights reflecting off the underside of the clouds had the same aubergine colour as the ink I learned to write with. There were rubbish bags stacked up all along the kerb. The odour of rot spread out over the Broadway. There was talk of moving the Army in — already it was being called the Winter of Discontent. The streets on the way to the tube station were empty, apart from the Turk, who was sweeping out his doorway. Nobody knew if the Turks ever slept — they were open for breakfast already and would still be open for dinner twelve hours later, when we were coming back. Dinner was the same as breakfast except for the addition of pork and lamb chops to the menu. Later they would serve kebabs until the crowds leaving the pubs had gone home. Then it would be time to get ready for breakfast again. 'Cold, *arkadash*?' he said as I passed. It was never warm.

I could see a group of men up at the corner. Spumes of breath rose above them like a racecourse on a frosty morning.

They hung back against the brick wall as if it might offer them some shelter. One or two of the younger ones were kicking out at thin air, some of the others looking on suspiciously, as if they envied this extravagant display of energy. Others still were rolling thin cigarettes from the remnants of dried-out tobacco — "Wormwood Scrubs Specials" as they were called. You could see their narrow points pulsing like heartbeats in the gloom. They weren't saying much to each other. There wouldn't be much to talk about in any case — words seemed to diffuse in the air. There was, in truth, a suspicion of words that went all the way up to the men they worked for, as if words should be measured against work: work left undone. Also, the men were suspicious of one another — why arm your enemy? The less he knew the better.

The vans that would take them to different parts of the country hadn't begun to arrive yet. The Broadway was where life was recycled; every day there was another chance. These were men whose lives were equally poised between a night in the Redcap or The Camden Stores and a trip to Golders Green Cemetery. What mattered was looking willing, as if a day's work wouldn't kill you — have boots, will travel. The older ones could tell of times when they had to have their own shovels. Murphy had his shovel with him when he came over on the boat from Cahirciveen or some place or other like that. You could see the Big Subbie of a Sunday, they'd tell you, their voices lowered in awe, emerging from his Roller up at the Priory on Malden Road for Mass. The Big Subbie and his marcelled, ermine-draped young wife. Him bent over. Some of them spoke with a note of pride, as if the Big Subbie's position reflected positively on their own.

That first morning I was only watching — or so I told myself — half-afraid to make a move. I knew that seven or eight pound a shift was good money on the Broadway. The going rate elsewhere was between eleven and fourteen. Fifteen or sixteen pound was top money and would never be got on the Broadway. A pound alone was the entrance fee, the price of twenty fags or some rolling tobacco and a couple of pints. Tax was something you might pay in the bookies. Men were paid every night or subbed up tight. You never knew if the man you were working for would be back tomorrow. You never knew whether you'd make it from bed yourself. Most of them would return to the Redcap or the Blackcap or the Mother Shipton to spend the day's money in any case. Some men would have subbed the price of the breakfast before they'd got out of the van and would continue to sub incrementally throughout the day. All that would be left at quitting time would be the entrance fee.

And there was always the possibility that you might be landed somewhere you mightn't get a breakfast. In a field the far side of London, left without shelter. Finishing a job in the rain, standing round in damp clothes until evening. Maybe left alone altogether to find your own way back, dodging fares on the train.

That first morning two men behind me — who seemed to have met for the first time in a long while — were unusually voluble.

'Who're you out with now?' one asked the other.

'Fallon from Ballycroy.'

'Any good?'

'A fuckdog to work for. A hungry bastard. Do you see that pair yonder?'

'What pair.'

'Over there beyond. That pair. The pair of auld Donegals. They smell each other, them fuckers.'

'What about them?'

'A right pair of toe-rags the pair of them. There's hardly a day's work in them. All they're fit for is tea-boys.'

There was a pause then as they looked about for another victim.

'Do you see that young fella over there? Pure Mayo.'

'The red face on him. Reared under the hen's arse. Too many fuckin' eggs.'

They both began to laugh. Just then a van drew up across the road and there was a desultory surge away from the kerb. One of the two men pushed me out of his way.

'Move there young fella,' he said, 'you're using good men's air.'

'Mr Fallon, Mr Fallon!' he shouted, pushing his way up to the butty little man who'd got out of a Commer van with the British Telecom logo painted over on its side. Fallon was wearing a check jacket, his trousers pushed into his high-sided rigger's boots.

'Push back the fuck there,' he shouted, as the men began to elbow each other in an effort to get into the back of the van. Fallon blocked their way. 'Push back the fuck and let me see ye. Ye'll not make breakfast half of ye.' He began to laugh uproariously.

'Mr Fallon, Mr Fallon!' the first man shouted again. 'Hearty, a townie of your own. A Partry man. I was out with you last week. Out in Barnes.'

'I remember you,' Fallon said, 'mouth in trousers. You're no townie of mine.' 'Mr Fallon, I can work sir. I'm a right handy man. Got a mate with me too. Galway but he can't help that.'

'Shut the fuck up and get in then,' Fallon said.

'What type of work is it and where are we going?'

Fallon rounded on him. 'You want a fucking job or a geography lesson? Get in the fucking van. You two?' he pointed at two men standing near. 'I'll try you two and that's it.' Seconds later the van had disappeared, its exhaust belching, off the Broadway.

By half-eight the last van had long left, beating the traffic on the roads out of London. I was still standing there. There were a dozen or more others, mostly late-comers. Old boys past work anyway. I'd watched the men jockeying for places in the vans. How they knew the subbies and how the subbies knew and avoided many of them. How the very young and the very old weren't wanted. How men with long hair were ignored. The seemingly casual glances that would take in the state of a man's footwear, whether he looked like he might have been out before. One man stood off to the side, his arms wrapped about himself as if to keep warm. He rocked over and back in motion to some music only he could hear. The skin on the right side of his face was missing. It looked as if someone had taken something abrasive and went to work on it. I could actually see his back teeth clattering. One eye was turned away in its own direction, cast off into another world. Every time he'd got into a van he was unceremoniously dumped back out onto the ground again. He picked himself up and tried again.

'Ah, the poor Rocking Horse,' the old man beside me informed me, 'the poor Rocking Horse.'

'Who is he? Why is he called the Rocking Horse?' I asked.

'He was alright one time. Well-to-do like, a subbie himself, like. They say he crossed some tinkers. Something to do with tarmac-ing. They came back and got him and rolled him in the hot tar. He was never the same again, they say. That's one story anyway. Sure he's here every morning. Everyone knows him sure.'

So there was myself and another young fella, the Rocking Horse and a few of the old men left. The old men held a desultory collection amongst themselves to see if they could raise the price of a bottle of cider. The newsagents beside the Turks was open. I drifted off down the road on my own. I was wondering what had brought me there. It was the beginning of the winter of 1977, though it felt like it could have been a hundred years before.

I'd left home at the start of the summer. I'd had enough. There was a new Government and the night I'd made up my mind to go I was in Mayo, in Castlebar. The whole town seemed to be celebrating the election of a new TD. The TD was there himself. He was wearing a black suit and every hair on his head was oiled into place. He was shaking hands and promising people everything. I could hear people going on about Frank Stagg and the way he could be buried now. Frank Stagg was already buried. He'd died on hunger strike in England and the Coalition Government refused him a paramilitary funeral. He was taken under armed escort across the country and interred under reinforced concrete in North Mayo. There was a permanent guard on his grave. It was one of a series of episodes that seemed pointless, beyond satire. I could hear people saying he was going to be reburied within days. It was like we'd fought an election over a man's funeral. I could hear a chef I knew, a Belfast man, whispering into my ear about Fianna Fáilers with guns. There was drink flying everywhere. The new TD gripped my hand. 'Congrat-ulations, Mr McBride,' he said. I wondered what I'd won. I wondered what I was doing there.

You could, if you were minded, learn a lot on the Broadway. The biggest lesson and the hardest to take was that you gave no quarter. That young fella with the red face, 'Young Mayo', might be about my age and twice my size but that made no difference. If you had to talk you talked fighting talk. You used words like flurries of punches. If you had to fight you fought. You lamped him off. There might be a scuffle in a pub where you'd hope the men about you would be interested enough to step between you, to haul you apart, back to your barstool where you could eye your adversary in the corner over a pint, muttering to yourself and your companions. There would be times when they'd be slow intervening — sixty seconds is a long time in a pub fight — or they might not be bothered altogether, they might relish watching two men fight it out. You realised quick you were no longer in the schoolyard, a realisation that happens to most boys when their bones harden and blows begin to hurt. You kept out of the other man's range, maintaining an eye on both his hands and his feet. When you struck you struck decisively. You hit first and as hard as possible and you followed it up immediately. A boot in the balls, the head between the eyes, these were the things that would do the trick.

As for the young Mayo fella with the red face, I would come across him again. One day of incessant rain he would slip in a trench and drop a sodden railway sleeper onto my foot. I saw stars and fell over backwards into the muck. The sleeper broke some bones and because I was only getting paid when I showed up for work, I continued to work. The bones eventually set back themselves. When the weather's cold I still remember young Mayo with the red face — he has yet to age.

2

THE NEXT MORNING I MADE IT INTO THE BACK OF A VAN. There was no great scuffle involved, neither was my worth mysteriously recognised. I left the house at six and was on my way to the Broadway early, passing the sacks of refuse that had begun to stink: thick, globular, putrescent trails running along the gutters. The tabloids were screaming for an election. We were in the middle of a recession, something that passed unnoticed on the Broadway, just as an economic boom might have.

I'd passed the Crown and was already beginning to shiver when a van pulled up. It was a newish Ford Transit, and unusual in that it had windows in the back.

'Looking for work young fella?'

I nodded.

'Six pound a day …'

I walked on.

'Alright then, I'll start you at seven.'

'There's no hurry,' he told me, 'none of my boys would be out of bed yet.'

He introduced himself as Frank Dunne before turning

the van around and driving off towards West London. We
pulled over at a café in the White City at the back of
Shepherd's Bush. All the roads around there were named after
battles in the Boer War or former colonies, Blomfontein
Road, South Africa Road, Canada Road, even the pub we
passed was called the General Smuts. I doubted that whoever
named them had possessed any great sense of irony,
nevertheless they would have been surprised by the
percentage of Black and Asian faces on the streets in the
White City. The place was run down. Dunne drove through
the flats complex and parked up. Then he thought better of
it and moved off again. I could see the central courtyard area
of one block of flats with the refuse bags stacked a storey high
like a vast potato pit. The stench was overwhelming. Dunne
bought me breakfast in the café. It was a quarter past seven.
The woman who served us said, 'Did you hear the one about
the Paddy who bought the Evening News? ONE THOUSAND
JOBS IN JEOPARDY it said. Off goes Pat to Euston Station.
"Give me a ticket to Jeopardy," he says.' She went off laughing
to herself. Dunne made an indeterminate sound. 'Fuckin'
English,' he said, 'think we're all thick so they do.'

We picked up two men outside the café. They were both
English. Dunne promoted one of them to charge-hand. 'You
know the score Bert,' he said, 'job's on Coyningham Road. A
week's work gutting out a house. It's not our work. I only
priced the gutting out. That's all we're doing. A week's work
now, do you get me? After Friday I won't be making money
and neither will you.' Then as an afterthought he added,
'Take this young lad with you and see what he's made of and
no swinging the lead.'

He dropped us off at the house and before he could get
back into the van both men had hit him for a sub. He subbed
them reluctantly.

Whatever I might have expected, this work was infinitely
worse. I spent the day pulling down ceilings. We made a hop-

up, two scaffold boards between trestles. The idea was to make a hole in the ceiling with a shovel. Then force the shovel into the hole and lever the laths and plaster loose. It was an old house. The plaster had been mixed with horse hair and spread on the wooden laths. It was impossible to see through the clouds of dust. There was soot in the ceilings and the soot adhered to the skin like grease. Within minutes I was coughing and spluttering. The two Englishmen left me on my own as soon as the pubs opened. Dunne had subbed them the entrance fee. I found out later that the best way to knock down the ceilings was from above. To lift the floorboards, shut the door on the room below and drive the whole ceiling down. Then wait for the dust to settle, water it all down and begin to bag it. It was a better way of doing things, though not by much.

And the bagging was just as difficult, the wooden laths ripping the plastic bags to pieces. They had to be carried downstairs and skipped. Bag after bag, room after room. It was afternoon when the skip arrived and there was still no sign of the two Englishmen. I had pulled down all the upstairs ceilings before they came back, smelling strongly of alcohol. Bert wanted to know why I hadn't the skip filled. I kept my mouth shut. The two of them began to shovel the debris into bags while I carried them downstairs. The laths with their small nails were cutting into my back and lacerating my hands. By quitting time I was dizzy from work, as all I'd had to eat was a sandwich and a bottle of milk since breakfast. Sweat began to form a frozen film on my forehead when I stopped.

'What about Dunne?' I asked. 'How am I supposed to get home?'

'If you facking think Yeller Dunne gives a fack about how you get home mate, you've 'nother think coming.' They both laughed, then Bert softened and explained that we wouldn't see Dunne until Friday. He'd expect the whole house to be done by then. We might be able to drag it out until Saturday but

Dunne wouldn't pay a full shift for a half-day's work. It was up to us. He told me to go off and clean myself up. When I asked him where, he said there was a water butt out the back of the house. I found the barrel under a down pipe. It was full of rain water. I caught sight of my reflection for the first time that day. The whites of my eyes were all I could discern. My face was blackened with soot and my hair stood on end. My torn hands ached as did my shoulder and back. There was a bruise on my shin where I'd got hit with a flying scaffolding board and I'd also managed to stand on a nail. I found a bottle of washing-up liquid. There was nothing for it. I immersed my head in the freezing water and lathered my face and hair.

It was almost completely dark before I reached the tube station on Shepherd's Bush Green. There seemed to be an ethereal glow about it, people ascending and descending into the depths, their eyes fixed in front of them, like fantasy characters. I drew some strange side glances on the tube with my torn clothes and bedraggled appearance. People edged away from me. One way or the other I'd arrived in London. I'd got a job. At that moment an oddly comfortless thought.

As the week wore on the amount of time the two Englishmen spent in the pub decreased. They were running out of funds. They cursed Dunne for staying away. They cursed the work itself: they said we should have masks and that it was only donkey work. The talked about good jobs they'd been on. 'Painters mate is what we is ...'

By Friday we'd almost finished gutting out the house. Pulling down the ceiling and demolishing the internal stud walls. Hacking sand and cement plaster off those walls that adjoined the neighbouring houses with a hammer and bolster, each blow sending a shock wave juddering as far as the elbow. Occasional blows missing the bolster and hitting knuckles. Everything bagged and skipped. We'd torn out the bathroom and ripped out the lead pipes. The Cockneys kept the lead and any copper they could lay their hands on. Beer money for Saturday they assured me. 'Scrap isn't what it used to be. Need a war Pat. Don't worry, you'll get your cut.'

Despite all the work done Dunne found plenty amiss. We hadn't cleared the nails from the joists. 'Like this,' he said, jumping on the hop-up and running the shovel along the timber until it was shorn of the small nails that hadn't come away with the laths. 'That's just more work for the tackers,' he said, 'and I'll hear all about it.' There were areas where the sand and cement had proved particularly difficult, patches still to be cleared. Bert told him we would need a Kango gun to finish it. 'Kango me arse,' Dunne said and took up the hammer and bolster. He hammered in a frenzy for about five minutes. 'That's how it's done,' he said.

Dunne took out a bundle of wage packets and looked through them. He gave the cockneys one each. Then he pulled out another bundle, this time of cash, from his pocket and counted out five five-pound notes and three ones. He gave that to me. 'I'm going your way,' he said, 'if you want to get in. It's four now, you're not going to set the world on fire in an hour.'

I sat back against the front seat in the minibus and seemed to feel each individual vertebra in my spine, as if they had been permanently twisted into position for shouldering bags.

'What do you make of it so far?' Dunne asked.

'It's OK.'

'You don't see your future in it then?'

I didn't answer.

'What about those two. You don't think a lot of them do you? Where did they spend the week? In the pub?'

I said nothing.

'It doesn't make much differ' to me. I know they're a lazy pair of cunts but what can a man do? There's not much else about. They leave all the work to you then?'

I still said nothing.

'I thought so,' he said. 'Where are you for the weekend?'

I told him I had no big plans, thinking I wouldn't want to, with £28 to show for four days' work.

'You're not scratching are you?' I asked him what he meant. 'Signing on the dole,' he said. I said I wasn't and he nodded. After that he didn't ask any more questions. We were stuck in traffic all the way up the Harrow Road, a continual belch of exhaust fumes, vans unloading men all the way along Kilburn High Street until St John's Wood where the gardens around the houses were bigger and there were fewer people on the streets, no corner shops or pubs and a better class of car in all the driveways. The glow cast by the streetlights seemed to gather in a haze about them. Already the pavements had begun to glisten with the first covering of frost. In the van the heater was on and I had to struggle to stay awake. Occasionally I came to only to discover we had hardly made any ground.

Dunne dropped me at the top of Kentish Town. 'You'll find,' he said, 'I'm not a bad man to work for.' Giving me to understand that I'd emerged successfully from some kind of a trial period and that I also had something to be grateful for. This, I realised, was as near as I would come to being offered a contract. I was being offered a job — of sorts.

'Can you make your way to Isleworth for tomorrow morning?' he asked. 'That is, if you want to earn a few bob.'

I asked him where that was and he gave me directions. It was on the other side of London, near the Airport. I told him that all this travelling was costing me money and asked where was I going on Monday. Isleworth was further away than the Bush. Dunne nodded ruefully and pulled £10 off the wad of notes.

'I'll see you tomorrow, half-seven sharp,' he said. There was almost a hint of menace in his voice, having been parted from his tenner.

I used to go to Hyde Park on Sundays, to Speaker's Corner to hear the religious revivalists and the rump of socialist agitators take on those who harangued them. There were always people about selling various socialist newspapers and tracts and I would argue with them — asking what they intended to do about Ireland. This interruption would cause a momentary pause in the rhetoric, an air of bafflement, like finding the wrong person in your bed. Ah yes, Ireland.

Well, I'd say, your army is over there isn't it? They'd nod acquiescence and then they'd confer. What was the policy on Ireland? Was there a policy on Ireland?

In those years, though we didn't know it, the great socialist experiment was skittling to a halt. The Labour Government was a minority one, and as my friends in Hyde Park would have informed me, wasn't socialist in any case. There were strikes everywhere. Britain had been admonished by the World Bank. The Speaker's Corner socialists saw all of this as the prelude to a revolution. Coming from a country that had just abolished rates and car tax and was giving out sizeable grants to anyone who wanted to build a house I was all for a bit of revolution. I had my doubts though. Anyway, what about that policy on Ireland? They said I should come to one of their meetings.

The meeting took place over a pub beyond the Angel, near Old Street, at that time a run-down part of London. It was a working-class area — how working-class an area was, I'd noticed, was measured proportionate to the amount of people not working — but it was the sort of place where revolutions historically festered. I was excited about the meeting, a bit of brigandage, consciousness raising, class solidarity — a good argument even. I bought a *Teach Yourself Marxism* book and would read it in the house where I was staying — much to everyone's consternation. I went straight from work to the pub that night and had two or three pints before anyone else arrived to settle my nerves. There was much of the small child about me: I lacked confidence surrounded by strange accents and wouldn't be far off pawing

glass or swinging off the door otherwise. The meeting started
late and the first, and it appeared only, item on the agenda
was newspaper sales or the lack thereof. Two hairy behemoths
rose to do battle over the division of sales' territory. It
appeared that one of the brothers had invaded another's
pitch. They argued back and forth. By this stage I was on my
fourth pint of insipid lager. I could feel it fizzing nicely inside
my empty stomach. I said I was going to the bar to get a drink
and made the mistake of asking did anyone want one. They
all did.

When I came back the conversation had turned to the
price of drink and whose round it was next. I remembered
from my reading that Karl Marx in London, exiled and in
isolation, an isolation 'corresponding to our position and our
principles', believed the revolution was about to begin in
1855, when an attempt was made to shut the pubs down on
Sundays. Half-a-million people assembled in Hyde Park but
the Government gave them back their beer. The incendiary
moment passed.

I could bear it no longer. I took to my feet.

'Ireland,' I shouted.

'Guinness,' someone responded, like it was a quiz
question.

There was silence then. The arguments stopped and all
heads turned towards me, waiting for me to make some sort
of point. I burped.

'I came here to talk about Ireland and it sounds like a
board meeting of the *Daily Mail*.'

'Now hold on,' one of the behemoths insisted, 'I say, the
Daily Mail …'

But I responded that I had spent the past few months
attempting to divine their policy on Ireland, and had been
assured that I would get an answer at this meeting. If I was
going to join I needed to know where they stood on Ireland.
Again there was that air of bafflement.

I seized the moment.

'Look,' I said, 'even the Labour Party … even the Labour Party has a policy on Ireland.'

There was a man in the corner who'd said nothing. He stood out because he had very short hair. There were murmurings about him. Anyway, he took my part.

'He's right you know,' he said.

'What — who asked you?'

'Well,' he replied weakly, 'I just don't think we should be over there.'

This seemed to galvanise them. I was asked to step outside the room for a few minutes while they conferred. I went downstairs for another pint of the fizzy lager. The barmaid served me and gestured upstairs.

'You with that lot of fucking wankers?'

I nodded and made my unsteady way back up to the room. The Rolling Stones were on the jukebox — *I was there when Jesus Christ had his moment of doubt and faith*. I was about to be put out of my misery, or so it appeared.

Well, they told me, it was simple really when you thought about it. Once the British Working Class had thrown off its shackles they would then turn and solve the Irish problem. What precisely that meant, even after Historical Determinism had taken its course, they were weak on. Perhaps I was thinking of the two Cockneys on Coyningham Road, for I wasn't convinced. I told them so. I said Ireland wasn't just an adjunct to Britain and that I wasn't a hundred per cent on what Labour's policy was but it couldn't be as bad as theirs — waiting on a revolution in England. Then, perhaps still thinking of the Cockneys, I asked them about guns. There was an appalled silence.

'Guns,' I said, 'you know. Bang. Bang. Things you generally need to have a revolution.'

This threw the room into confusion. Someone said I was obviously the Fuzz. Some sort of *agent provocateur*. My friend with the short hair said I had a point. He was told to shut up again. Someone else said I was drunk, and I heard one of the girls I knew from Speaker's Corner say no, I was like this all the time. They turned on her. She'd obviously been taken in by me. I was about to be expelled from the cadre before I could properly join. I left the room quietly, amidst all the confusion, and had a last pint in the bar. I was getting to like that beer. I told the barmaid that I agreed with her diagnosis of the custom upstairs. She asked me if I'd noticed the man with the short hair — a copper, she said. I asked how she knew and she said she knew to see him around. Then she said she thought I'd come in to plant a bomb.

My jaw must have dropped because she winked and said, 'But you wouldn't do that Pat, would you?'

'Would you?'

Unwittingly she'd stumbled on the crux of the whole matter. We were on dangerous ground in those years, in the immediate aftermath of Guildford and Birmingham. One man I knew swore the people serving time for those atrocities were innocent. His was one of the very few voices raised then and he wasn't in the audience the night those jailed for Guildford appeared on Irish television, sporting Louis Copeland suits. That was when I truly came to understand the meaning of historical determinism. But that was all well in the future. What was happening in London in the mid-to-late Seventies was both insidious and almost universally pervasive. It was like the soot from those ceilings. It could be washed off, but would somehow always re-emerge from the pores. It carried the unmistakable tinge of fear. It meant you crossed the road to avoid trouble. If you were Irish you kept your mouth shut.

Of course there was an Irish MP for Islington North back then, strange as it is today to think of the Islington Labour Party run by the Irish. Not that you'd have known then either. The Irish vote had long Labour associations and the Irish in

Britain had a long history of radical politics, going back to the Chartists. But there was something else afoot in those years. The Labour Government had lost its impetus, had failed to deliver to its own supporters; the words "Trade Union" had increasingly negative connotations; the Tory Party were lead by a woman. There were also National Front marchers on the streets, and although some might argue that they achieved little, their language and agenda did filter into mainstream politics. In any case, any thoughts I had of radical politics foundered after that night with the bar-room Politburo.

That Saturday morning in Isleworth Yeller Dunne became the first of many Irish I met who would refer to that Tory woman as someone who meant change and change for the better. Isleworth was a substantial suburb just past Richmond on the map. A quiet place with lots of large, detached houses with gardens where you could hear birds singing. There was a cricket ground near the house I arrived at. There was I thinking that Dunne was keeping a low profile — the way he had his minibus pulled well back from the road. It took me several minutes before I realised that this was his own house, and it only occurred to me because of the way he lumbered about the kitchen, the way he knew where everything was. For Christ's sake, I told myself in retrospect, wasn't he wearing slippers? His wife, he explained to me as he made a cup of tea, cooked school dinners. She was back in Ireland on holidays with the children. I had a days' work clearing out his garage. He kicked out at the uncollected rubbish bags lining the side of his driveway. The unions, he told me, were a scandal. The days of their power over. He was voting Tory. He'd never voted before but someone else deserved a chance. Labour had made a mess of the country.

I spent the day sorting bandstands into their various sizes. Lining up scaffold boards along the walls, deciding which pots of paint could be reused and which skipped. His garage

was full of the detritus of ten years' site work. Everything
lumped together. He had enough lead bagged to keep the
Cockneys drinking for many a Saturday morning. There were
bags of tools for every trade, men he'd subbed who
disappeared: they could be all dead now for all he cared, the
cunts, he told me. Shovels, spades, forks and brushes. He also
had a 1965 Jaguar up on blocks that he'd taken in part-
payment for some job he'd done. By lunchtime I'd filled a
skip. He returned and made sandwiches, asking me into the
kitchen. He watched me looking at the washing machine and
dishwasher, the Aga cooker and utility room with a shower
built-in.

'Not bad for a bollocks from Mullinahone,' he said.

I said I never knew he was from Cavan.

'It doesn't matter much where a man's from over here.
There wasn't much Mullinahone ever did for me. Not a lot
back there anyhow. I'm going back though. I'm going to buy
a pub just to show them, the fuckers.'

I had little need to ask him why. His little eyes lit up
when he said that. Vengeance is like a genetic defect in us. It's
what's stiffened many a man's back. I watched him cross the
kitchen floor to make more tea. The crotch on his trousers
was down about his knees. Dunne was about five-and-a-half
foot and his tailor must have had a time of it with him. His
toes turned inward as he walked, giving him a shambolic
look, as if he was without direction. His face had the colour
and blandness of a bucket of wallpaper paste, not that of a
man who'd spent most of his life outdoors. He had altogether
the aura of a fire that had never quite ignited. But what he
had, suited him. Everything about him made others under-
estimate him, but there were, in truth, few men whose
opinion Dunne held in any regard, nor was I one of that few.

When he'd told me he wasn't the worst to work for he
was right, by his own standards at least. He was a subbie
after all and all subbies remembered the men they'd worked

for. The Elephant Johns that would boot a young fella up
the arse to see what his reaction would be. Then mercilessly
beat the head off him if he squared up to them. The men
that would set you on the wrong road, that wouldn't pay
you. What mattered was being a man of your word — even
if it was just your own word. If others didn't like it, then
they could just fuck off. There were rakes of men out there
looking for work.

On the other hand I could go up the Archway Tavern
on a Sunday morning and meet men from Inis Meáin. They
would explain to me that the subbies were crippling the lot
of us. One of them was in the union and working for
McAlpines on the cards. He had his money every week
whatever the weather was like. But it was around that time
that the big firms, the Wimpeys and McAlpines had taken
to laying men off. Firms were taking on apprentices,
keeping them on the books until they'd got their
government pay-outs and then letting them go, two years
before their time was finished. Then they took on a new lot.
Direct labour was finished. If our past had been cursed by
the subbie, our future too was pledged to them.

'How long are you over now?' Dunne asked, returning
with the pot of tea.

'Six months or so.'

'Are you going to stay or are you going back yonder?'

I said I hadn't made my mind up. I was thinking of
staying.

'You want to get out of this business. There's no future in
it. Who have you at home? Have you land?'

I said we had no land. My father was dead and my
mother still alive. He nodded.

'At least you want to get a trade. You went to school.'

When I told him I'd done my Leaving, he looked up,
astonished.

'Then what are you doing at this crack. Couldn't you get

a job in a bank or something. Jasus, anything's better than this. Anything where you don't have to dirty your hands?'

I had no real answer to that. What I had in mind was only half-formed and I feared he would think I had a few wires loose — ends all but casting dangerous sparks about the place — were I to try to make my thoughts cohere on his kitchen floor.

He left me as far as Hammersmith that Saturday afternoon and pressed another crumpled tenner into my hands for my efforts. He would see me, he said, at the gates of Terminal Three, at Heathrow Airport on Monday morning.

I made my way back to the house in Kentish Town. The house was maybe ten years old. It had an extension as big again built onto it. It was purely functional with only one concession to luxury — a black & white television. There was a fridge that it was impossible to keep food in. It's difficult to explain a house like that to anyone who hasn't lived in one. There were anything between twelve and sixteen men living there. There were fights over everything, over food, over cleaning, over who left the window open. Fights in the middle of the night in the room you were sleeping in. I once saw two men fight over who would hit the third man first. It was ten pound to share, thirteen pound for the single-room and there was just the single single-room, as the landlady told me.

I shared with three others. Who they were varied, sometimes by the week. There were two men in the house who were near my own age. One was Fermanagh Tony and the other called Diffley came from Galway. I was to become very friendly with him. There were essentially two types of people in the house: there were those like myself and Tony and Diffley who, with some degree of luck or ambition even, might escape the place eventually. Escape the place in the sense that the house was generic, that it was typical of any one of hundreds of houses, flats, B&Bs, self-styled hotels and glorified flop houses that the likes of us gravitated towards. Then there were the older crew, those who'd been well through that list. And for them, as long as they could muster the rent, this house was as good as it would get.

The Boxer Finnegan who came from Athlone was emblematic of that crowd. He was on his last chance, except that nobody had told him. We were all afraid to. He'd return from the pub every night and do a few rounds, shadow boxing, awakening anyone who was asleep with his own commentary: 'And Finnegan has the great Ali backed up against the ropes … a right and a left and the champion goes down on the canvas.'

He claimed to have been an Irish Army Champion. I was afraid of him — the way you might fear an unpredictable animal — and watched the way he asked questions continually, not through any pursuit of knowledge but in an effort to keep conversation going, like a child. He had a great fear of silence. In that sense living in the house suited him. It was rarely quiet. There were always ongoing spats over who had eaten whose food. It was, in its way, as tiring as work. Eventually it would quieten down, only for the silence to be disrupted by Johnny Lambe's return from The Adam and Eve, his unsteady progress upstairs, his coughing fits, while he muttered to himself, 'Die you bastard, die.' Then The Boxer would come in, and in the dark of our room, throw a flurry of punches into thin air. A discarded item of clothing might catch his foot and he'd keel over — wakening anyone who'd slept through his entrance. No one ever told him to stop and he'd invariably run out of steam of his own accord. When I rose to go to work I'd see him crumpled, half-on/half-off his bed, fully clothed in the thin morning light. In truth there wasn't much to him. He looked spent and deflated, a trickle of spittle running constantly from his mouth onto the pillow. The ends of two Sainsburys' bags poked from his boots as he slept, one hand in his pocket and the other clenched on the pillow above his head.

—————————————

3

FOR THE NEXT TWELVE MONTHS HEATHROW AIRPORT formed a kind of axis in my life. It was a place I would return to again and again, the return determined time after time by work. It was true, I'd flown in there six or so months before from Dublin, on the evening I finished my Leaving Cert. I had £10 and some loose change in my pocket. The Irish pound was linked to Sterling. The conductor on the bus looked down at the Irish coins I handed him. 'That it, Pat?' I nodded. He dropped the money into his pouch. 'Same size anyway,' he said. I got off the bus outside a pub. Went in. Asked for a job and was pulling pints ten minutes later.

Terminal Three was an altogether different experience. The Yeller took me through the gates and onto the site and introduced me to the agent. He was a man with a clipped moustache and an obvious military bearing, standing to attention in an office full of plans. And he obviously wasn't happy to see Dunne either.

'This,' he said lugubriously, 'is not all that I'd hoped for.'

He looked me up and down like a miniature Montgomery, unimpressed with the latest batch of recruits sent his way in the sands of North Africa. Outside, the site hummed in the early morning, men shouting at each other and concrete mixers chugging relentlessly. Everywhere there was activity. Dunne drew him aside, far enough out of earshot so that all I could hear was an occasional word or two. 'I'm working on it … no reneging … better tomorrow.' Then drawing me by the arm down the stairs from the office, he took me to a relatively quiet corner of the site and handed me a scaffold pole.

'Stick that on your shoulder and hold onto it like you wanted to shag it,' he told me. 'Keep moving. No matter what happens, keep moving. If anyone asks who you're working for, you don't know. You were landed out here this morning and you're getting picked up this evening. That's all you know. And keep out of your man's way. I'll have it sorted for tomorrow. Just keep moving. Give the fuckers nothing to talk about.'

So it was I spent my first day on a building site, walking in endless circles with the same piece of scaffolding on my shoulder. Like a conscript again, on the eve of a great battle, ignorant of what, if any, design my superiors had in mind for me. It was not at all what I'd expected. I watched the other trades at work and noticed how there appeared to be a demarcation among them. How they worked independently of each other. The agent emerged from his office once or twice and I scurried out of his line of vision. I noticed how he appeared to direct only a gang of Asian labourers who seemed to be in charge of keeping the site clean. Like myself there were several of them whose sole job it was to walk about with the implements of their trade on their shoulders — in their case yard brushes. There were more of them than there was work. On the other hand they were at everyone's beck and call and were asked — unfairly I thought — to clean up the mess created by other people. I began to feel that the choice

of a scaffold pole was a good one: it gave me a status of some
sort, though of what sort I couldn't be sure. For the better
part of the day I was ignored. After a while I began to believe
that the Asians were truly vital to the cohesion of the site: no
sooner had an obstruction fallen in the way than they swept
it up or stacked it in a neat pile with others of its type,
knocking back nails and, towards the evening, covering great
heaps of sand with heavy canvasses as protection from the
overnight frost. I didn't know it then, but those Asians were
already virtually redundant. The time was coming when
everyone would be responsible for their own mess. On sites
driven by the price-work ethic, men would move as if on sea-
legs across great piles of rubble and discarded timber, nails
protruding dangerously. But that was a future then only half-
realised.

I gradually began to realise that my hours were more or
less my own. If I wasn't supposed to be there, then who would
notice if I wasn't? I had decided then to head for the tube
station when someone shouted, 'Here mate. Throw that up
here.' I looked up to see a man perched above me on a single
plank. 'The tube, mate. Pass the tube up.' I took the pole off
my shoulder and eased it towards him. He gestured to a pile
of similar tubes behind me and I passed those to him as well.
He in turn passed them to two men above him who attached
them to the frame already built. After about an hour of this
he told me it was time to knock off. 'Will you be back
tomorrow mate?' he asked as we moved towards the gate. I
said I didn't know. He asked who I was working for and I told
him what Dunne had told me to say. He shook his head.
'Fucking typical,' he said. 'That's the thing about these big
jobs, mate, no one knows what the fuck's going on in this
place.' The scaffolder was right. It occurred to me over time
that while the likes of an agent or engineer might have plans,
and the likes of Dunne had schemes, the likes of me was
caught somewhere in the nexus between the two. It was a

while anyhow before I had an inkling of Dunne's intentions and, even then, I questioned whether he was wholly informed of them himself.

The next morning I met him in the same place, only this time he told me to get into the van. There were four men already in it and I could tell that they'd all seen better days. Dunne made no introductions. He drove off towards the far side of the Airport and stopped in the middle of nowhere. Heathrow is vast and from where we were there was no human habitation visible on the horizon in any direction. We'd pulled up beside the only feature of note in the landscape, a large heap of gravel. Dunne bundled us from the van and handed us shovels. 'Start spreading,' he shouted.

We began to spread the gravel in all directions. Within minutes the other men had lost interest in what we were doing and had begun to talk amongst themselves, rolling cigarettes. Dunne roared at them and they started to work again. Their work pattern was fitful though, as they were given to inertia, to staring off into the distance. I worked on anyway, beginning to wonder what was the point of it all. A machine would have spread the pile of gravel in a few minutes but to what effect? What was the point in spreading a pile of gravel in the middle of a field? Only later would I spend a day shovelling muck into the bucket of a digger while the driver sat smoking, only starting the machine once the bucket was filled and emptying it into the skip directly beside us. Either I could have shovelled straight into the skip, or the driver in less than an hour could have cleared all the muck off the road. But that wouldn't have kept both of us gainfully employed — an agent looking on.

The gravel wasn't half-spread before Dunne told us to stop. One of the men decided he was spokesman for all the others and demanded to know where we were going for breakfast? Dunne ignored him. He tried again, pointing out that every working man had a right to know where the canteen was, where the bookies was and where the pub was. The other men looked at each other uneasily. Dunne told us to get in the van. As we sat into it, we watched him walk about the pile of gravel, placing shovels and forks standing in the ground at strategic intervals. He came back and dragged some old coats from beneath our feet. These he draped over the tools. Then, nonchalantly, he reached into the van and dragged the man who had questioned him from the front seat, and immediately began to pummel him about the ears. 'Talk back to me would you, you toe-rag!' he screamed.

The man lost his footing on the pile of gravel, stung by the ferocity of Dunne's attack. As he fell over backwards, Dunne swung his boot into the man's ribs. He drew back to kick again, struggling like a small child does to maintain balance and kick a ball at the same time. His second blow went high, glancing off the fallen man's cheekbone. Dunne then fell over the recumbent form on the gravel, onto all fours, panting. Drawing himself up, he turned back to the man who was now curled into the foetal position.

'You can fuckin' make your own fuckin' way home. It's youse,' he said, turning to the rest of us, 'it's youse has us the way we are. Youse and the bookies and the pub landlord. Well if that's what youse want, youse can fuck off too. Fuck off back to the Broadway where I found youse, youse shower a shite.'

He got back into the driving seat. I was sitting beside him and could hear him muttering, hunched down over the steering wheel. We took off in a shower of gravel. He was going on about no man being subbed and how he would get a day's work from everyone, even dossers. All this was under his breath. I could see where his knuckles were pure white on the wheel. There were small stones embedded in his hands.

We moved onto another site and repeated the process. Scatter a bit of gravel and leave evidence of our having been there behind us. It happened four times in all that day. After what had taken place in the morning the mood was sombre for the rest of the day. It hadn't lifted by the time he'd dropped us off at Hatton Cross tube station, at the edge of the Airport that evening. Dunne made some effort to mollify things, there was a weak joke about subbing money and he thrust five pounds on each of the men without asking whether they wanted it or not. We were almost in Hammersmith before anyone spoke. The oldest of the men, whom I'd vaguely recognised, asked me if I was long out with Dunne. I realised it was the man who'd told me about the Rocking Horse. I was half-embarrassed by the question.

'I got the start last week on a renovation up in Shepherd's Bush. There was only a week in it.'

'He shouldn't have done what he did to Geraghty. Auld Geraghty is harmless. He was only having the crack with him, all that about the bookies and the pub. Wouldn't any right man be able to see that? There's no need to raise your fists to any man.' The other men nodded. The old man reached across to me. I shook his hand.

'So you're not one of his men?'

'No,' I hesitated, 'didn't I tell you I never met the man before last week?'

'He's the worst kind, jumped up. Spent all his life working in the Hoover factory on the Westway. Took his redundancy and set up as a subbie.'

'How do subbie,' one of the other men said.

'What do you mean?' I asked.

'Well sure that's not right work. He has some class of a deal going on there with an agent or something. Oh, he'll make a killing if he can keep it going long enough. But how'll he keep it going if he can't keep men there — he'll have to keep some class of men there.'

'How'll he make a killing?'

'It's easy knowing you're not long off the boat. Dead men, that's what he's at.'

'Dead men?'

'Isn't it as plain as the nose on your face? He has four sites, if that's what you'd call them. Say he has five men down on each. All day-work. He's getting paid no matter what's done. That's twenty men in all. I don't know what a subbie gets for a man but if the good ones are paying £14 a day then it has to be £20. There has to be some cut in it. What's twenty times twenty?'

'£400,' I said.

'Smart, isn't he?' They all laughed.

'Well, don't stop,' I said.

'So, say he's giving the agent a backhander. Say he's giving him £100 a day. That would be plenty but say he's giving him a £100 a day. Then take the likes of us. How much are you getting?' he asked me.

'I think it's £9 now.'

'You only think. You'd want to know with that greeshen. We're all getting seven. Alright, you couldn't class what we're at, work. Still, even taking his petrol, just say he's paying off two hundred a day between us and the agent. He's still making two hundred. That's a thousand a week for driving a van round in circles. That's good money these days and they go on about a recession. There's never a recession for them fat fuckers.' The man thought for a minute, then said, 'The likes of you, a young lad'd want to get out of this game. There's no future in it.'

No one said anything. We sat looking at our feet on the journey into central London. It was a long way back to Kentish Town. When I came out of the tube station I was no longer thinking of people disappearing into the subterranean depths. I was thinking of Dunne. How everything he did appeared deliberate. He waited before he picked the fight with Geraghty. I could see him weighing up what the opposition would be like, whether or not he could catch it off-guard. Even losing his temper seemed like a ruse. Everything was designed. Like the windows in the van, not for the comfort of the men, but so that anybody looking could count the number of men he had. It was a numbers game.

I confided in Diffley back at the house. It was a Sunday morning and he was standing at the cooker. When I'd come in to the kitchen he'd been giving out to the bacon he was stirring about in a pan. Calling it English bacon and saying it was useless and full of water. When he realised I was watching he turned round and grinned and asked me if I wanted some? I said I didn't mind, I'd give it a go. He turned back to the cooker, muttering under his breath now, as much as anything for my benefit, I felt, as if he believed I'd been entertained by his monologue. He was wearing a suit. It was a good suit I knew. I'd seen the jacket lying where he'd left it, hiked on the backs of chairs, without a label and obviously hand-made. Yet he seemed ill at ease in it — as if it weren't quite properly buttoned or one sleeve was longer than the other. I thought he cut his own hair but perhaps I was being charitable. This was the era of DIY hairstyles — some of which cost a lot of money. Still, it was wild and wiry, protruding from his head at angles. He grinned again as he tipped four slices of bacon onto a plate, taking care to keep the white liquid in the pan. Grinning broke the look of furrowed concentration that was usually on his face, as if everything were riding on the moment. I like to tell myself that I saw then, for the first time, how he was one of those people whom strangers readily approach. That he had that rare gift of empathy, was one of those people you unburden yourself to and then wonder — later — at what you'd done: telling yourself ruefully that your secrets are safe with him. We ate in silence. Our breakfast was almost the antithesis of food, there being little difference between the limpid bacon and the sliced-pan that tasted like cardboard and stuck to our teeth, heaped on a plate in the centre of the table, coated in greasy margarine that looked like a skein of motor oil on a puddle. Diffley poured tea from a tea-pot, giving out about how unnatural tea-bags were, though the tea actually tasted good, strong enough, with a jolt to it that might have been described as bracing. He then asked me about the other people in the house. There wasn't much to say about them, I said, I was only there a few weeks. 'They are alright,' I said. 'You have to watch your food though or it gets stolen. Anyhow it isn't the Paris Ritz.' He asked me if I was going home for Christmas? I told him I likely was. And then I told him about Dunne. I was, I suppose, less than happy. Diffley didn't really say anything. When I finished talking he left enough silence so I could take up again, saying, 'But sure what can I do? I'm stuck with him till after Christmas one way or the other?'

We went up to the Adam and Eve that Sunday morning. It was still a local pub then and every Sunday the same crowd was at the bar, done up in their Sunday best. The bar was bedecked with plates of sausages and cheese and crackers. Men and women called for drinks that seem arcane now, pints of mild, light & bitters, black & tans, Martinis and velvet porters. There were tables of twenty-five players and darts matches going on. English pubs which had a tradition of admitting children on Sunday mornings shut at half-two then. We emerged into the winter sunlight, light-headed, half-defeated by alcohol, and went back to the house where we sliced up and fried the roast I'd bought. Two of the old boys were snoring on the couch.

When Fermanagh Tony came in he suggested we go to the cinema. He said there was a new film showing, called *Close Encounters*, which was meant to be very good. We took our places in the cinema. Tony went off to the toilet and, upon returning, took up a seat separate to the rest of us. Diffley elbowed me and I looked across to see Tony take a slug from a whiskey bottle hidden in a brown paper bag. The film, as it turned out, was worth seeing. That was until the closing sequence when Tony stood up on his seat and proclaimed to one and all: 'None of you believe it but I saw it. I saw it. They came for me.' He looked across at myself and Diffley, who was already moving to the entrance. We made our way hastily up the street, turning back to see him accosting people as they emerged from the cinema, an evangelical glint in his eyes.

At that stage the Adam and Eve was just reopening its doors. Myself and Diffley entered and ordered two pints. We thought that Tony would by now have made his way home. Instead he'd followed us.

'No one believes me,' he said, joining us at the bar. I made to move away from him but Diffley tugged at my sleeve.

'So what happened then?' he asked Tony.

'It was like this, I was going down this alleyway, see — you know the one, between the Paki Shop and the canal — it was a week or two ago. It was dark when I seen this light in the sky, see? Cigar-shaped it was and it came down and hovered over my head. Then it turned and disappeared back up where it came from. It was moving so fast I could hardly keep up with it.'

'Obviously no sign of intelligent life,' Diffley said.

'Fuck you,' said Tony who then moved down the other end of the bar.

'Well,' Diffley said, 'you have to say it's a bit of crack.'

I told him he was alright: he didn't have to share a room with Tony and The Boxer.

Diffley was on the road most of the time and never had to put up with what went on in the house on a daily basis. He had a job on a drilling rig and travelled all over the south of England soil-testing for civil-engineering projects. He earned almost as much in subsistence as he did in wages. Diffley also had a big romantic streak in him. He was always going on about the poetry of work, about rowing currachs and the perfection of motion. He drew up images of lying on his back in a boat on a fine day, the waves off Inis Oirr flapping dolorously against the gunwales. He could talk to anybody and on almost any subject. He was affable without being in any way diffident and had the ability to let you feel — in an argument — that you'd talked yourself out. That he was holding fire, letting you get away with it. Even The Boxer liked him. All of this cast my own tribulations into relief. I was almost ashamed to describe what I was doing as work, although work it increasingly was.

For a start the supporting cast varied almost from day to day. The original four men were long gone. The nearest Dunne could get to keeping a steady crew was to sub them half what they were due every day. Enough for a night's drinking and even then men disappeared, sent their friends as far as the van on a Friday to pick up what they had coming. Dunne pulled over at the Adam one evening and got talking to one of the men at the bar. He was complaining about the quality of labour that was available. The man finished his pint and said, 'What do you expect and the money you're paying?' I looked down into my own glass, feeling the odd itch of shame. Dunne finished his own drink and left.

He had taken to confiding in me — exactly why I never knew. Perhaps he thought I could understand him. Maybe he saw something of himself in me. Both his son and daughter were attending good schools in the Home Counties. His son was a rugby player. 'That'll be useful in Mullinahone,' I said in exasperation but it passed over his head. There was no element in his make-up that questioned how his teenage children would adapt once they were living back in the middle of nowhere in Cavan. He took what I said at face-value. What was important to him was that his children understood what it had taken him to get where he was. I could have told him that I didn't doubt they knew where he came from, but what meaning did that have for them?

Once I heard him arguing with one of the men who'd failed to turn up for work the day before.

'Jesus Christ, you're only working three days a week. Why's that? What good's three days to any man?'

'Well,' the man says, 'if you were paying right money … do you think if I could earn enough in two days to go drinking for three days I'd be working three?'

The logic was irrefutable and there was little Dunne could do except live with his frustrations. Every day brought the pub in Mullinahone that bit closer.

It was a Friday evening that he first detoured about the back of King's Cross and pulled the van over at a point where we had a view of the deserted gasworks.

'That's where a man should be pitching in,' he said, 'places like that that no one thinks anything of. The future you'd say.'

'How's that the future?' I asked, looking out at a wild overgrown wasteland, a no-man's land between the council flats and canal, five minutes walk from street corners and pubs filled with whores.

'There's a change coming in this country. There's an election coming and there's going to be big changes after it. No more unions. No more useless Paki labour like on that site out at Heathrow. The men that sees that'll be able to make money.'

'Aren't you making handy money now? What more do you want?'

'A drop in the ocean,' he said, 'that's the problem. Youse boys don't understand that. I'll tell you this though, this country's gone to the dogs. The change is wanted. We have to stand up for ourselves. The country has to stand up for itself.'

I supposed he was just short of saying the white man had to stand up for himself, though he wasn't. It was his use of the word 'we'. He had never voted in an election in his life. I always voted, would always vote Labour. I was even, on occasion, to canvass, forlornly, for Labour. But I could never rise to use the word 'we'.

In terms of work the burden was coming increasingly my way. Dunne was still driving relentlessly between four or five 'sites' on the boundaries of the Airport. It was as if miniature civilisations grew up around the piles of gravel. One day a lorry load of kerbs would arrive in one place, in another a load of pipes. Dunne would get out of the van and set out a roadway, a radius and a run of kerbs leading from no defined point to somewhere farther off. I would spend a few days laying the kerbs on my own. Hard work in that a kerb which weighed almost as much as I did had to be individually wrestled into position, boned into line using a wooden mallet and two pieces of timber fixed into a T, then backed up with a dry concrete mix. It was the same with the pipes which serviced nothing. No doubt the fiction was that the rest of the Airport would eventually catch up with us. Occasionally the work was even inspected and on one occasion the pipes tested. Blocked off at both ends by a Clerk of Works and filled with water. Despite the apparent pointlessness of it all, I still took delight in that there were no leaks. A good job was being done.

I'd moan to Dunne about how hard I was working. At that stage I was on £11 a day and getting Saturday work. My outgoings were £10 for the room, as much again for food and another £20 to see me through the week. Once or twice, almost involuntarily, Dunne reached into his pockets and dropped me an extra tenner. I was expecting to have about £300 going home for Christmas. Atavistically almost, I understood that what you showed at home was far more important than what you actually had.

Diffley was sick of the road. The Donegal man he was working with barely spoke to him. Most nights they slept in the back of the rig to save their subsistence money. He was working in towns on the south coast where there were naval bases: places, he said, where Paddy wasn't welcome. He was half-fed in B&Bs and grim lodging houses. He was so hungry, he said, that he was forced to eat that ham in plastic packets, the one where it was difficult to distinguish the ham from the packaging. It was then that he first began to talk about going to Germany to work.

In the house things were getting worse. The Boxer's behaviour was growing increasingly erratic. Half the time he didn't have the money to drink and lay on the couch before the television. He was either elated — usually when drunk — or a morose and brooding presence, objecting to everything and existing on a diet of TV soaps he'd increasingly come to view as reality. One of the characters in a soap was on the run for something he hadn't done. The Boxer had begun to identify with him, blaming the politicians for his plight. He complained that it was a story the News refused to cover. At first the rest of us treated this as a joke until it became obvious we were the only ones laughing. I'd lie awake at night, waiting for him to come spluttering into the room. Sometimes he walked past the door, muttering to himself, 'Fifteenth and final round. Seconds away.' Some of the other men complained of waking up to find he'd joined them in bed. They insisted that there was nothing improper in this beyond the act itself. Fermanagh Tony was talking of leaving the house. He'd got a job in Bracknell in Berkshire on a concrete gang. The idea of collective action against The Boxer seemed beyond us. It was like the school bully — what if we did gang up on him and then the first man to act found himself left on his own? We could see no other way of dealing with him other than confronting him on his terms, by fighting him. Tony said we might try throwing a few fucks into him but what difference would that make? 'He'd be too thick to notice. What we want to do is go up to the room some night he's asleep, pull the bed-clothes up over him and beat the head off him.' Tony was staring across the bar at the optics when he said that, and neither myself nor Diffley made any comment. The subject was not broached again.

The house was deserted most of the time. If he wasn't there we feared his return. There was nowhere else to go except the pub. This was a very common condition and it was why pubs thrived: companionship. It was still possible to get three pints for a pound. Men talked of a full shift as ten pints or more. They made their way from their work vans to the pubs and stayed there, wending their ways home, anaesthetised against their surroundings. I tried — mostly unsuccessfully — to think of ways around this. Tony had totally succumbed and hardly even bothered to wash his clothes any more. Every Saturday he bought a new outfit, a cheap suit which he wore to the dance in the Galtymore on Cricklewood Broadway or the Gresham on the Holloway Road that night and out onto the site on Monday morning.

I went home that Christmas into what in a few brief months had turned into an irredeemably different world. I got off the bus in the town and went into the chip shop to see if there was anyone about I knew. There wasn't. It seemed a new generation of school-goers had sprung up over the few, brief months I'd been away, although they still had Neil Young's mislabelled 'After the Goldfish' on the jukebox. The house was warm, quiet, and there was good food on the table. I stood beside my mother at Midnight Mass and felt almost cosseted. But there were people there I barely knew, younger people who'd changed, who'd grown somehow, yet they all knew who I was. I recognised few of them. What I did recognise however was that I was beginning to grow apart from where I'd grown up. That I was more impatient than I had been. That I had to stop myself from expressing this impatience, something I wasn't entirely successful at. I watched my mother look at me as if I was someone she didn't really recognise. She remarked on my hands and said there was little excuse for the condition they were in. I felt this was her way of making a wider point. All the while one question lay between us — was I going back and if I was, for how long? It was a question that was never directly asked, nor was it answered, except insofar as I got on a bus back to Dublin after two weeks.

There was a lull in work at the Airport in the aftermath of Christmas. Either that or Dunne was falling out of favour. Even if some of his schemes were in abeyance, his demeanour hadn't changed. He was using the time to retrench. He commandeered a Portakabin and installed a gas ring. One of the old boys was detailed to cooking duties. There were always three things on the menu — in line with a great London Irish convention — namely meat, meat or meat. London was full of conventions like that: another one was that you shouldn't jack in one job without having another one lined up to go to. Things, I was told, would begin to improve after St Patrick's Day and into the summer. I knew I couldn't stick another three months with Dunne. It was Tony who came to my rescue. He said there was work going with the concrete gang out in Bracknell. He talked about concrete all the time. He made it sound like hard-going. There was something in what he was saying that suggested, deliberately I was sure, that I wouldn't be up to it. Dunne had a pork chop halfway to his mouth, there was grease running off the end of his chin, when I told him I was jacking it in.

'You've something lined up then?' he said.

'I'm going out with Duffy's to Bracknell … Concreting,' I added, as if unsure of myself. It was all he needed. I could see the gleam appear in his eye.

'Do you think you'll be fit for it?' he said. 'It's not every man can stick that sort of work.'

He spent the next three days acting as if I'd personally affronted him. He didn't speak a word to me. If he wanted me to do something I was addressed through a third party. There was no offer of more money and certainly no thanks. It was as if he'd turned his back on me and walked away, hiking up his trousers.

4

LONESOME TOM WAS THE NAME OF THE GANGER ON THE Bracknell job. I got into the van beside him and Tony the following Monday. Tom was over six-foot tall and had an appetite to match. He'd spent most of his life digging tunnels underground and was, as I found out later, something of a legend. He was of that generation that elevated physical strength above most else, and, when it came to strength, Tom had few parallels. I once saw him lift a bag of cement with his teeth. There were a group of post-office engineers on a floor of a building we were working on — this at a time when one of the most successful programmes on television was about feats of strength — and they were placing bricks in a line and attempting to lift them up. Tom walked over, set a bag of cement on its end, bent down and picked it up with his teeth. The veins in his neck were bulging like canal systems seen from aloft. The post-office men scattered silently in all directions.

He had a fierce type of morality. Most of this, I believed, resulted from being the father of five daughters, some of

whom had reached adolescence, and he had a keen sense of
what men were capable of. In the big things you told the
truth, played it straight and lived with the consequences.
Authority had to prove itself and was something you were
always suspicious of. In these arenas men like the Yeller didn't
measure up. Tom also had his own prejudices, based not on
creed or colour but on where a man came from. A West
Corkman himself, he was hired out at the age of eleven in the
north of that county to a strong farmer from Mallow. He
mistrusted those from that area and Cork City men, who, he
said, made their way from one Fords Factory to another. He
had a developed sense of injustice and a long memory. He
talked about how he'd been let go from a heading — a
tunnelling job — in the week before Christmas because it was
discovered he wasn't from Kerry. Kerrymen also rated near
the top of his list of dislikes, up there with time-servers, pen-
pushers and factory workers. He was all for a rumbustious
lifestyle, where there was nothing wrong with settling things
with your fists. I never saw Tom fight, he never had to. What
he had done more successfully than anyone I'd ever met was
create his own mythology. He suggested things about himself.
His sheer physical bulk was off-putting enough. There were
stories about how he'd cut the rungs off a ladder and left a
Clerk of Works stranded in a tunnel shaft over a weekend or
how he'd chased one of Murphy's agents — a man with a
wooden leg — down the Holloway Road with a saw in his
hand. Tom would smile at these stories. If something
rebounded on him he would say, 'Well I never told you that.'
He hadn't, but neither had he denied it. In that way he was
an inveterate storyteller. When I first expressed doubts about
something he'd told me, he smiled and muttered something
about there being nothing wrong with the odd white lie.
Something that was told to move the action on, if you like.
He was a master of the wind-up. Even now, years later, I still
find myself wondering about some of what he told me —

doubting the veracity of it or wondering just exactly where 'the white lie', the exaggeration, began or indeed ended.

On my first day in Bracknell I discovered that the concrete gang only existed in Tony's imagination. Instead we were part of that great class of worker, 'general labourers' or what later became known as 'general operatives'. Diffley probably defined what we did as well as anyone one night in the Bunch of Grapes in Kensington, when the two of us were approached by a pair of Englishwomen.

'What do you do?' one of them asked him.

'I dig holes,' he said.

'And what does he do?' she said, pointing at me.

'He fills them in after me.'

That first day in Bracknell was the day I spent shovelling muck into the bucket of the digger while Roy the agent looked on. Roy, needless to say, was on Tom's list. I once got talking to an old Irishman in a pub in Camden Town: 'The English,' he told me, 'think we're all thick. There's two ways of going about it. You can prove to them you're not thick or you can go along with it. But if you go along with it you can get away with anything.'

That was how Tom dealt with Roy. Roy didn't really believe Tom was stupid but he didn't see what he could do about it. Roy was what Tom classed as 'a firm's man'. 'He'd be up the road the same as the rest of them if things got tight,' he observed wryly. In this at least, he was right.

The digger on the Bracknell job was an RB, a machine that even then was antiquated. The only other place I've ever seen one since is in a picture. Whereas modern machinery works on hydraulics, the old RB bucket was guided by chain and swung dangerously loose. It was also extremely difficult to drive. Our driver was John McHale, better known about Hammersmith Broadway as 'Fighting' McHale. If there were ten men alive who could drive the RB, John wasn't one of them. He struggled to come to terms with it. In the afternoon the first of several lorries arrived on the site. McHale was to fill them and at the same time clear a road about one side of the foundations of the new building. This development meant I had no longer to shovel into the bucket. Myself and Tom were to oversee the filling operation, clearing away any scaffold tubes or lengths of timber that ought not be part of the load. We watched with amusement as McHale swore continually. Several times the bucket got wrapped up in its own chains and we had to mount the front of the machine to free it. Within an hour there were four lorries backed up and the first one as yet unfilled. Tom was back talking to the lorry drivers as McHale grew increasingly frustrated. A level of paranoia had also begun to set in, and he kept asking me what the lorry driver was saying. Tom told me to tell him that the driver reckoned he wouldn't drive nails. The driver had said no such thing. McHale jumped down from the cab of the machine and made his way back to where the lorry was in line. He reached up and pulled the driver from the cab.

'What would you know about it, you Black and Tan bastard?' he screamed, throwing the man into the muck. 'Drive the fucking thing yourself!'

Despite what Tony had said, Bracknell proved to be a much cushier number than the Airport. And even when a couple of days later my first problem arose, it was as much a matter of whether or not my face fitted in as anything else. The real concrete gang who were inexperienced had made a bad mistake. For all the talk about concreting it isn't exactly an art form. Indeed, the major prerequisite is common sense. The concrete has to be kept moving at all times or it will go off. What happened at Bracknell was that as it began to go off they added water to it. An obvious enough ruse and one that would be seen as nothing untoward as long as you didn't get caught. You wouldn't do it knowing that the concrete was subject to testing. Or you would make sure that what was tested was what was poured before it was adulterated. This time however one of the columns the gang had poured failed the slump test and had to come down.

The column was eight feet across, two feet wide, and reinforced with steel. What you do to take it down is hook its top to a crane to take its weight and begin working on the bottom with air guns. An air gun is about two-foot long with a point another eight to ten inches in length. Powered by compressed air, they have a kick that would knock you backwards if you weren't prepared for it. When the air-line opens the compressor begins to rev up. The air fills the gun, the trigger twitches into position and the gun begins to shift involuntarily. It has a rattle that could shake the fillings in your teeth loose, that spreads up your arms and into your shoulders. The only respite is to bury the point in something and deaden the vibration, momentarily at least. Beginning on opposite sides of the column, myself and Tom were to cut into the base where the starter bars for the reinforcing steel had been tied into those from the foundations it arose from.

In normal conditions water begins to condense inside the air-line and in the gun. In freezing conditions the water also freezes, seizing up the gun, and it was well below freezing that day. My gun was continually jamming and that, coupled with the fact that I had never used an air gun before, meant that, to say the least, I looked awkward. On my side of the column I was making meagre progress, whereas Tom was going at a faster rate. In an effort to combat the water we were pouring diesel into the air-lines. The diesel sprayed out like blackened oil from the sump of a car, covering our hands, our clothes and splattering our faces. All of this was being watched by Geoff, the Contracts Manager for Wilments, the main firm. My gun was either jammed or stuck in the steel for most of that afternoon. No one else could work because the crane was held up. There was a great degree of humiliation in all of this. I felt I was being found out. It wasn't altogether my fault, but the fact that Tom was making greater progress than me told its own tale. We did eventually get the column over and then stopped work for the day. Tom was called into the site office. He told me later that Geoff wanted to get rid of me. He said I wasn't up to it. He was looking for experienced men. Tom told him that experienced men were difficult to find and how did he expect the likes of me to get experience? He refused to let me go. There was a stand-off that ended when Geoff backed down and said I could have a second chance.

At the time I was grateful to Tom for taking my part. I couldn't have faced the ignominy of going back to the Adam as someone who'd failed on a site. Tony would have made the most out of it. But — for what it was worth — there is little doubt that my future in the building game was assured that day. Within a month we had to take down another column, working well into the evening. The second time I had no problems with the gun and managed to keep pace with Tom. I remember walking back off the site and a relieved Geoff thanking me. The fact that a second column had failed was a major embarrassment for them. It was something they wanted to cover up and that was why it was a rush job to get it down. When Geoff thanked me I walked past him. I didn't open my mouth.

Within a week of my starting Tony disappeared. Tony had never been the best timekeeper and always missed too many days. On a job like Bracknell perception was very important. At times there might be little real work to do other than keeping the general site in order, but it was expected that a full gang show up all the time. On some jobs like that a foreman or ganger might come to an arrangement with the agent whereby they would book in a couple of men between them, splitting the take, but there were no dead men in Bracknell. Diffley had said it would suit Tony to have me working with him. I would make sure he got out of his bed in the morning. Tom's belief was that if a man began to miss

the occasional day he was in danger of the trend accelerating.
There wasn't all that much, he'd point out, between that and
the situation The Boxer had got himself in — especially for a
young fella. Tom, I found out, was suspicious of Tony. He
mistrusted his intent. What evidence he based his
observations on he never let on. Tom rarely questioned his
own judgement and saw himself as a shrewd judge of
character. He made his mind up about people very quickly
and rarely changed it. He had Tony marked for a downward
road. It was the Monday of the second week that Tony
refused to get out of bed. 'He can go fuck himself,' he said. I
didn't tell Tom this and said he would be in tomorrow. When
I got home that night everyone was in bed, everyone except
The Boxer. He had the lights off and the living room was lit
by the flickering television. There was a snooker game on and
he was traversing the room in his underpants as if he were
taking part in the game. I watched him as he bent over and
studied a shot, as he chalked his imaginary cue and stroked
the imaginary ball towards an imaginary corner pocket.

'You alright?' I asked.

'Never felt better,' he said.

I went upstairs. There was no sign of Tony anywhere. I
had an overwhelming feeling that we were building towards
something in the house. That Tony was liable to confront
The Boxer. It wasn't something that I wanted to witness.

By the end of the week I had subbed Tony a tenner. I
told Tom when he asked what Tony was doing for money.
He observed that it was cheap at the price. I asked him what
he meant and he said that it was often better to give someone
a few bob on the understanding that they couldn't come
back and ask for more. 'Still and all,' he said, 'I'd stick to a
fiver. A tenner's a fair bit. It's nearly a days' work to you.' He
didn't believe I would see the money again. But by the
following week Tony had another job. He said he was in a
concrete gang. I did get my tenner back, but in a sense it was

never really mine again. Tony had begun a series of peregrinations between different jobs. He never spent more than a few weeks anywhere. He'd borrow the money back in his time between jobs and pay it back as soon as he started again. There was nothing wrong with Tony as a worker. I never did get a handle on what had got a hold of him, on what was the difference between me and him. Eventually he got a reputation as unreliable, as being able to stick at nothing. For all that London is a big city, Tony's reputation began to precede him. He found it increasingly difficult to find work. He was left with a choice between casual work on the Broadway or moving on. He spent a few fitful weeks getting in and out of different vans. Then he disappeared, owing the landlady a months' rent and me the ten-pound note.

'It was,' Lonesome Tom said, 'typical of Tony to do a runner when there was work coming up.' Tom was in high spirits, the phoney war was over, our period of site maintenance was coming to an end. There was a big hole to be dug to service a series of post-office ducts. 'Some of it,' he told me, 'they'll have to dig out with a machine. But the machine'll not be able to get tight in. That's where we'll come in.' Roy the agent was looking for more men as well but instead of turning to Tom he'd asked Fighting McHale, the RB driver, to do the recruiting. This was site politics. The man we were working for wouldn't like it, that was for sure, Tom said. He blamed Geoff, the Contracts Manager and wouldn't talk to McHale. But McHale had no great design. He was trying to be obliging. He was hurt that Tom had taken to ignoring him and questioned whether he should have volunteered to look for men at all. It turned out to Tom's advantage though. McHale brought two clients out from Hammersmith Broadway. I used to spend a good bit of time about there and knew their faces well. They were dossers, more of the type who worked for Dunne. Tom could see that straight away the morning they got out of McHale's van. One of them had a limp. He was young enough, probably in his early thirties, but his head lolled from side to side and his eyes wandered off into the distance when you tried to talk to him. The other man was too old, too old in the sense that the likes of Geoff and Philip, the engineer, believed any man who was over fifty was too old. You could see that he could have coped rightly with steering a brush around if that was what was wanted. Roy the agent looked them up and down. He pursed his lips.

'I thought,' he said to McHale, 'you said you could get me good men?' At this stage McHale was fed up with the whole exercise. His face reddened and he swallowed.

'Well, if you think they're bad now, you should have seen the fuckers this morning before they threw away the crutches.'

They didn't last and Geoff had to come to Tom after all. That was how our gang more than doubled.

We picked them up on a Wednesday morning. One of them was Joe Hopkins, a Mayo man. A handy man, Tom said, he could build manholes and stuff like that. The other was an unknown quantity. When he got into the van he told us to call him T-Bone.

'And where are you from?' Tom asked.

'The good part ...' T-Bone said. I could see Tom's jaw stiffen. 'Kerry bastard,' he muttered under his breath. Then he brightened up.

'I hope you're fit for some heavy digging T-Bone,' he said.

The heavy digging didn't materialise — at least not the way Tom thought it would. McHale excavated the big hole and Wilments brought in two of their own men to mine under the Post Office and put in the ducting. They were both Cockneys and claimed to have been born within the sound of the Bow Bells. They described themselves as heavy-digging specialists. I watched Tom wince. We were at the start of a period of guerrilla war, though none of us knew that then.

I missed its early stages. I had been set to dig a series of trenches about the building for cable laying. I'd never done much digging before and Tom soon put me right about how I was holding the shovel. I held it with my hand over the top, rather than under it. I was effectively working against myself, an ergonomic disaster. Bad work was like biting your nails, Tom said. He showed me how, once I'd opened out the trench, I could cut a sheet of plywood and place a length of it in the bottom. Then, using the pick, I could knock the spoil onto the ply and have a level surface for shovelling off. If the ground was wet or when it rained and the muck was sticking to everything, I could coat the blade of the shovel in diesel which would form a protective layer over it.

Digging was all about rhythm and once you discovered that rhythm it would never leave you. It wasn't something that was given to everybody. He left me at it once he discovered that I had some sort of an aptitude. I was partnered with Hopkins, or Hoppy as he was called. Hoppy wasn't too gone on work and was relieved to see I was. He'd leave me alone for long periods. Sometimes I'd think of him and look up, resting on the shaft of the shovel, to see him wandering off somewhere, his head down, deep in thought. He had an odd way of walking, in which he kind of dragged his left foot behind his right one, kicking across the back of it. In time I found he had badly damaged his ankle after it caught in a piling rig. He walked with his head down and his hands clasped behind his back. If you didn't know him you might think he had the weight of the world on his shoulders, but he was usually only studying form. Then he'd come over to me.

'You alright there?' he'd say, nodding to himself. 'Boy, you can work boy. I'm going up to put a bet on. Do you want me to put on one for you?' Then he'd disappear until lunch time and I'd get lost in my subterranean world.

Lost was the correct term. The trenches were about three-foot deep and eighteen inches wide. Strictly speaking, at that depth they should have been timbered to stop the sides caving in. But the ground was good and held fast and there was no need of timber. Every man, they said, was his own safety officer and really nothing should be left to chance. A man I knew was killed in a trench that depth. He bent over to pick something up. A box of matches it was said. Everyone had gone off on a break. The sides came in on him. He would have been like someone in water. He panicked and couldn't distinguish up from down. The new, unlit cigarette was still between his fingers. Most people who died on site died like that — in undramatic ways.

What Tom had taught me about digging was to stand by me over the next few years. At times it proved an embarrassment. Men would say you'd want to keep at least one gear in reserve. The rhythm I worked with was fierce and unrelenting and often I had to be prevailed upon to slow down. You're not on price-work, they'd say. Make the job last.

I loved digging. Loved that half-subterranean world where there was only the smell of the ground, newly opened up and fecund, or hard, arid and abrasive underfoot. I learned to use the least amount of motion needed, conserving everything, pivoting in a short arc to fling the spoil far back from the sides of the trench. I could hear the short silences before the shovel bit again into the ground, my body rising and falling in fluid motions. I learned to recognise ground without opening it up. To largely avoid water. When I was working like that my mind was totally empty of thought, my whole body had a single purpose.

Whatever Tom thought about Kerrymen, he had a considerable ally in T-Bone as the two of them set out to ruthlessly undermine the Cockney Heavy Diggers. Tom appeared sympathetic, listening to the two men as they complained of the conditions they were working in. The job wasn't as straightforward as they'd hoped. They'd hit water which was seeping into the hole on top of them. It wasn't an insurmountable problem. It wasn't spring water, which has an awesome force, but was flowing in from under the road. Water has a relentless logic and will always find its own level. That, coupled with the speed it moves at — much faster than most people would estimate — means what appears as a trickle is lapping about your ankles in half-an-hour. Tom could have solved the Cockneys' problem: it was a matter of common sense. All they had to do was sink a sump hole and steadily pump the water from the excavation, but they were allowing it to build up overnight. It took the best part of the morning to pump the hole out and then they had to begin work. At lunch time they'd emerge sopping wet and caked with muck.

Tom sat with them in the canteen. He pretended he was learning from them. They boasted about the work they'd done. They'd been with Wilments a long time, as had their fathers. They talked about how they knew old Roger. They were, Tom said, out of earshot, firm's men, and they haven't the sense to see the firm doesn't give a fuck about them.

'It's not right to have two good men like you boys working in them conditions,' he'd tell them. 'You should go to young Roger and tell him. You deserve better than that, the years' service you've given this company.'

The two men nodded, bought more tea and contemplated drastic action. How could they get near Young Roger in his Rolls Royce? Their complaints grew more strident. The whole site avoided them. Though they didn't know it they were the butt of everyone's humour. How do Heavy Diggers!

While this was going on T-Bone waged a guerrilla war on them. When they left before us at night he would go down

into the hole and ease apart some of the timbering they'd
done that day, dislodging them just enough so that the water
could work its way about them, undoing much of what they'd
achieved during daylight. When they were in the hole he'd
sneak up and drag the pump from its mooring, so that it was
sucking air instead of water from the hole. An occasional
piece of timber was dislodged from where the shuttering
carpenters were working above them. They began to
complain of danger.

'Well,' Tom advised, 'I'm only surprised two men like you
aren't getting danger money anyway. It would make you
think ... that's all that is thought of a working man after a
lifetime's work. I was just telling Philip the engineer up there
about the two good men you were and how lucky they are to
have you.'

At this stage their plight had drawn the attention of head
office. The job was behind schedule and every day Connelly,
the Contracts Manager for the Southern Region, appeared on
site. Panic was fermenting in the office. Connelly was a man
who was usually best avoided — but Tom sidled up to him
and shook hands and they'd have a brief conversation. It was
a trick Tom had: he could smile on a person whose whole face
would then change. He left people feeling specially favoured.

It all reached a resolution that was sparked by the
Cockneys' use of the word "we". They referred to everything
collectively: it was *our* compressor, *our* shovel, *our* pump, *our*
air-lines.

'They don't belong to them,' Tom used to say, 'they
belong to the firm. They own fuck-all no more than the rest
of us do.'

What was happening was that the situation had dragged
on longer than Tom had anticipated. The two men were
probably more resilient than he expected, either that or he
was running out of patience. They'd asked Connelly to bring
their own tools from another job they'd been working on.

The tools were shovels with sawn-off handles, cut down for use in confined spaces. Something that might appear to be of little significance had talismanic properties for the two men. For once they weren't moaning in the canteen. Ebullient, one of them lifted his shovel onto the bench beside him.

'See that, Pat,' he said to Tom. 'Could you guess where I got that Pat, me old mate?'

Tom shook his head.

'I got that on me first day with the firm. There ain't many Heavy Diggers left now, Pat. Not many men who'd look after a shovel like that over the years ...'

'How long are you with the firm now?' Tom interrupted.

'Thirty-two years, man and boy, Pat. Hard to believe ...' And he was off now down the road about his father before him. Tom interrupted him again.

'I'll tell you what, Pat,' Tom said, 'they'll never let you go now.'

But the Heavy Digger was at cross purposes.

'You ever have your own shovel, Pat?'

'Never,' Tom replied, 'always some other bastard owned it Pat. I suppose I saw as much of the shovel as any man but to be honest with you, Pat, I never was that fond of it. I suppose you could say I was glad enough to see the end of it and the end of the day.'

'It ain't just that, Pat,' the other Cockney joined in. 'What I mean is ... I mean it's a matter of pride. It's about the way a man keeps himself ...'

'Yeah, well I'd see no pride in it. What are they going to do — cast the fucking shovel in bronze when you throw in the towel, Pat?' Tom snapped.

The Cockneys were nonplussed at the sudden change in the tone of the conversation. They looked at each other, bewildered, already beginning to deflate. Eventually one of them spoke.

'My name's not Pat, Pat,' he said.

'Well neither's fucking mine,' Tom replied, rising to leave the canteen. He usually walked back with myself and Hoppy, enquiring about what progress we were making. But when the rest of us followed him outside, he'd taken off ahead of us. We could see him working his shoulders, his jacket stretched tight, then bunched and wrinkled. In the van going home he wasn't his normal self either. Nobody spoke. It was obvious the war of attrition had run its course. T-Bone got out of the back of the van at a set of traffic lights. He came round the side and rapped on my window. I wound it down and he half-leaned in, across me to Tom.

'Leave it to me,' he said, 'I have a plan for those fuckers.'

I never got to witness exactly how it ended, as I was finishing my first manhole. This was where Hoppy was supposed to come into his own, he being the expert on building and benching manholes. As he set out the work, I laid the engineering bricks which were impervious to water. Benching meant building up the bottom of the manhole about the pipes with sand and cement. A smooth finish was vital. Then the manhole was tested, which meant plugging the outlets with bungs and filling it with water. The Clerk of Works oversaw this part of the operation. He lit his pipe and dropped a match into the centre of the pool of water.

'I'll be back at four,' he told us.

'They always do that,' Hoppy said.

'Do what?'

'The trick with the match. Boys o boys but they always do that.' He shook his head sadly, like a teacher who had witnessed successive generations of pupils trying the same hackneyed ruse.

'You see if it's leaking and we want it passed?' He looked at me. I nodded. 'Well then, if it's leaking we'll fill it up with water before he comes back. He'll know we were at some tricking around if the match has moved. That's why you always keep an eye on where the match lands.'

Hoppy had watched me work that morning, stopping me to put me right when I went astray. We were both absorbed in what we were doing. Neither of us was thinking of the Cockneys so when we entered the canteen at lunch time we were taken aback to see Tom in such a good mood.

'Where's your two mates, Pat?' I asked him.

'We'll not be seeing them toe-rags again,' he said.

'Boys o boys, what'll we do without them?' Hoppy said and we all laughed. 'What happened in the wind-up?'

So Tom told us how T-Bone had gone down into the hole while the two men were at breakfast and cut the shafts of their little shovels in half. That was all it took. When they found them they went mad. They came up just as Connelly arrived and went over to him as he got out of the car.

'They blamed us and all,' Tom told us. 'I think that crack yesterday was the last straw: they copped on what we were at. You should have heard them going on about Paddy bastards and danger money and the length of time they were with the firm.'

'What did Connelly say?'

'He said nothing to start with. What could he say? He didn't know half what they were on about. He let them rant at him. They got worse and worse and then one of them says, "If you don't get rid of those Paddy bastards we're jacking." Connelly says, "You'll jack?" "That's it," they says, "we'll facking jack if you don't get rid of those Paddy bastards." Well it was worth it to see Connelly's face. He didn't even move an eyebrow. "Fine," he says, as cool as you like. "I'll take it then you've jacked. Your cards will be in head office for you on Friday night." He turned on his heel and walked away.'

'And that was it?'

'That's all it took.'

We were to start in the hole the next day. There was only one thing bothering me. How could two men who'd spent as long as they had with a company be let go like that? Tom said we were all the one thing in the end, whether they called us labourers or skins or dogs. The Cockneys' mistake was in thinking that there was such a thing as loyalty in this business, or that any man couldn't be done without. Maybe it was a thing that Wilments wanted to get rid of them anyway. If the men hadn't jacked they'd have had to go through a whole disciplinary process to get rid of them. There would have been redundancy money involved. Neither were they very smart in going on to Connelly about Paddys. Connelly's father and mother were Irish. He mightn't sound it but he grew up listening to that shite, Tom said.

Diffley had escaped the taciturn Donegal man who never spoke to him. He was drilling in South Wales and I saw him irregularly. He wrote letters about how everyone believed the mines were gone, about the sort of places he was visiting, the slag heaps and the scarred landscape. He was back for Easter and we met up in the Adam on the Thursday night. The place was thronged with men. It was the first night I'd been there since Christmas and I was surprised at how it had changed. A new landlord Chris had taken over before Christmas. His first move was to sack the barman, Blacky. Blacky was from Laois and was popular with the Irish clientele. Then Chris ran a Teddy-Boys weekend. Maybe it was the culture shock, too much Brylcreem in the air, these new customers in their brothel creepers and drape jackets, for without any organising the Adam was boycotted. Most of the customers just walked up the road to the next pub. Within days Chris had taken Blacky back and was down the road buying drink for anyone he even thought he'd seen before. We knew even as we gradually drifted back that he had already effectively given control of the place to the customers and after that he was ignored. That Thursday night the place seemed wired to some new, lethal circuitry. There was a charge running through it that had a

hallucinatory quality to it. Men were drinking in vast
rounds. There was alcohol splashing about everywhere. One
man I knew vaguely had improvised a stage out of a bar stool
and was standing — no swaying — above the rest who
completely ignored him, singing: '*I was born and bred in
Boston, a place you all know well, Brought up by honest parents,
the truth to you I'll tell ...*'

At one point I was drinking in three rounds. All night
long there were running skirmishes along the bar. Fermanagh
Tony had reappeared from nowhere and was involved in
several of these.

Diffley got us two stools at the end of the bar. He reached
behind the counter and picked up a cloth and began to swab
beer slops and empty the ashtrays in front of us. That was the
thing I admired most about him, the air of calm that seemed
to insist that if he waited everything would come to him. He
wasn't going to be disaffected. I, on the other hand, always
felt as if I'd gone out having left something vital behind me.
A glass went flying over our heads. Diffley was talking so he
ignored it.

'A man,' he told me, 'a man in Galway once said to me, if
you were digging a hole in Galway you'd always be only a
digging a hole. But if you were digging a hole in Paris you'd
be learning a language. If you get what I mean.' And then
Diffley added, as if an afterthought, 'it wouldn't be the same
hole though.'

At this point the man who'd been singing, who everybody
called the Full-Back for the County, probably because he used
to claim he'd played in that position, started to call me 'a
jumped-up South Monaghan cunt'. This was news to me, but
he went on about people from South Monaghan looking
down on those from the north of the county, he being from
a place called Aghabog in North Monaghan. 'What McBride
are you anyhow?' he said. I glanced at him. The pint glass in
his hand looked like a baby's bottle. Diffley ignored him but

then the man started forward. I moved to block him but he began laughing uproariously. He clapped me on the back. '*She was lovely and fair as the rose of the summer*,' he sang.

'*She wore a silver locket with a picture of her home*,' Diffley interrupted. '*Just a lonely little cottage on a hillside on its own …*'

'*Twas not her beauty alone that won me …*' the Full-Back continued.

'*If I had you lovely Martha*,' Diffley cut in again, '*way up in Inishowen, or in some lonesome valley, in the wild woods of Tyrone …*'

'*There's cute little girls in old Strabane*,' the Full-Back changed tack, '*and just as pretty in Monaghan …*'

'Go on about you,' Diffley said laughing and I handed the Full-Back a pint from the two or three before me. We watched him lumber up the bar, lurching aggressively against two or three customers. He found a place in the corner, singing to himself. Diffley turned to me again. 'What I was saying there … did you get what I was saying there?'

'About Tyrone?'

'Jesus no,' he laughed, 'about Germany. That's what I mean, this …' he gestured, looking round the bar at the scene of increasing mayhem. Chris had emerged as if from hiding and was buying drink for everyone. For a brief few moments we all seemed to be united, magnanimous even, there were even men saying that Chris wasn't the worst of them. I caught sight of The Boxer at a table on his own. His head was resting between two full pints, the drink untouched. His eyes were vacant, the sleeve of his jacket soaking up spilled slops. The Boxer wasn't the man he'd been. He'd grown increasingly remorseful since Christmas. He talked about a family, young children he'd left up the country somewhere. He was spending whole days moored to his bed.

'A right man,' Diffley said, 'should take to the road. There'll be time yet for the 2.5 children. That's what wrong with us. There's too many *Connaught Telegraph*s and *Donegal Democrat*s in this town. The likes of us is tethered to Hammersmith Broadway.'

Tony had come back from the toilet. The Full-Back for the County pulled the barstool from beneath him as he went to sit down. Tony landed with a bang on the floor.

'Watch this,' I said to Diffley. Tony got up and loosed off a flurry of punches. The Full-Back reached over a paw and spun him around. Then he drove a steel-toe-capped boot as hard as he could into Tony's arse. After which he picked him up like a bale of hay and threw him through the plate-glass window into the street. It was probably more humane than hitting him.

'Come on,' Diffley said, 'let's get the fuck out of here before the cops arrive.'

Outside Tony was sitting on the edge of the pavement, brushing shards of broken glass from his hair. Apart from an abrasion on his right cheekbone the glass hadn't cut him. Diffley hauled him to his feet.

'Come on,' he said.

Tony followed us down the road, clutching his bruised backside.

'About that tenner,' he said.

The next day was Good Friday. We walked up to Ladbroke Grove where you could see all the Paddies lined up waiting for the pubs to open, the West Indians in their Sunday best on their way to and from religious services. We made our way down the Edgware Road to Hyde Park Corner. We crossed the Park to the Serpentine and hired a rowing boat, spending the afternoon racing a group of young Asians up and down the artificial lake. Diffley was a good oarsman. He told me it was the same as digging and God knows I went on about digging often enough. It was all about timing. After a while I did get a handle on it of sorts, although I was no more than barely competent. The highlight of that afternoon was when we let the Asians gain on us and then took off, rowing furiously towards the waterfall. At the last instant Diffley called out and we dipped oars and spun the boat about. Our competition overshot the falls and ended up dry-docked in the stream on the other side. They called us Paddy bastards.

5

By this time we could have sleepwalked our way around the Bracknell job. The summer was coming. There was incessant talk about money, who was getting what and which subbie was paying what was called 'the big money'. We were on £14 a day, which was very good money for what we were doing. Lonesome Tom used to say that there was no point in any man jacking a job for a pound or two a day. You could end up having to travel, your face mightn't fit in. He'd say this knowing that Hoppy at least was looking around. But Hoppy was vacillating so Tom drove his point home. Hoppy, he'd suggest, in a roundabout way, wasn't getting any younger. He should be looking for a sinecure, some nice factory job. Hoppy knew Tom was working at unravelling him but still it affected him. One way or the other he seemed determined to at least preserve the fiction that he was after another job, flitting between groups of men in the pub, picking up information. He studied the construction-jobs sections in the evening papers. He talked about a big money number he had lined up. It was up the country somewhere.

A General Election had been called and the feeling was we'd see a change of government. Tom didn't believe the government had much to do with the likes of us. It was like one lot or another were fighting a war somewhere else, though he felt instinctively that the Tories were the better choice. Money, he said, would flow back into the buildings. He remembered when Heath was Prime Minister. It seemed, the way he told it, like far-off halcyon days when a man could walk onto a site and ask for whatever he wanted. T-Bone however was a Labour man.

'Them Tories is all about big business,' he said. 'Labour's for the workers.'

'Listen to who's talking about work,' Hoppy said.

T-Bone said he would concede that the Tories were better for Ireland. Not many Irishmen would agree with that, but T-Bone said Labour were afraid of showing themselves up. English Socialists made the best Imperialists. The Tories, it had to be said, would gut their mothers for political gain.

Hoppy said he was talking shite. 'The only man,' Hoppy said, 'who ever did anything for Ireland was Hitler. He rose the price of rabbits during the war.'

We all started to laugh but T-Bone wasn't having it. Tom said it didn't matter if there was a united Ireland tomorrow. The likes of us would still be for the boat and the same big farmer's sons would be running the country for their own benefit. T-Bone went on about that being no way for a man from West Cork to go on. 'Wasn't Mick Collins up on Shepherd's Bush Road. Didn't he write about seeing a donkey and cart and them all cheering and thinking of home?'

'The only thing I ever cheered on Shepherd's Bush Road,' Tom said, 'was the subbie with my money.'

'The problem with ye boys is that if the English came back yonder tomorrow, ye'd walk out into the water to meet them,' T-Bone said.

That was when Hoppy sprung the big job up the country

on us. A week's work, he said, for three right men. And T-
Bone could look after things here. We'd have jobs to come
back to. Tom was sceptical.

'I've heard all about a week's work before,' he said.
'What's the pricing like and what's the ground like?' He went
off to get a drink. Hoppy said he was fed up with men talking
about the ground. He was fed up with men arguing about
what was the best Murphy to work for — the Green Murphy
or the Grey Murphy. He turned to me.

'Me and you'll do it,' he said. 'Take off by ourselves.'

That was a forlorn hope. We had no van. Tom had the van.

But we did end up on the great road north, to Bradford.
Hoppy swearing to show Tom the difference between good
and bad ground. Tom, even as he drove, maintained his air of
scepticism, the half-relayed notion that he'd been dragged
into something against his will. We travelled up on Sunday.
Work began on Monday and it was obvious by the afternoon
that we were in serious trouble. We had a compressor,
jackhammer and air-guns, all the shovels, spades, forks, picks
and cut-off sheets of ply we needed but we were in bad
ground. We might as well have been using spoons.

We had to lay a run of pipes four feet beneath the earth.
But the ground was bad and collapsed away from under us. It
was soft and clabbery: like trying to shovel water from a
swimming pool. A reddish colour, it adhered to everything
like glue, then dried into a carmine dust that got into the
folds of all our clothes. I'd wake up in the morning, hoping
for the first time ever to see the familiar shape of The Boxer
opposite me. Instead I'd see Hoppy in the next bed — hear
him snoring before I'd rightly opened my eyes. Then I'd get
out of the bed, and even that motion would start clouds of
red dust winnowing across the floor. It was inescapable.

There was no bookie's for Hoppy anymore. He had some
theories about gasworks and the Ministry of Defence but no

one wanted to hear them. Even so the ground did appear to have a gaseous quality and to move of its own volition. Myself and Tom staged each other shovelling. The further we threw it back the faster it seemed to seep back in on top of us — slithering like a live thing. It was a taste in our mouths, it was in our noses and ears and streaked across our faces where we'd wiped the sweat away. And worst of all, the whole site was English and we had the overwhelming impression they were laughing at the thick Paddies trying to dredge soup.

We'd expected to finish that Friday. Instead we worked until it was dark and then made our way to the Bricklayer's Arms pub near the digs we were staying in. Nobody spoke for a long time. It was one of those nights when you'd be afraid that whatever was said could change things in an irreversible fashion. Hoppy had begun to go on about one of his theories until Tom silenced him with a look, saying to me that the Rocking Horse knew more about groundwork than some men he could name. It was also a sign of our dejection that he ordered two pints and left Hoppy out of the round. I looked around the bar and could see the last of the pink evening light diffusing through the windows. A few old men played dominoes in a corner, studiously ignoring us. The barman slapped the pints on the counter and shuffled off without speaking. There was a very fat skinhead alone at the top of the bar, glaring at us, his shorn head in the pink light looking almost the colour of the ground we had been digging. He had the self-satisfied look of a snake that had swallowed a small goat and was ruminating on it while awaiting better fare. I surprised myself when, for an instant, I thought about walking up to him and levering my head into his dismal face. At last Tom spoke.

'We have to face facts. There'll be no draw here unless we do something fast.'

'What can we do?' I said. 'We'd be as well to cut our losses and head home.'

Both of them looked at me like I was demented.

'A man can find a way out of every situation,' Hoppy said.

'Well you should know. You landed us in it.'

'That's not doing anyone any good,' Tom said. 'We know Joe landed us in it. We have to get out of it and get out of it ahead. Getting out ahead's the problem.' Tom looked at me. 'Look. You're tired. You've done your best. It's me and him took you up here. Why don't you go home and get an early night. Get a Chinese or something.'

'I came up myself. It was me wanted to come. You're the one who wasn't sure.'

'Leave that for now. Leave it to me and him.' He handed Hoppy some money. There was something approaching relief on Hoppy's face. It was the first time in several days that he'd got a civil word from Tom.

'Go on up there and get a pair of pints and you go on back.'

I didn't need any more encouragement.

The following morning we got up as usual. Even the breakfast seemed depressing. The eggs swimming in a glutinous sea of grease. The bacon half-cooked, its rind transparent and the sausages deep-fat fried, hard and tasteless. I pushed the plate away from me. Tom and Hoppy ate without thinking, shovelling the food into their mouths. Tom reached for my plate: 'Not want it?' I shook my head. Although he didn't say anything I felt I was being admonished. I was always going on about working on the road, threatening to go to Germany and places like that. He was, in some way, pointing out the reality of all of that to me. The reality of poor food and bad work.

When we got out to the site Tom told Joe to pull the van over to the JCB. He got out the coils and jump-started it. 'You,' he said to me, 'gather up all the tools and clean them. Put anything we didn't bring with us in the hut. Then go back to the digs, pack the bags and pay that woman what

we owe her. Then go back to that pub we were in last night
and wait for us.'

I began to protest.

'Look,' he said, 'who's in charge here? Me or you? For
Christ's sake — just for once ... do what you're told. OK?'

It took me an hour to get back to the digs. I packed the
three bags and went downstairs. The landlady was lurking
behind the door.

'In a bit of a hurry then Pat?' she said.

There was no one in the pub when I got there. I bought
a paper and sat reading it. It was over an hour before Hoppy
showed up. I bought him a drink.

'What's going on?'

'That man's mad,' he said. 'He's mad. You don't want to
know. It'll never work. I'll tell you one thing, I've always said
a man's better off working for the Englishman. The
Englishman's straight. A man would know where he stood.
None of this flying off the handle. A man could keep the
canopy. If you had any sense you'd go and get a proper job.
You're a smart boy. Go and work with the Englishman in
an office somewhere. None of this digging. It'll get you
nowhere.'

I bought him a drink. He drained it in one swallow and
bought two more. I didn't want to push him and was relieved
when he said he was going out to look for a bookie's.

He returned over an hour later. 'Even the fucking horses
aren't running for a man,' he said. I began to get a vague
impression that we were pulling out of town and cutting our
losses. Tom came in soon after and refused a drink.

'Well?' Hoppy said. Tom ignored him and told us to
throw the bags into the van. We were well south of Bradford
before anyone spoke.

'I'd eat a horse,' Tom said, 'I don't know about you two
but I'm pulling into the next service station.'

In the cafeteria he told us to pile as much as we wanted

on our plates, then pulled a big envelope of money from the pocket of his donkey jacket at the cash-desk. We stared at it, transfixed. He paid for the three of us with crisp new notes. When we sat down, he said to Hoppy, 'I had you there.'

'You had in your arse. I knew. I knew if any man could pull it off it was you. I always believed you could do it. No better man, boys o boys. How do the last of the Heavy Diggers!'

'What happened? Jasus, will youse tell me what happened?' I said and they told me. Hoppy had driven the JCB. He dug up the surface of the ground the whole length of the run of pipes we were to have put in. Then he banked it up and drove over and back on it. Then they'd dug down four feet at the beginning of the run, sunk two pipes in place and backfilled them, leaving the ends uncovered. Then they'd hidden the rest of the pipes. We were lucky there was nobody else on site. It was a matter of leaving the JCB back where it came from. At that point Tom dropped Hoppy off at the pub and continued on to the contractor's house. He picked the man up, took him back to the site and showed him the job. He was paid on the spot. Tom counted the cash in the envelope and split it into three piles. There was £370 in each with short of £100 left over. That, he said, was for expenses. I could take what I'd paid for the digs out of it. Then there was the grub. The rest was beer money.

'No more Pat this and Pat that,' said Hoppy, 'I'll be glad to get back to me own place. What did I tell you, the Englishman's the best of the lot. You can't beat the Englishman.' He let a whoop and smacked the table. 'How do the last of the Long Distance Kiddies!'

'Funny enough,' Tom said, 'he wasn't an Englishman, he was one of our own. He must be up this way too long. He had a nice Bentley in the drive. A swimming pool I'd say at the back of the house. By the cut of him now I'd say he threw

a few fucks into men in his time and all. He just must have
forgotten how he came by it all.'

There was a new man in the house. Another Tony in Tony's
bed. This Tony was from Laois. He was in his late forties and
had got a job in a sausage factory. Nobody knew where he'd
come out off. A man of his age might have a family of his own
and even though we knew little about him, nobody would
ever try to learn more than what a man might willingly
impart. Tony from Laois appeared overwhelmed by the
mayhem in the house, the comings and goings at all hours of
the day and night. He was a shift worker and from the start
his sleep patterns were disturbed. He wandered about the
house at odd hours making tea. 'The tea won't make itself,'
he'd say. Or 'Flat-land man, good man.' Repeating these two
phrases like a mantra the way in which people often do repeat
the familiar, as if a few words had the ability to ward off
chaos. Laois Tony though was inoffensive and in his current
environment that wasn't a positive.

I had got a girlfriend. Sheila was her name, from Sligo. I
met her the evening after I'd gone boating on the Serpentine
with Diffley. I met her in the Bunch of Grapes in Kensington.
After that I seemed to keep on meeting her in a variety of
places and we drifted into going out with each other. She was
working in the Civil Service. I used to meet her on weekends
which meant I spent less time with Lonesome Tom, Hoppy
and T-Bone. I told her about the type of work I was doing. I
knew that a lot of people then who knew me considered I was
working on the buildings until something better came along.
As if it were — at best — an elongated student holiday I was
on and someone, someday, would come along and offer me a
job as a brain surgeon or recruit me for NASA. Tell me: 'Hey
man, we need you in Florida.' I had a way of masking my
intent by allowing people to make whatever assumptions they
wanted and letting them stand unrectified. This practice

meant that from the beginning Sheila and I were on, as I might have said then, bad ground. She believed that my job was a transient one, a temporary aberration. She listened to stories of my workmates with a detached bemusement, as if they belonged to another era, weren't quite what the Irish were meant to be these days. All of this was inchoate, wasn't quite voiced. She urged me to look for other work from time to time, clipping an advertisement from the *Irish Post* for a bank job. She was moving up in the Civil Service whereas I was shunting sideways, if shunting at all. She was in the tax office. I wasn't paying tax. If I took the bank job I could get a cheap mortgage. Not paying tax meant I didn't exist — and what was I going to do for a pension? Whereas to me a pension seemed like an existential notion. I dissembled, as I've said. I had other plans I was less forthcoming about. Germany was cohering into more than a notion in my mind.

Germany was on the minds of all building workers at that time. Everybody knew somebody who'd gone there. I was playing soccer on Saturday afternoon and Sunday mornings and Gaelic football on Sunday afternoons. The manager of one of the soccer teams had a wholesale butchering business. He offered me a job. He'd start me on £70 a week. Within a year I could be clearing £120, on the cards — after that it was up to myself. He was expanding and offering me a chance to get in on the ground floor. He bought me a pint, as if to give me time to consider. He could understand, he said, a young fella like me wanted a bit of 'Saturday Night Fever'. There'd be plenty of 'Saturday Night Fever'. But what I truly wanted was the big money — even if it was only to say I'd earned the big money.

It was an innocuous offer but still it somehow seemed to define my position. Every Irishman who'd ever left Holyhead was after the big money, but the big money was largely delusory. The problem with the big money was that it became an end in itself and I was well-primed for that — after all, as

I've said, I only wanted to be able to say I'd earned it. I was ready to work relentlessly at a fierce pitch for weeks, months even, on piece- or price-work. I had no aptitude for accountancy so that when that period of work was at an end there'd be a hiatus. Price-workers are an elite. They drink together, usually copiously, and disdain the daily rate — whatever that might be — as beneath them. There might be a gap of weeks between jobs but who would ever average out what we earned?

Germany was Hy-Brasil to people like me, the land of rumours. When I mentioned it to Lonesome Tom he pointed out all the men who'd come back from there after a few days. Where would you be there if your face didn't fit in? Occasionally, with Sheila, I would refer to Germany in an oblique kind of way, mentioning someone — a hypothetical person — I knew who was there. On the whole she seemed to believe it wasn't a good idea. In this she was at one with Tom, who was otherwise suspicious of her and warned me against talking to anyone from the tax office. Diffley though was still on about Germany. He was at me to set a date to leave on. I was in thicker with Sheila than I would have articulated then — quivering between twin attractions. See, the problem with Germany wasn't the ones who came back after a week or so — it was those who didn't.

One weeknight, towards the end of that summer, I met Sheila on the Fulham Road, near where she lived. We used to trawl several pubs in that area. We'd begin in the Rose and usually end up in a place with literary connotations, run by a Galwayman whom the Irish papers would turn to whenever they displayed any concern for the Irish abroad. I had work the next day and had to catch the last tube by twelve o'clock at the latest. I saw her onto a bus and shouted my goodbyes. I turned away and straight into trouble. There was a group of skinheads coming towards me, chanting 'Fuck the IRA'. I knew they must have heard me shout after the bus. I had already started towards them. I could have turned on my heel and walked off in the opposite direction, away from them, but I knew that wasn't a solution. They would surely set off after me. There was also a possibility that they wouldn't do anything if I kept going. I didn't know my skinheads then, didn't know enough about blood and hunting and things like that.

The first football match I had gone to in London was at Stamford Bridge. Conditioned by black & white television, Match of the Day and The Big Match, it was as if I'd emerged from a kind of fugue state as I took my place in the stands in a world of colour and turmoil. Chelsea had the makings of a good, young team, mostly home-grown. They played Spurs that Saturday. Instead of a full-throttled roar of anticipation as the teams emerged, a low angry hum reverberated round the pitch. Then the chanting started. The crowd surged spasmodically, more intent on each other than on anything that passed before them, as the chanting reached crescendos. The players seemed intimidated by what was happening. The match was a non-event. The following morning it made the front pages of the tabloids: a photograph of a young policeman, isolated and covered in saliva on one of the walkways that divided the fans, cowering as the fencing above his head yielded and gangs of skinheads clambered towards each other.

That night in Kensington there were few people on the streets. I counted at least ten skinheads in the group coming towards me. They were in full regalia, braces, jeans at half-mast, Doc Martin boots and Fred Perry shirts. I moved off the pavement and walked around them. Someone muttered 'Paddy bastard'. There was a rivulet of sweat running down my back. All my tiny hairs seemed on end. I got past them and had to concentrate hard to stop breaking into a run. I walked on. I knew they'd stopped and were conferring

amongst themselves. Someone shouted, 'Oi Pat, you in the
IRA then?' as someone else shouted, 'IRA bastard come over
here to blow us up. Fack off back to Ireland Paddy.' And with
that they were upon me. I knew enough to go down straight
away onto the pavement. To curl up into a ball and cover my
head with my arms. It felt as if the blows rained down on me
for a long time. They kicked my back and legs. As they kicked
at me they called me an IRA bastard. One of them attempted
to jump on my head. He fell off-balance onto the ground
beside me. I could see him through my fingers as he
attempted to spit in my face. I could smell the reek of alcohol
off him. Then as quick as they'd attacked they left, running
down the street, laughing. I waited until they'd gone out of
earshot before I began to pull myself together. I sat up on the
pavement. The few passers-by tried studiously to pretend I
wasn't there. I had the beginning of a ridge of lumps on the
back of my head. My nose was bleeding and there was blood
all over my shirt. I thought that I probably had a black eye
and I knew from the way my breathing was constricted, the
first sharp intake of breath that sent a jolt of pain searing
through me, that I'd broken some ribs — or that they'd
broken some ribs.

In the circumstances you tell yourself you were lucky. I
lost a week's work over it, a week's work without pay. You
know that the bruises aren't your fault, that you were in the
wrong place at the wrong time. But it's not altogether that
simple. There was a degree of guilt that compounded itself
every time I walked down the street with my black eye and
swollen nose. Every time someone pretended not to look at
me. For a while I wondered how many people saw me as an
IRA bastard. Wondering was there some form of collective
guilt for what had happened in Guildford and Birmingham.
The truth is the average Englishman didn't give a damn. The
average Englishman was completely ignorant of Ireland. They
heard on their radios and television about 'the Irish problem'.

They read about it in their papers. Saw the cartoons of Paddy
the ape with his sticks of gelignite. Of course, we were told
that those cartoons weren't aimed at the likes of us. The
decent Paddy who was trying to make a living, who'd built up
a devastated country after the war. The Paddy whose children
went to school with your children and my children. 'But
you're not like that,' they'd say to you after some new atrocity.
There'd be a pause then as they waited for you to affirm what
they'd said.

I had gone back to Ireland about a month before that
night in Kensington. I was at the Fleadh in Buncrana and
then visited Sheila at her parents' house. I spent a week in
Sligo. That's where I was the day the IRA blew up Lord
Mountbatten   at   Mullaghmore   and   killed   eighteen
paratroopers at Narrow Water near Warrenpoint. There was a
sense in which I dreaded going back to London. But when I
did return a week later there was little mention of what had
happened. Someone like T-Bone might have said, 'That was
some doing back there?' and I'd have nodded. The 'some
doing' was in itself noncommittal. By nodding I was giving
nothing away either. My first day back at work in Bracknell,
on my way onto the site, one of the English fitters stopped
me. 'What's white and does a thousand miles an hour?' he
asked. That's a new one I thought and told him I hadn't a
clue. 'Lord Mountbatten's slipper,' he said.

For Sheila it was different. There was a charge in the
atmosphere at work, she said. Someone had come up to her
and said what had happened didn't do the Irish any good at
'all. Some people didn't talk to her for a time. It always
puzzled me that what emphasis the English did place on an
event like that was placed on the explosion at Mullaghmore.
The soldiers at Warrenpoint were barely mentioned. The class
that largely provided those soldiers was that of the fitter who
told me the joke. Of course London was far removed from
the towns in the north of England that those bodies returned

to. It was odd too that the English middle classes were the ones whose reaction hardened fastest. It was amongst those people that Sheila worked. A friend of hers told me that her mother wouldn't buy Kerrygold butter, something that appeared both disconcerting and vaguely futile. Even the English liberal press found the Irish a strange conundrum. There were articles and editorials about 'the Irish problem'. There was some vague notion of an historical wrong, something that was never quite defined. And behind it all a belief that we'd given them our great writers and playwrights, so why did we have to go and spoil it all? Something that in those days was very apparent in their coverage of the affairs of the Republic, in how they reported the Irish solutions to Irish problems as whimsy: the teachers in the staff room bemused by the deliberations of the students' council.

As for the Irish in London, for the greater part they didn't want to know. They were the ordinary decent Irish the tabloids occasionally championed. The bombings and killings did nothing to make life easier for them. Through the Seventies many of them witnessed their own children turn their backs on any idea of being Irish. There were few outward displays of belligerent Irish nationalism in London in those days. One time I saw a group of men chanting 'IRA all the way. Fuck the Queen and the UDA' on the Fulham Palace Road. They were Scottish football fans on the rampage after they'd been routed by England in a home international. On another occasion two men I knew from the nationalist enclave of Ballycastle in County Antrim were set upon by Red Action as they returned from the pub late at night. Their offence was that they had talked while the band played the Irish National Anthem. To be fair to them they saw the irony of their situation: that what were by any standards Northern nationalists had been beaten up by English left-wingers in the mistaken belief that they were Orangemen. There were others, like myself and T-Bone, who played our cards close to our chests, becoming the inscrutable

Irish, the Paddy with two faces, who lurked in many an English imagination. Others still directly sympathised with what was happening in Northern Ireland. Some, no doubt galvanised by occurrences like what befell me in Kensington. Believing that if you were going to be classed as an IRA man you might as well start to talk like one — if nothing else.

6

THERE WAS A SHARP SENSE OF CLOSURE ABOUT WHAT happened in Kensington. I got over it because I had to. Indeed what little sleep I lost arose from the discomfort of three broken ribs. It made me mistrustful and edgy for a while but that too passed. What had happened had happened on a personal level. It reflected, in reality, no further than myself. I was back at work soon enough. What it was though was one of a series of minor events that made going to Germany an increasing reality. I was at one with Diffley on that. In my mind I was casting about for a reason to set a date. The only problem of course was that it was now too late in the year.

I was spending most of my time in the basement of the job in Bracknell. In reality, the job was over. There was still at least twelve months' work — but it meant clearing up after the tradesmen, pushing a brush. Whatever cohesion we had as a gang had evaporated. T-Bone and Hoppy had dropped any pretence that their verbal sparring was just 'having the crack' and were like a pair of feral cats. The excavation for the post-office ducts had long since been filled in, but underground there was still a big service chamber. Access to that was provided through a manhole opening. The manhole passage was about twenty foot in length. It was narrow and claustrophobic. I spent a week in the chamber, putting off-cuts of timber and brickbats into a bucket which Tom pulled up on the end of a length of rope. That I was a week in the hole was a statement about the condition of the job; we were at the stage when we were making it last, manufacturing work for ourselves. I could have been out of there in a day. Tom kept telling me to slow down. In the end I took a book with me and spent most of the day reading, stopping only when there was a tug on the rope and the bucket, which was always ready, began its jerky, upward motion.

Then I moved into the basement. I had to work with Philip, the engineer. He had the theodolite — the donkey level as many men called it — and I was in charge of marking levels on the walls. The levels were reference points for the floors and false ceilings. The basement was where the bulk of the sensitive post-office machinery would be situated. Because of that perhaps, the operation of the theodolite had all the complexity of theological exegesis for Philip. For my part though the job filled me with rancour. The word used to describe it was chain-boy. I wasn't yet twenty, although I acted as if I were older, and the word 'boy' held an unwanted significance for me. I was convinced I was more than that. It also appeared — not only appeared — that it was a job anyone could have done. It was repetitive and boring and I often found my attention wandering — not so much distracted as a victim of its surroundings. The basement had flooded, naturally enough as it was at the bottom of the building. We had to pump it out. Large pools of water still coalesced on the uneven concrete sub-floor and stained the reinforced walls. It seeped in everywhere. To dry the building out blast heaters were brought in. One of these would go through a five-foot bottle of gas in a day. The levels of heat were incredible. The water began to evaporate from the floors, but because we were in a basement and there was nowhere for it to go, it condensed on the ceiling and fell back on us like irregular droplets of rain. I began to imagine I could see the condensation happening in front of my eyes, waves of shimmering heat surrounding me. The whole basement took on a greenish hue. It was as if I were in the bottom of the Monaghan lake where I'd learned to fish, moving in slow motion against the water's resistance, the water cold and deep and murky, green and secretive, promising opulence like some woman's eyes. Then Philip would shout at me to move to the next position. He worried about me, worried that I was unbalanced, I think, and what I was day-dreaming about started to obsess him. At times I really believed I was somewhere else altogether. Those were hallucinatory days.

I had also begun to think about the nature of the work I was doing. I wondered if there was an end to it. I thought about Lonesome Tom. Tom told me about the secret Ministry of Defence tunnels he'd worked on beneath London. He made it sound as if nobody really knew where they were located. Apart from the fact that he'd got paid for the work they might not be there at all — who could prove it? It could be just another of his stories. I thought of the motorways and power stations those men who had come before me had helped build but who was to say they'd been there either? In this way I began to look for the significance of the job we were doing, as if all work were an existential problem.

I started to complain then, but there was no use in complaining. The site had effectively wound down as far as we were concerned. If I wasn't in the basement I would be cleaning up after plasterers or stacking wood for chippies or moving pallets of bricks around. The worst that could happen was that I'd be put scabbling. The scabbler was used for breaking up the surface of the concrete floors to provide a key for the screeders who would lay the sharp sand and cement. The scabbler itself was about the size of an electric lawnmower. It lay inert until the compressor was switched on and then it jerked upright and pulsed on its three little hammers. There were no wheels on the scabbler, which strained from side to side, bouncing up and down. It took strength and persistence to keep it in a straight line. Scabbling was somewhere about the seventh circle of Dante's Inferno. That was the general labourer's condition.

Diffley returned for a weekend about a month before Christmas. I met him in the Adam at Saturday lunchtime and filled him in on the latest comings and goings in the house. He saw it all like a soap opera and I grew frustrated trying to explain to him how it all begins to wear you down after a while. We sipped our pints and watched two customers argue over which of them could eat the most pickled eggs. They began to compete, forcing the white, slimy eggs down their throats. Diffley had a philosophical bent: he saw what they were at as some kind of commentary on the human condition.

'For fuck's sake,' I said, 'they're both English.' We both began to laugh, dissolving the tension that had been building between us. We had decided to move on somewhere else and were on our way out the door when we bumped into The Boxer — rather The Boxer bumped into me. He had his head down, but he looked up and made some effort to acknowledge Diffley just as he swung his shoulder hard against my chest. I stepped backwards. I must have sounded fairly strident because Diffley said I sounded just like Fermanagh Tony. He said it was obvious The Boxer had a serious problem and it was best to ignore him.

'That cunt wouldn't box eggs,' I said.

'I'm telling you,' Diffley said, 'just like Tony …'

By now I had become firm friends with Lonesome Tom.
Whatever else, there was something about me, some capacity
that made some men look on me as a surrogate son. This
trait was a trap Tom had fallen into. There was no doubt that
from the beginning he'd looked out for me. On one occasion
one of the casual labourers we'd brought out with us
borrowed some money from me, a fiver. It wasn't a
significant amount of money, or so I told myself when I
realised I wasn't going to see it again. This man was another
of those Tom took instinctively against. I remember him
coming out in the van and talking incessantly about
Germany. He said he was a shuttering carpenter and all a
man needed there was a hammer and an auger. The mention
of Germany was probably enough for me but Tom
recognised a chancer when he saw one. He wanted to know
why a shuttering carpenter was working with us. He laid the
emphasis on the 'us' like the man believed we were really
beneath him. On Thursday — pay-day — when I got into
the van Tom handed me a fiver. I protested and he gave me
a sharp look. I was saying it wasn't the money, fuck the
money if that's what the man was made from. Tom told me
not to be stupid. He'd tried to have one up on me and hadn't
got away with it. I was an idiot if I thought there was a lesson
there for anyone, the same man would do the same thing
again next week, with a deal more success. It's the way he was
made. I remember that man's face when Tom handed him
his wages. He counted the money and said he was short.
Tom told him why and I knew from the way the man's
mouth twisted into a sour grimace that Tom had been right.
He was wholly vindicated when a Kango hammer and our
friend disappeared together the same day. The hammer

belonged to the plasterers. A man's tools were his own concern. To steal from a working man was regarded as the lowest of the low.

There were many other ways in which I was looked after. I never became a target for other men's humour — or for what often passed for humour. A new man, somebody as obviously green as I was, could be a source of great fun, not all of it wholesome. There was an element of bullying about it. The mistaken belief that by demonstrating to someone that cynicism was the only defence mechanism you were doing them a favour. Even the week I had off because of what happened in Kensington was eventually covered, an extra day a week turning up in my wage packet over the following two months.

Correspondingly I began to take on many of Tom's characteristics. My hardening attitude to The Boxer came from him for instance. Tom knew more about The Boxer than he let on: the antagonism he felt towards him was deeply sourced and no doubt genuine. I also learned from him to set up a running noose of white lies; to lay false trails everywhere; to recognise the weaknesses in what the men I worked with said, how they reinvented themselves and then tripped up through periodic repetitions as if all the time having to convince themselves of what they were saying. I learned to worry at these things, to return to them again and again, picking at the lies like a knot until they loosened and the frailty of what lay behind the construction was exposed. There was little to be said for this. These men were for the most part weaker than I was. They did not have the benefit of an education beyond what they'd gleaned on the building sites. They did not have my sureness of purpose or the glinting belief I had that I was not going to spend all of my life labouring. That was my greatest deception — although I knew this or felt I knew it — I masked that purpose. I was, as far as they were concerned, one with them. Few of them saw through it.

I had begun to see survival as a kind of guerrilla war where you always had one up on the other man. He didn't know where you were coming from and you had his trajectory marked out. What you had on him you might never use but the fact was, you did have it. To some people it might make no sense in having some form of power — however shallow — without demonstrating it on occasion. That that didn't arise in my case only compounded what I was doing. Finally, with The Boxer, it was to prove more than demonstration, no matter how logical it might have seemed in the moment.

It happened the Saturday night after myself and Diffley had run into him in the doorway of the Adam. It was late that night and I was asleep in bed. Tony from Laois was in the bed opposite mine. I knew when I'd returned to the house that he wasn't asleep. His breathing was too irregular. I listened to him twist and turn fitfully before I drifted off myself. I was awakened though when The Boxer came crashing into the room. There had been that strange leakage over the preceding months of the person he was. Whole weeks when he'd appeared marooned in a twilight place of his own design. He had frayed considerably — but then had spent the past few weeks as if determined to make a stand, to reassert himself. When he swept into the room he began his usual tirade of a commentary wherein he fought Mohammed Ali. I lay awake listening to him, my resolve hardening. I'd had a good bit to drink that night and he had lurked at the back of my mind all the while. I was waiting on him to make a move. He didn't disappoint. When he crossed to Tony's bed and pulled the covers from him, I leapt from mine.

'Where's Tony?' he shouted as if he'd never met the Laoisman before.

'I'm Tony,' Tony said.

'No you're not. You're not Tony. Tony was a fine man.

Who took Tony? Tony wanted to fight me. Are you going to fight me?'

The Laoisman snatched at the bedclothes and pulled them back over his head.

'Go 'way,' he said, 'I don't want to fight no one.'

I was now standing facing The Boxer in my underpants. He was fully clothed. In those moments everything seemed to telescope into a funnel. His face grew exponentially before me. For the first time in my life the whole room dissolved into a red miasma.

'What have you to say for yourself, you cowardly fuckdog?' he said. I hit him. I hit him with everything I had and I also got lucky. I connected with the point of his jaw and he catapulted back down the funnel. He landed, spread-eagled beside his bed, cracking his head off the bedside cabinet. I moved to follow up. Time just seemed to hang there, to run in those red colours. The anger surged through me and I became aware of Diffley and another two of the men in the house hauling me back. I struggled to get away from them. All I could see was red, literally red. The Laoisman was helping The Boxer to his feet, but The Boxer brushed him aside and staggered groggily from the room. I heard him clatter from side to side down the stairs as my heartbeat subsided.

He never came back. I never saw him again. None of us ever did. It became the final impetus I needed to leave the house. I had done no one a service and that was made apparent to me. If I'd wanted to hit him I should have done it twelve months before, when there was more of a real target in place, whether he was a boxer or not. For the few weeks I remained there I would have to get out of bed every morning and look over at where he'd slept, his pillow still bearing the distinctive greasy imprint of his head and beside it the form of a clenched fist. His cardboard suitcase lay half-hidden beneath the bed. I knew that whatever it contained, photos of children, mementoes of some sort, would be another admonition. One of the old boys in the house was the only person who ever referred to what had happened, when he told me sadly that there was no need for what I'd done. That The Boxer was the victim of some other malaise. In the few words he spoke there was the distinct message that what went about came about, of Irish karma. Perhaps it is some form of karma to carry memories — for while I never saw The Boxer again I've borne him with me, like some secret memory of a distant childhood perfidy.

7

IRISH KARMA — OR FATE — IS SOMETHING I'VE NEVER BEEN
much of a one for. I've never bought a lottery ticket minutes
before the draw and felt, as many I've known have done, that
I would win. Felt anything other than that I was getting
caught up in the churn of things, fulfilling some obligation
and wasting money. There has been no great tide that's borne
me in one direction, nor any riptide that's dragged me in the
opposite. And yet, for a while there, in the wake of that
incident, things did spiral irrevocably downward. Diffley gave
up the job in Wales and returned to London and we rented a
bed-sit off Acton High Street. The landlord was Yugoslav —
more appropriately he was a Croat, a people with an even
more convoluted history than our own. He had difficulty
understanding myself and Diffley. He saw no percentage in
being in a foreign country if your every effort wasn't bent
towards making money. In this we disappointed him greatly.

It was also all off with Sheila. I told myself that I had
initiated it, something that was, at the absolute least, an
evasion. I was in shock at the manner in which she'd broken

it off. A good part of the summer had been — for me at any rate — an idyllic time, spent wandering the streets of London. I went home that summer and then went up to Sligo with her and got on well, I thought, with her family. Lonesome Tom left me to Euston Station the night I left for Ireland. We were early. I had already bought my ticket. He came onto the concourse with me and we went for a drink before the train began boarding. There was maybe up to a hundred people queuing for tickets, families standing in knots together and men and women, of all ages, on their own. It was Tom who pointed out to me how close some of those people stood to their belongings, as if those battered, cardboard cases somehow contained all of themselves. They looked like mostly the people who'd come over in the Fifties or earlier even. They looked like those cases defined them — a definition of perpetual movement with no particular object to it. The suitcase as near to an idea of home as many of them would ever get.

I had all of August off that summer. The weather was balmy. Around my own place the whitethorns and fuchsia were in bloom. The things you take for granted when you've grown up amongst them. An uncle of mine was back from America. He was my mother's favourite and for a while there seemed to be some respite for her, for the first time since my father had died she seemed happy. I hitched to Sligo across Cavan and Leitrim, through town and villages, past signposts for places I'd heard people talking about. Mythical places that seemed to shimmer like mirages in that August heat. Places that weren't quite as they'd been described, streets deserted but for a few cars, collections of habitations that hardly merited the name town. A single street and then you were gone. These were places that appeared emptied out, half-asleep, as if awaiting some event that would start them into reality. The memories of those who described them to me their only, real realisation. More of those people with the

cardboard cases. I stood between lifts outside a pub sipping a
warm bottle of Harp. There was a young girl playing outside
a deserted garage up the road from me. She had her ear
pressed against a rusting, galvanised iron fence, as if she could
hear life's great thrum accelerating somewhere else.

That was the summer they'd blown up Mountbatten and
the only thing that struck me as strange, in Sligo, was Sheila's
parents' reaction to it. They were grim and tight-lipped like
nothing out of the ordinary had happened at all, nothing that
wasn't expected. At the same time there was more than a hint
of jubilation in the air, knowing looks exchanged, and her
father muttering something about a car he'd seen reversing
out of the road down to the bog that morning. That's where
we were when it happened, the bog — a bog in Sligo — and
we heard a kind of whumping sound. The sound as a child I
always imagined the giant's feet would have made as he
chased Jack off the beanstalk. I remembered the looks they
shared as the deaths of the soldiers at Warrenpoint on the
same day became known and they could only barely suppress
their feelings. We all went to the pub that night and it was all
anybody talked about. There were glasses raised to the
audacity of it, the confusion the act had sown and the sheer
atavistic joy it evoked. This was happening while politicians
on the television were condemning those who'd carried out
the bombings. It was like we were living in two different
countries. I was disconcerted: I didn't know which country I
belonged in.

Back in London everything returned to normal, or so it
appeared. I was in a pub in Hammersmith with Sheila one
night, where there was a band onstage playing Republican
songs and the audience's response was alcohol-fuelled. I was
all against bar-stool Republicanism. As with many things
with me, this began as a general feeling and ingrained itself as
conviction. Look at them, I was saying, the idiots. She didn't
make much of a response at first but I kept dragging at the

subject. Eventually she came out with some weak line about them being harmless. That did it. I made the point that where I grew up you wouldn't get away with something like this — it was too close to the border. You'd get asked what you intended doing about it.

'How far from the border is it,' I said, 'where you're from?'

She didn't reply. She didn't have to. I knew what I was going to say next anyway.

'Yeah,' I said, 'forty-what miles? It's easy to be a Republican when you're near as far from the border as Dublin.'

Of course these were small, if emblematic, things. It was like putting together a jigsaw wherein the first few pieces have little real relevance by themselves — only after a while do they begin to belong to part of a greater pattern. It was there anyhow that the mistakes were made. Like the argument in the pub, I had developed a habit of hacking at things, in what I believed was an effort to clarify them, when in fact I was really beginning with an answer I already knew and working backwards.

When she did finally say she'd had enough she did it well. She allowed me room to manoeuvre, enough room so that I could conclude that it was me who had called it off. After Christmas she heard her father was dying. It's clear to me now, the evening she told me, the two of us sitting in The Hoop at Notting Hill. The gloom outside that hadn't lifted all day. The slop of rain. The traffic whooshing by on the wet streets. The feel of damp clothing and the smell of it drying indoors. The sound of the football results coming through. The cigarette stains between my fingers.

'He's dying,' she said.

And I was too preoccupied. I was thinking about her, about the way I'd held her folded against me the night before, about the colour of her hair and her eyes and the way she tasted of iron. I was thinking of all that and there was no room for what she might have been thinking. I could see it all in retrospect: how she winced and the sheer pitying look she gave me — half-defiant, half-cornered.

Though it had ended it seemed to me like a record still going round in circles on an old-fashioned turntable, long after the music had stopped. Nothing audible beyond a series of inane, repetitive noises. I lay on the bed in Acton bereft. The sense of loss I felt was spectacular. It was my own fault and it also might have been just what I wanted.

And then Bracknell came to an end. A new gang had arrived on site. The promise the new Tory Government had given hadn't materialised. Work was tightening up. The place to go was the M25, a long-vaunted Civil Engineering project that was to rescue everyone. Its real start was imminent. We all knew that work was ongoing: there were engineers and contracts managers and surveyors and clerks of the works outside London, in undoubted bucolic bliss, putting the final touches to where it all went. And, we felt, working out the proportions between us and them as they might have gauged concrete: was it two managers per worker or could they get away with 2.5 or … 2.75 even? In the meantime the subbies were prepared to cut each other's throats. The new gang had that look of permanency about them that comes when a slightly newer, more durable article works out cheaper than its predecessor.

Our gang was disintegrating at the same time so we were complicit in letting them in as well. Hoppy went home for Christmas and never came back. T-Bone's ex-wife had left his two sons with him one weekend and hadn't come back. He was taking his duties very seriously and was casting about for a job that would better accommodate their needs. Diffley replaced Hoppy and we both began to miss time. This was the crucial factor in our replacement, or so we were told. In reality we could be no more blamed than the man who fired the first shots in a war could be said to have determined everything that followed — or so Diffley said. Lonesome Tom didn't know whether to be relieved or not. Time had turned leaden. We missed Hoppy's natural mastery of appearing busy when there was nothing to do. One day before he left we were looking out the window at the street below us when Hoppy turned abruptly, grabbed my head and held it backwards, muttering something I couldn't make out as he stared into my left eye. Then I heard the agent asking what was wrong?

'He's something in his eye. Can you see it there?' The agent had a look before sending me off for the first-aid kit and a bottle of eyewash. 'And when you're hiding,' Hoppy'd urge, 'always keep an eye on the top of the ladder. If it moves there's someone coming.'

_____

8

WE WERE OUT OF WORK FOR TWO WEEKS THEN BEFORE A JOB came up and I was landed back at the Airport. We pulled up outside a Portakabin in the middle of nowhere, and both Diffley and Lonesome Tom were taken aback that I could describe what was in it before we'd opened the door, down to the fridge, table, cooking ring and the map of the Airport. I could also have told how there was a run of pipes about somewhere, starting at approximately nowhere and ending up at nowhere. The ground had reverted to what it had been like before myself and the Yeller had torn it all up, leaving it up to future generations to unearth Dunne's scams and muse over them as they might the archaeological remains of a Roman bathhouse: another failed attempt to impose civilisation.

That was our first day back at work. We were out with McGee. Now McGee had a reputation as being a good man to work for. We'd spent the Easter hungry and were glad to be working anywhere. McGee was expanding. No Irish company, despite the history of Irish involvement in the

buildings, had ever operated on the same level as the big
English firms. The Irish were too smart for that — there was
a price on near self-sufficiency whereas the real money was to
be made subcontracting specific areas of work. No
bureaucracy of your own and fewer bureaucrats peering over
your shoulder. McGee was groundwork and demolition.
They had a big presence at the Airport. Many of the men who
worked for McGee had been with him for a while. They acted
like he was a small god. They'd tell you about the time the
machine, the Poclain, got stuck in bad ground. McGee
arrived in the Rolls Royce and hitched the car to the machine
and began to haul it from the hole it was in. It tore the back
off the car which was brand new. They'd tell you that, shaking
their head as if to say 'What can you do about a man like
that? … And then he took the Roller back to the garage and
Rolls Royce refused to replace it. What can you do? That's
why he drives a Merc.' Other men would argue with that:
'You ever see a donkey saying no to a carrot? Of course Rolls
Royce took his money. Didn't he get a trade-in on the
damaged car. Wrote a cheque on the spot, so he did.' Some
said he asked Rolls Royce what they'd allowed him on the
trade-in, then wrote a cheque out for that too and went home
with the two Rollers — the arse hanging off the one. You
could say what you wanted about McGee — he was an
ordinary man. Didn't he play cards and pool with all the
other subbies down at the Halfway House in Southall for big
money — men he could have bought and sold?

   'Bide your time,' they'd tell you in moments of near
privacy. 'Bide your time. You could do well with McGee and
he's going places. The money's good.' The money was above
the average but they didn't say he paid by cheque. Cheques
were a novelty then. Kites they were usually called, and kites
were associated with flying, and flying a kite meant bouncing
a cheque. You wouldn't really trust them. Any right man
would want cash. Money smelt. Anyhow, to change a cheque

you had to have a bank account. McGee had a way around that. You could change McGee's cheque in McGee's Club in Northfields. There might be a couple of hundred men there by the time you got there. You'd get a tenner straight away, up-front like, the price of a night's drinking and you could queue for the rest at closing time.

McGee was the harbinger of a new order. McGee stopped thirty-three per cent tax off the top. I was now legally self-employed. There was, in truth, a novelty in seeing the name McBride on an envelope for the first time in a while. I was — I was told at any rate — a subcontractor who was subcontracting my labour to another subcontractor. I was being paid by cheque. Over the coming years more and more men would joins queues clutching cheques in places off the Holloway Road, in Kentish Town and Kilburn. Places like McGoverns and the Archway Tavern had offices with hatches and security that specifically dealt with cheques — taking upwards of five per cent off the top. When the bust came much of this business retreated to the back streets. Men were signing on and working. There were multiplicities of false names flying about. Almost everybody you worked with was working illegally to keep ahead. Lines of pints of lager on the counter, fewer specifically Irish accents, the air rancid with the smell of cigarette smoke and stale beer — circumvented lives. This was money laundering on a grand scale.

At the Airport though we knew that worrying about changing cheques was a short-term problem. We had a date for going to Germany. We hadn't told Tom yet because we were half-afraid of the scorn we would face. How we'd be told we would never stick it. We'd be back soon enough like cowed dogs.

At the Airport we kept our heads down and our traps shut, at least for the first few weeks. Tom was scornful of McGee's men. Many of them knew him, at least by reputation. They were uneasy about him — as if he was an expensive acquisition they didn't know quite where to place. McGee had an agent called Larry Murphy who was from West Cork — a townie of Tom's. I heard them colloguing. Murphy was saying that Tom would be made up to ganger. That there was a future with McGee. Your money went up every year automatically. A man would be looked after. Tom grinned and said little in response. He nodded. The problem with Tom — if you knew Tom at all — was that what looked like assent meant nothing.

We were put digging trenches. We were all glad to have work again, particularly work with a direction to it. Diffley had begun to go on about digging like it was some form of Zen. Tom used to grin listening to him. 'That man can sure talk some,' he said.

The day Tom was made up to ganger man I decided to see if I could figure out what he was thinking. We were bottoming out a trench. I was in the trench. He was shovelling the spoil clear.

'He's not the worst, McGee,' I said. Tom didn't answer. I was thinking to myself of how McGee wasn't anymore approachable than Roger Wilment in his Rolls Royce. Besides I'd never even seen McGee. Yet I decided to try again, as if he couldn't see me coming.

'Anyhow,' I said, 'you're well-fixed now you're made up to ganger.'

'We're all well-fixed,' he said, throwing a shovelful of clay behind him.

'That auld Murphy's alright too.'

Tom's roll-up had gone out. He stopped to light it, took a draw, then said, 'He'd be the first man you'd ask to drive your car if Ted Kennedy wasn't about.'

It was shortly after that myself and Diffley went and stalled the dumper in the access tunnel. It was a Friday and almost going-home time — the best time for a disaster to happen.

Neither of us could drive properly, although Diffley was
much better than I. We had to move the dumper and a jack
hammer from the main site at Terminal Three to one of the
smaller sites off the Bath Road. The agent told us that this
was a rush job. Get the gear together, get over there and do
what was to be done. We knew better than to ask questions.
The Bath Road was where we'd begun, where Dunne's old
Portakabin was. Getting over there was an end in itself. Your
time was your own over there. The problem with working in
Terminal Three was that we were back to being general
labourers again. We'd spent two weeks clearing up after
brickies and plasterers. If we could only get back to the Bath
road we'd show them what we could do. Tom was somewhere
over there. He told us he'd get us shifted but we'd have to bide
our time. He had to deal with Murphy's original gang. They
were entrenched, literally, over there. None of us mentioned
that they were all Cork men.

Anyhow a driver was supposed to hold a valid licence to
drive a dumper beyond the confines of the site. It was
something nobody ever paid much heed to. In any event
neither of us had a licence, so when it stalled in the tunnel we
were thinking of the Airport police. We knew we were in
trouble. We jumped down and ran. By the time we got back
to Terminal Three there was traffic jammed all the way back
up the M4 into London. There was an inquiry under way. It
took over two hours to get the dumper moved. Two hours at
rush hour on a Friday evening. I remember watching it on
television that night, the aerial pictures of the tail-back and
the news commentator saying that the chaos was caused by
an abandoned works' vehicle. At one point the Bomb Squad
were involved. I remember your woman's voice on the news,
how deceptively calm she seemed.

It was the following Monday we began digging the hole.
Tom had come to our rescue. He didn't say much. No doubt
his anger had dissipated over the weekend. He drove us down

the Bath Road and turned off it, driving across the vast area
of unused land that surrounded the main Airport. He drove
far beyond anywhere I'd seen on Dunne's travels and I
believed I'd seen everywhere. Then he stopped. He got out of
the van and opened the back. He pulled out four shovels, a
sledge hammer, a fork, two picks and a wheel barrow. Then
he began to search about in the front. He emerged with an
empty cigarette packet. He marked out dimensions on it.
Then he told me to follow him and we transferred the
dimensions to the ground, marking out the perimeter with
pegs and twine. He handed me the tape measure.

'Now lads,' he said, 'you boys like a bit of heavy digging?
I'm going to leave ye at it. I want it dug out like it's marked.
Straight sides and a level bottom. I'll be sending a machine
over later. Ye can make yer own way home tonight can't ye?'

We said we could and he got into the van and drove off
in a cloud of dust. The two of us sat down on the ground.

'How big is it?' Diffley asked.

'Big enough,' I said, 'Eight by ten. It's four feet deep as
well.'

'A handy enough few days work. I suppose we're lucky to
have jobs. I wonder what it's for?'

'Who cares?' I said. 'We better make a start.'

We began to dig down four feet in opposite corners. It
hadn't rained for weeks and the ground was hard and
compacted. My wrists ached from the shock of the pick
hitting the ground, but we were making headway. Although
we looked about for pieces of ply to shovel off, there was
nothing in sight apart from a few scaffold boards and we'd
need them as a run for the barrow. We decided to
work through breakfast. We were a long way off from the
attractions offered by canteen food: the sight of aeroplanes
taking off and landing and air hostesses sashaying past. The
early-morning haze disappeared and the sun came out,
strong and unrelenting. There was no shelter where we

were. We stopped early for lunch, then sat wondering which direction to head off in. Heathrow is on flat, featureless ground. Every direction looked the same. Then Diffley stated the obvious and we moved off towards where the planes were circling. It took us thirty-five minutes to reach the canteen, ten minutes there and then the long walk back. We were supposed to have a half-hour for lunch, even allowing for no breakfast, and if anyone found out we could be docked. We were in enough trouble. We finished dead on five that evening. We sat on the sides of what we'd dug out, our legs swinging as we smoked. The machine hadn't arrived. What machine, we were thinking, we could do this by ourselves. There were worse things than digging. We argued about which direction we should head home in, the tube station at the Airport or take a chance on a bus from the Bath Road. The Bath Road was nearer. As we began to make our way across the open ground we could see a storm boiling in the distance. It was moving towards us fast and even though we began to run there was no shelter to run towards. The rain left the ground pock-marked about us, cutting runnels through the dust. We made the road and eventually a bus came along. We were both soaked to the skin.

'At least it'll loosen up the ground,' I said.

'He's likely to leave us at it for the week,' Diffley said. 'We'll not see him till Friday with the wages. We should be finished by Thursday.'

I nodded in agreement, though even then I was suspicious of Tom's intentions.

The following morning a JCB was perched on the side of the hole by the time we arrived. I knew the driver to see. He was from Longford.

'Hey Longford,' I shouted at him, 'you come to help us?'

He looked at me as if I'd uttered a heresy. He blinked a few times and twisted his small head about, as if he were trying to loosen a crick in his neck. He took a while to answer too: like the cathode in an old radio warming up.

'I have me own orders,' he said, 'what Tom, your ganger, told me. He told me nothing about helping out you boys. He told me to come down here and not help youse. It's all the one to me, sure I'm on day-work anyhow, but I can't go against the ganger man.'

'Are you saying you were told not to help us?' I could hardly believe what I was hearing. 'That Tom told you not to help us?'

'I'm not saying nothing more. Youse boys heard what I said.'

To compound our difficulties the rain had done nothing to loosen the ground. We redoubled our efforts and by that evening we knew we'd only have to level out the bottom the following morning. Then Tom arrived. He admired our work. Then he told us there was a change of plan. The hole would have to be bigger, twice as big in fact. It was only then that our true situation began to dawn on us.

It continued like that. We'd finish making it bigger and he'd return and say it needed to go deeper. We said it was getting so deep it would need to be timbered. He tested the ground and said we could go another four-foot down before we'd need timber. We'd get to that yet. So we'd go deeper and he'd say bigger. Bigger, deeper — deeper, bigger. We never mentioned Longford sitting watching us in the JCB. Tom could also tell if we'd wandered off anywhere, how long we took for lunch, when we arrived and left, how often and for how long we stood up smoking. Tom never really criticised us for any of this. He couldn't in theory and by his own standards the job was getting done. But for us, the fact he knew all this was enough of an admonition. We began to call Longford a stool pigeon.

'I'm telling the man nothing,' he'd say. 'He just knows you boys too well.'

'This,' Diffley said, 'must be the biggest hole known to man. I mean barring those open cast mines in the Amazon where there's hundreds of them at it. You,' he'd say to Longford, 'you could dig that machine in down here and get us out of here in a day.'

'I has me orders,' Longford said, 'what more can I do? I'll tell youse what, I'll leave youse up to the bus stop the night? Sure if I did help youse he'd only make it bigger again. What more can I do?'

We didn't refuse the offer of the lift.

We were by now in a deeper phase, sweltering in the heat, the weather had got hotter. Even a bottle of water would be tepid by eleven in the morning. We were deep enough however to have some shade in the bottom of the hole — in fact the cold down there soon bit into your bones if you weren't moving. Then the jibing started. Longford had turned the machine round in a circle, facing the opposite side into the sun.

'Look at that bastard,' Diffley said, 'he's too lazy to get out. He's just getting the other side of his face done.'

Longford must have heard him.

'How do local boy makes good in London?' he said. 'What were you boys at, stalling that dumper? If it was me now, I'd have stayed with her. I'd a got on television.'

Obviously our fame was beginning to spread. Anyhow it was then we started to tell stories. Diffley would tell us about ghost currachs and drowned fishermen, siren voices drawing men to rocks.

'All them stories of yours is weird,' Longford told Diffley. But to me he said, 'He's an educated man. You'd know by the cut of him.'

Longford had a few stories himself. Mostly about fights with bouncers on the Holloway Road. Then he started talking about home.

'There's an island on a lake on our land,' he said, 'and if you went out there — they say there's an entrance to Purgatory on that island.'

'Now, that's weird,' Diffley said.

'You're the boy to talk about weird and them dreams you have.'

'What dreams ... ?'

'Well — there's that one about you being dead and having to cross a river, in a boat, and the man that's rowing the boat's called Sharon. Whoever heard of a man called Sharon?'

'You might have a point there,' Diffley said, 'but that's what he was called.'

That was when Diffley told us about the dream he had about a man rolling a stone up a hill. Every time he'd get to the top, off it'd take ... on its own ... back down the hill.

'And what happened to your boy?' Longford asked.

'I don't know,' Diffley said.

'That's what I mean ... weird ... sure what's the point in that?'

'That's what I thought myself,' Diffley said.

In the distance we could see the clouds of dust thrown up by the grey Commer van. Lonesome Tom was on his way back.

It was the Friday of the second week. At this stage we were dwarfed by the hole, had grown sick of it. Those of our friends who knew little of the building industry refused to believe us. What's the point? they wanted to know. Why would anyone carry on like that? We'd been told to knock another two foot off the bottom. This would take us to twelve foot, dangerous territory without timber. Tom assured us we would be going no deeper. If we were, we would get timber. We had given up asking what the hole was for: we knew what it was for.

That was the day I struck something metallic with the pick. I felt the jolt and heard it ring out. I raised the pick again but Diffley grabbed my arm. 'Wait,' he said before he climbed out of the hole and returned with a claw hammer. I said it was alright, it was only an old water mains or something.

'We don't know that,' he said, 'Tom says there's no services around here. Look around you. There was no one here before us. You wouldn't know what it would be.'

He began to hoke the ground out from beneath what I'd hit. After a few minutes you could just make out the fins.

We called to the Adam that night on the way home. Tom was at the bar as arranged. He bought us both a drink and we waited until the local news round-up came on the television. Tom turned to the other drinkers and told them to be quiet. There was Longford on the television, standing outside Terminal Three.

'Hand-digging I was,' he said, 'hard auld going in this weather, when I came across her. I just upped with her into the bucket of the machine and took her over here.'

'What happened then?' the woman interviewer asked.

Longford savoured his moment. He gestured behind him.

'Well, I carried her up the steps there into the office and I lands her on the agent's desk. Boy, you should have seen them clear out of there. Never saw anything like it, so I didn't.'

'Then they called the bomb squad?' she asked.

'Then they calls the bomb squad,' he agreed.

We turned away from the television.

'What do we do now?' I said.

'Back-fill the fucking thing. Back-fill it if you have to work all weekend.'

'And what about the machine? Can we use the machine?'

'Use the machine. Use the machine,' Tom said. 'That bollocks has to be some use.' He glanced up at Longford who was still talking.

'How do Andy Warhol and the fifteen minutes of fame,' Diffley said.

Longford's fifteen minutes passed, but the incident with the bomb wasn't forgotten. It became part of the folklore that

circulated about the Airport, like the story about the two
workers who came out of the bar and drove a dumper out
onto the apron as a Pan Am jet landed, welcoming the
passengers to Europe on behalf of the British and Irish
Governments. The part myself and Diffley played was never
fully uncovered. What happened on the peripheries of the
Airport was never subject to much control. No doubt the
work there had some long-term plan but most of us were in
the dark about it. We were ordered back to Terminal Three.
Now and again, over the next few weeks, one or the other of
us would meet someone who appeared to be in the know.
We'd get winked at, or someone would nod in passing and
mutter an aside about 'prime boys'. It meant we were known
— though most men wouldn't know why — and being
known meant we were on our ways to becoming
untouchable. We'd be at the Airport for as long as we wanted.

Then Larry Murphy the agent was promoted to a
Contracts Manager. Murphy's first move was to abolish our
afternoon tea break. Although we were on day-work rates
at Terminal Three — getting paid by the main contractor
regardless of whether we worked or stood about all day —
we were not entitled to a break at three o'clock. Not by
McGee's rules. Murphy's decree was officious, his way of
telling everyone he'd arrived. Still he wasn't altogether
happy with his promotion. It meant giving up his fiefdom
on the Bath Road, where he had a gang of men he knew
well, who socialised together in Camden Town. They were
like a firm within a firm. McGee's were full of gangs of
men that had come aboard at different times, arriving
together from other sites, other sub-contractors. Much as
myself and Tom and Diffley had. Men who looked out for
each other. This meant that there were inevitably a series of
fiefdoms on a job the size of that at Heathrow Airport.
There were specific gangs who looked after paving, others
who were in charge of pipe laying, while other men who

came in from outside with no links to one of these gangs
ended up on day-work. Murphy's promotion was an effort
to come to terms with this: an attempt, the latest of many,
from McGee's Head Office to impose some form of
cohesion on the job. Murphy though was the wrong man.
He was weak and vacillating. A man from outside was what
McGee's needed. Murphy was like a tribal leader brought
into national government, yearning for the desert wastes
he'd emerged from while also trying to pillage where he
could.

His mistake was that he'd moved against the men whom
he perceived were weak. The men in Terminal Three owed
fealty to no one. They may not have had a protector who
could ensure that they got paid for days they missed at work,
but neither did they have to spend their weekends drinking
with someone they didn't particularly like. Because of that the
whole job began to go awry. There were mutterings in corners
which by themselves amounted to little, but taken overall led
to widespread disaffection. Work was done unwillingly, and
Murphy's orders were deliberately misunderstood. Jobs were
left uncompleted, days were missed, and missed days meant
lost income, lost for McGee's. The rumours had begun to
circulate: the M25 was on everyone's lips. Sean Hennelly had
another big job up at the Target Roundabout. Men drifted
away. Lonesome Tom got the start on the M25 and the
money out there was very good. Murphy was becoming
exasperated, and the more exasperated he grew the more
things spiralled beyond him.

One day I met Frankie Dolan in the canteen. I knew
Dolan to see from the time I'd worked with Dunne at the
Airport. I also knew him from playing Gaelic football. Dolan
had played county for Armagh. He was a bit of a legend. But
he was also an agent for the main firm. He asked me what I
was doing, and when I told him I was mainly sweeping up,
he said he thought I was a kerb layer. I said I could lay kerbs

but made no great claims to it. 'If I remember,' he said, 'you can do rightly.'

Two days later Murphy came looking for me.

'You've got a friend somewhere,' he said. 'I'm told you can lay kerbs. Why didn't you tell me that?'

I said he'd never asked me what I could do.

'Get your gear together and follow me.'

And so I started as a kerb layer on the side of the road that lead to the Terminal. I was working with a man named Tom Sweeney. Sweeney, from Kerry, was an old hand with McGee. He knew everyone, but knowing everyone had done him no good. He was one of those men whose face never quite fitted in, the man in the team photo that nobody remembers. He was aware of his own situation and was growing restless with it. He had seen other men promoted over him. Some of these men must have made good gangers, were no doubt better paviers, but not all of them. This rankled with Sweeney and he complained about it all the time.

The run of kerbs we'd been set was awkward. It was on a radius that curved from one 45° turn into another one before it straightened out. The straight run itself was over half-a-mile long, on both sides of the road. It would make someone a lot of money. Sweeney was sure that it had already been assigned. One of Murphy's cronies was eyeing it up. We, he believed, would be dropped as soon as the difficult work of finishing the turns was completed. He harped on about this all day. He wasn't made for price-work. In fairness to him he fundamentally disagreed with the idea. He said anyone should be able to make their living without pulling and dragging for a few extra bob. While he was saying this, I was pulling and dragging. Every morning I got to work before him, went into the depot and placed two kerbs across the wheelbarrow. Then I pushed them up the road and left them in position for laying. A run that was repeated fourteen or fifteen times. When it came to laying them I stood them up

and positioned them. A kerb was about half my body weight.
As with any weight, handling is the problem. Knowing the
point of balance, although this can be learned. But all
Sweeney did was bone them into position. All the time he was
forecasting what would happen in a few days, once we got the
corners built.

Murphy arrived with our wages on Friday. He seemed
pleased with our progress and asked Sweeney when would we
reach the straight? 'Monday week,' Sweeney said. Murphy
nodded thoughtfully. 'What then?' Sweeney asked.

'I'm not too sure yet,' Murphy said, 'but isn't there a run
of kerbs near enough to London Town after that.'

'Will we be on that?'

'I don't know yet, sure anything can happen. What I don't
want you doing is going mad. This is all day-work and all we
want is a day's work.'

Sweeney agreed with that. That suited him anyway.

I met Lonesome Tom that night. There was work coming
up on the M25. They were paying £26 a shift, £8 more than
I was getting. 'A week or so,' he said, 'stick it out.' I told him
about Murphy and the kerbs. He thought Sweeney was right.

'They'll have the hard part on day-work. You'll not see
price-work right enough. That'll be all their own crowd. It's
all sown up already. If I was you,' he said, 'I'd go and see your
man Dolan.'

'What would I say to him?'

'Say nothing. Let him do the talking. But I'd say you were
as well giving him a backhander as someone else giving
Murphy one. '

I didn't have to go to see Dolan, he came looking for me
one day the following week. He wanted to know if we were
deliberately going slow. I told him what was happening and
he proposed a deal. He could get me the job on a price if I
wanted. I didn't even have to worry about the price: he would
sort that out too. He even said he could get me a man on day-

work to help me. Of course I would have to look after him.
We shook hands on it. The only thing that worried me was
the man on day-work. I asked him if I could bring my own
man with me? He agreed to that. In any case I knew Sweeney
was back off to Dingle for the rest of the summer.

That night I went to the Adam with Diffley. Lonesome
Tom was there. He said we could both start on the M25 the
following Monday. I told him I wanted to make a go of the
kerbs on a price.

'So you talked to Dolan?'

'I did. He even agreed I can take a man with me on day-
work.'

'And who had you in mind? Wait now a minute,' he said,
'Joe Sheridan.'

'Joe Sheridan,' I agreed.

I had never worked with Joe Sheridan, but I knew how
everyone said he was as good a pavier as there was to be
found. Joe Sheridan had near legendary status, as a worker
and a drinker. He was a Second World War veteran and had
been decorated. He'd played county football back in Ireland
and had been on the verge of that famous Cavan team before
he'd emigrated. Joe never talked about any of this, apart from
when he had a few drinks and then he'd sing "The Gallant
John Joe". His status resulted from all of this and from the
way he coped with anything that had come his way. He'd lost
a wife and son. If a man was complaining, he could be sure
someone would turn to him and say, what are you on about
— look at Joe Sheridan. The only problem with Joe was that
he didn't work much anymore. He was getting on. He was
too old for lifting heavy slabs and kerbs. His back was gone.
Yet when I went up to the house that night to look for him I
knew none of this.

He told me he wasn't too bothered about work. He didn't
get out and about much anymore. What was there left for
him but more of the same? I explained that he wouldn't have

to do much. All I wanted him for was his advice — I was told
he knew all there was to know. He could sit on the kerbs and
watch me. The money was £18 a day and depending on what
I made I'd make it up. Wouldn't it get him out of the house?
That was probably what swung it. He went out to the kitchen
and came back with two bottles of beer. He stood looking out
the window as the sun declined across the playing fields at the
back of his house.

'Do you know,' he said, 'it's fierce good weather to be
inside. Do you think you could get me a bottle of brandy? I
does like a drop of brandy with a raw egg if I has to go out
early in the morning.'

Before I left we shook hands.

Back at the house Diffley had a big red mark around a
date in July on the calendar. That was the date we agreed:
there'd be no reneging, he said, no matter what big money I
got myself on. I argued that the date wasn't important. Going
to Germany was important, whenever we went. No one ever
did anything on the date they said. I did agree though that I
wouldn't be looking for more than a week's grace. It was
already the middle of May. We had six weeks left. Six weeks
took us into July, which was late enough to go looking for
building work in another country. But, he said, it gave me
plenty of time to show what I was made of and him another
stint with Lonesome Tom.

That weekend he went back to Ireland, and I went on a
march. A march that assembled at Hyde Park Corner and
walked up Picadilly, turning down Regent Street, where we
were attacked by the National Front while the police looked
on. The head of the march turned towards Trafalgar Square
where it was turned away — refused the right to assembly —
and made to skirt down the side streets, now under a heavy
police escort. We were herded down the Strand and across
Waterloo Bridge and into the bullring at Waterloo. A vapid
punk-rock band mounted the back of a lorry and played a set

for a crowd that could hardly raise a cheer. Then a woman who had indeed once caused men to storm barricades rose to address us. All about us and above us, on what resembled battlements, were lines of policemen: the visors on their helmets down, shields raised and batons drawn. They outnumbered us three or four to one. After the woman had finished her address the desultory crowd made its separate ways home. We were pushed and jostled by the police as we passed. They called us Paddy murderers.

Back at the Airport I was now on price-work. I didn't give too much thought to what losing the job would mean to Murphy. I reckoned it wasn't my job to tell him. We were working within the Airport security zone and had to carry passes. Parking was strictly prohibited. I was progressing better than I'd hoped. Dolan was also easing my way. We had the use of a forklift, pallets of kerbs were dropped at regular intervals. Joe Sheridan too had proved to be a real boon. He spent most of the day sitting on a stack of pallets, his spindly legs swinging. Where I'd have had to use a tape measure, he trusted his eyes. He was never wrong, and was teaching me to trust my own judgement. The only trouble we had was when a safety officer came along and asked us where our helmets were?

'I wore a helmet for you before you were born,' Sheridan said, 'I wore a helmet all across North Africa chasing Rommel, and Hitler himself stopped me on Monte Casino, and I'll be fucked if I'm ever wearing a helmet again.'

I thought the safety officer might have made an issue out of it but he didn't. After that he just walked past us, chastened.

We already had our first draw of the money we were earning by the time Murphy came around. We'd half-finished the first run of kerbs when he arrived on the Thursday afternoon. I looked up as he drove past, then heard him brake sharply and pull his Granada over on the opposite side of the road. His face was livid as he stalked back up the road in our direction.

'If that's our man,' Sheridan said, 'I'll leave it to you. I reckon I could do with a quick pint. Or maybe I'll find out how my horses are going.'

'What the fuck are you at?' Murphy ranted. 'What the fuck are you at? Are you trying to ruin me? Who the fuck told you to start on this section? This is fucking day-work. What are you being a hero for?'

'What's the problem Larry?' I asked.

'The problem? The problem? Look at what you're doing. I told you this job is to last. There's two weeks in what you've done already. And who the fuck's this man?' he asked, turning to point after Joe's retreating form.

'But I thought you knew,' I said. 'I took this work myself. Priced it and all.'

He leant over into my face. I could smell alcohol from him, his fists bunching and unbunching. He was unsteady on his feet. Behind him I could just about see Sheridan — coming back down the road and trying to attract my attention.

'If you took this job, then I'd untake it if I was you. This is McGee's work. No one fucks with McGee. Do you know what you're doing? No one fucks with me and gets away with it. You'll never work for this firm again.'

'Larry, can you hold on a minute,' I said, 'there's something wrong over there.' I stepped around him. He seemed transfixed in position, as if it would take too much effort to move his head and shoulders to follow me. Sheridan was pointing up the road. Up where a tow truck had already levered the Granada into the air. It had only taken a few seconds and the driver was already back into the cab. By now Murphy had turned around to see what was happening.

'My fucking car!' he shouted. 'My fucking car!'

9

THERE WAS ANOTHER QUID PRO QUO WITH DOLAN AND ONE I hadn't altogether reckoned on — football. When I came over to London first we used to play Gaelic on the field at Bothwell, on the edge of Southall. I had a few runs out with the Brendan's. It was my romantic entanglement with Sheila and a growing fondness for drink that had put an end to my career, or so I had thought. I never had the requisite zeal required — not since I was fourteen and used to practise, over and over, the dummy that Gerry McElhenney, the Derry footballer, used to sell. McElhenney would drop the ball from his hands, as if to kick it, and then snatch it back as a defender lunged to block the kick. Then he would step imperiously over the fallen man and continue with his progress. I had a cousin who was playing in the half-back line for the county at the time. I knew he practised religiously, on his own, banging the ball off the gable end of his house for hours on end. I also always remembered seeing a television programme about the great Kerry footballer, Mick O'Connell. O'Connell used to run the roads of Valentia on his own. It was easy to tell he was well within himself: the camera showing him leaping upward and touching the branches of trees with his fingertips. Those branches were, I was well aware, far beyond the leap of any poor mortal. It would have been impossible not to have been impressed with the grace of O'Connell. To watch him, as a player, rise upward, field the ball and place a kick in a single fluid motion, like the half-seen dart of a deadly snake, so quickly that it might never have happened. There was too the first goal I ever remembered — or half-remembered — a ball that came back off the upright in the 1968 All Ireland Final, in black & white. A ball that all the other players watched except for Sean O'Neill who buried a volley past the hapless Johnny Culloty in the Kerry goal. Those were the images I carried with me. In one game only, as a fifteen-year-old, I fetched well beyond what I could have expected, ending up with two goals and six points. But as a rule I settled for the odd, opportunist score, though others would wonder whether I really had meant to lob the goalkeeper or whether an effort to put the ball over the bar for a point had fallen short instead. With the McElhenney move I had considerable problems: never quite pulling it off and losing confidence after I landed in a tangle of limbs with the opposing defender on a couple of occasions.

So, by the time I was playing in London, dreams of greatness were beyond me. Football had been as much about a social occasion when I knew nobody, and by the time I had a range of friends its attractions had waned. I could hardly be troubled to train. Men like Dolan were evangelists for the game and what I felt for his zeal was genuine fear rather than awe. There were men who would have stirred you from your bed on a Sunday morning in the parish I came from, no matter how useless you were to their cause. By now I was truly inured to being shouted at, being told as a corner-forward not to stray upfield, that half my job was to keep the ball in play. To lurk on the edge of the penalty area, as if I were no more than a glorified ball boy. And when it did come my way I would twist and turn, trying to bamboozle my opposing number with pure chicanery, while they roared at me to release the ball. Being from Monaghan they felt I would be well able to look after myself. There was a dash of truth in this proposition: after all, I had been sidelined as a seventeen-year-old in a Junior match in Mayo for being dirty. But also what passes for good football at an underage level can notoriously dissipate in the years afterward, and not just because of lack of interest. The boxing adage that a good big un will beat a good little un holds also for Gaelic football — not always, but enough times so that it counts — the good big un being likely to weigh the odds in his favour by crippling his opponent.

Still, I had my moments for the Brendan's. I played well on the Saturday of the London Sevens, then failed to show up on Sunday. I'd scored the equalising goal, having laid on the one before it, to draw a semi-final of the Tipperary Cup. It hardly mattered that we were hammered in the replay: we weren't meant to get two chances anyway and like all teams who emerge onto the field with that attitude, we were happy to settle for the once-off headlines in the *Irish Post* — BRENDAN'S SPRING SURPRISE. I also provided great entertainment in a Junior game against Aer Lingus out at New Eltham, where their corner-back spent most of the first half chasing me about the pitch after I'd clipped his ankles on several occasions. He was overweight and breathless and ended up getting sent off. The haymaker he swung would have finished me off, had it connected. When it didn't, he fell forwards and ended up panting on his hands and knees in the muck.

When Dolan approached me to play in the first round of the London Championship there wasn't much I could do but agree to show up. Dolan was obviously the sort of man I needed to keep in with. The game was being played in the

new London County Grounds at Ruislip. If I said no I would
have to face him for at least another ten days at work.
Agreeing to go and not showing up wasn't an option either, as
he informed me straight off. The game was on a Wednesday
evening. One of those June evenings that would have
delighted me four or five years before, an evening that you
knew would stretch inexorably into night. When all that
would be visible in the waning night would be the white
O'Neill's ball in constant flight. The type of evening on which
I still stop and listen for the sound of leather hitting leather
and the shouts of frenzied boys carrying from a great distance.
We were playing The Kingdom, who were then dominating
London football, and might have expected to be put to the
sword early. The Kingdom were the current Champions,
though the older players on our team spoke of them as if they
were in transition. There were mutterings in the days leading
up to the game that they were there for the taking. For the first
time in years the backbone of the team was no longer solidly
from Kerry. They had a Cavan County player in midfield —
a shoo-in — fixed up with a fancy bank job. London football
was like that. Many a team was supported by a subbie.
Prestige companies like Aer Lingus and Guinness fielded
teams. We had one great asset — our midfielder was Terry
Sheridan, Joe the pavier's son, and it was well known that any
team in London would have had him. Why he was loyal to us
puzzles me still. We had one or two other useful players,
including Dolan, who didn't know the meaning of giving up.
I once saw him continue on a solo run after the final whistle
had gone — oblivious to anything other than the ball.

My welcome in the dressing room that night was less
than effusive. For once each player seemed sunk in his own
reverie. I already knew that this would be my last game for
some time and the odd silence heightened the elegiac feelings
I had about it all. Barely twenty, I was hanging up my boots,
for the time being at least. I didn't expect to be picked to play

and I wasn't disappointed. I was on the sideline beside the
mentors, passing the time. I was thinking that we would put
up a show for the first half, fade early in the second and I
would get thrown into the corner for the last few minutes. By
that time Dolan and Sheridan would be reduced to humping
any ball they got long into the square, looking for the break.
For anything that might take the bad look off it. The usual
bad taste from our mouths. We would all go for a drink
afterwards and remember how well we played in the first half-
hour, wondering as we always did was there something
elusive that other teams knew about, that we didn't. Some
secret ingredient we all knew in fact was a mixture of
diligence and confidence.

But that wasn't the way it transpired. Nobody had
explained to the Kingdom that they were vulnerable. Perhaps,
like many teams that have been told they've peaked, they used
that as motivation. Knowing the best thing to do was to
annihilate the opposition. To start the rumours: 'You should
have seen the Kingdom. By fuck they stuffed the Brendan's.'
In truth too there was no great belief in us that they were
assailable. Nobody told us to go for the quick score or two
that might have opened a fissure in their armour. Within
fifteen minutes we were down a goal and six points to one
point. Moreover our single point was opportunistic — a long
ball launched into the sun by Dolan that their goalkeeper
could have safely caught. Instead he fisted it over his own bar.
Sheridan was out of sorts. I watched him, before each ball was
kicked out, drawing out at clumps of grass with his boot, his
eyes cast downward. The game was passing our midfield by.
Dolan was like a hod carrier looking for a ladder, buffeted
right and left by their half-forward line which was wreaking
havoc. Only for Noel English in goal we would have been
completely buried. Bending and twisting like a will of the
wisp, he was pulling balls down that seemed bent on bursting
the net, even catching above his own crossbar. The one thing

evident to any of us watching was that the Kingdom were intent on beating us early — they were going for goals, even though their own mentors were shouting at them to take their points. 'Take your points,' they roared, 'the goals will come.'

When Denis Donnelly on the sideline told me I was on, I was sure he'd taken leave of his senses. What use was I in the corner when the ball hadn't got that far?

'Centre-half,' he said, 'you'll not catch a cold there.'

I was half-elated.

'Centre-half forward,' I said.

'Centre-half back.'

I had never played anywhere in the back line, never mind that their half-forward line was rampant. Meanwhile Donnelly was making one other change, putting Frank Cagney, who was normally a back, into the half-forward line.

'What'll I do?' I said, as Cagney was already handing his slip of paper to the referee. 'I've never played there before.'

'You'll be facing the ball,' he said. 'Win the first one. Then take that ginger fucker out of it.'

The Ginger Fucker was the centre-half forward. He was also one of their best players. He played for London, and some said he would have been there or thereabouts if he was back in Kerry — he'd at least have got a run in the League, they said. That was some compliment in an era when Kerry were unstoppable.

The Ginger Fucker told me from the off he would do me. If I had any sense I would give him the run of the pitch. The first ball I went for I went for with my fist. It was breaking between us and when I made contact with it I also hit the side of his head. He was clutching his ear. The ball bounced into Dolan's hands. He cleared it up the field. I watched Paul Reilly swoop low to cover the bounce. He side-stepped his man and dropped the ball over the bar. Reilly ran back towards us with his fists clenched. The next ball that came between us favoured me. I had the hop judged when I was hit

from behind. Bowled over by something that seemed to carry
on right through me. I didn't see much more of what had hit
me than the green and gold bands on his jersey. The Ginger
Fucker had the ball. He played it out, took a return pass and
lobbed it over the bar. To be fair to him there was no more
movement in what he did than what was absolutely required.
He was a mathematician — a master of oblique angles — hit-
and-run and fade into space. Except that he came back to tell
me: 'I told you, you Orange cunt, I'll do you.' I could hear
Donnelly shouting at me not to let him see the ball. It seemed
unnecessary, overstated even. I knew that as a forward if you
missed a ball there would always be another one. If you had
a bad game you were useless — yet people would forget that
after a goal the next day out. For a back a bad game was a
disaster. You were immediately at fault. It was there for
everyone to see and most likely there would be no go at
redemption. The percentages were different. I didn't need
Donnelly on the sidelines to tell me that. If my man had the
angles worked out, it was my job to cut off the supply. Every
ball had to be marked down, fifty-fifty.

From that until half-time I held him scoreless. I had a
nagging suspicion though that that had as much to do with
him conserving energy. We briefly got the better of them. We
racked up two points before the break so that it came,
surprisingly, as an unwelcome respite. We were still six points
adrift. I sat over near the sideline on my own with my quarter
orange. I looked over at them and knew that they were
worried. They were clustered about my man and their two
midfielders. They had a sense of their own vulnerability. They
were looking for leadership, for someone to tell them — to
reassure them — that they had the beating of us. There is no
great secret in what is said at half-time. None that I ever saw.
Keep at it, you're doing great, or For fuck's sake lads. There's
usually some wit with a comment like 'Every man
a man and two on the big fella.' And there is often an under-

lying suspicion that it just mightn't be your day. A suspicion that can be contagious.

Terry Sheridan came over to where I was sitting.

'You have him in your pocket,' he said.

Sheridan never said much. For all his abundant talent he wasn't a talker on the pitch. He wasn't a natural leader. Dolan was and Dolan did the talking. You could watch Sheridan. In the middle of the night you might think you could emulate him. But it was not a thought that would last for long. He wasn't a talker off the pitch either. He'd have his few pints and go home. Men said he was a family man. To me he seemed to have some problem he carried within himself — constantly mulling it over. He was withdrawn, almost isolated somewhere on his own. He'd never spoken much to me. Nothing beyond an acknowledgement, mostly a nod or monosyllable. Yet none of us cared much what ailed him as long as he wore our jersey.

'I know,' I said, surprised at myself.

'Right now,' Donnelly shouted. 'Back out there lads. There's only two goals in it. Two goals and a point — three scores and it's ours.'

There was a change in Sheridan in the second half, as if he'd stirred himself from his reverie. A players like that always has the ability to mesmerise the rest of us. When I was playing Sunday League soccer and was first asked to play Saturday League, I asked what was the difference? 'A yard,' I was told. Sheridan had that yard in any league. The first ball he fielded that half he landed in space, the space that a player like him can find, that gives him a few seconds in which the likes of him can't be touched. The only measure of players like that from game to game is what they do with those seconds. This time he set off at a run, ghosting past tackles. You could almost have etched a circle about him with a compass — as close as any of the opposition got to him in motion. He then drove the ball past the goalkeeper, low and hard, like you were told to from the time you first kicked a ball. Low and hard and think of the net bulging. It would make you cry to see something like that — something you could only dream of.

That was all we needed. It was the first time I'd ever played on a team where every player seemed to know what the others were doing. Those few brief moments of telepathy. For a while pure kinesis. Even Willie Cassin above in my corner seemed to dart with purpose. To make the runs I used to make, except no one was calling him back. Runs out of position that worked as a decoy, his position being filled by other runners. By the full-forward, the half-forwards, by Sheridan, by Dolan even. I began to realise that I had spent years facing the wrong way. That having to turn with the ball was mostly beyond me. Facing the ball — with the ball travelling towards me — was completely different. I must have been watching. I must have learned something. I knew everywhere the ball was going to bounce. I watched the easy way the opposition built up their movements from their half-back line, saw them building their way down the field like weather fronts, and moved to intercept them. All the months of working had bulked me out. I felt I had a fierce upper-body strength. I was buoyant as cork. I put my head down and ran with the ball, feeling like I was wearing armour. Maybe it was all those years in that corner that I'd learned from, or maybe there was something atavistic about it all, some gene I shared with my cousin who played for the County. Either way, it was the first game where I was assiduous and relentless. Where I followed every ball. Never stopped running. At the start of the half, as the Ginger Fucker stood beside me, shouldering me, I looked into his face. 'Jasus,' I said, 'you're going bald.' He put his hand up to his hairline, then caught me laughing. I could hear Donnelly roaring at me. 'Ride the fucker,' he shouted, 'ride the fucker.' With ten minutes to go he was moved off me. Moved into the corner. It was, for him, I knew, equivalent to exile.

We scored four more points, one after each other, and after that traded scores with them. We were a point to the good coming to the close. But in the underdog there's always the spoor of a belief that you'll always end the underdog. That the other team will get what luck's going. The merest shaving of a decision, that fraction of momentum added to their forward thrust. The infamous stasis, for instance, that can strike a referee's watch. And that's what happened to us. We knew we needed another score to lever the game beyond their reach. We looked around at each other and we knew it. We knew it as time elongated. It all went into slow motion — and still is. At least that's what I was thinking when I let the ball bounce over my shoulder. When I failed to cover the hop. In slow motion when I tried to turn and the back-two studs in my boot hooked into the turf, spancelling me. The way the ball fell into the hands of the Ginger Fucker — back from exile in the corner — moving to crowd the midfield. The way his shot drifted wide, and then drifted back, as languorous as a wayward balloon. Spiralling of its own volition until it dropped over the bar and the referee raised the whistle to his lips and blew full time. We were still looking at each other when Ginger came over to me and shook my hand.

'Great game boy,' he said, 'no hard feelings. What's your name? I'd say you're a ringer.'

We had a replay we told ourselves in the dressing room, and in the bar in Ruislip, afterwards. We could turn them over. We could, not would, turn them over. Nobody said it was my fault. They all said I had a great game. I made the difference. In myself I felt I'd made fuck-all difference. I said as much to Noel English, the goalkeeper, at the bar, who was telling me how well I played.

'You'll be at training next Tuesday. We'll do them yet.'

'I'm going to Germany,' I said.

'Jasus, the first good game you played this last two years and you're fucking off on us. What are you going for?'

'For work,' I said. Donnelly joined us.

'What type of work?' he asked.

'Shuttering.'

'Did you ever shutter before?'

'No,' I said.

'You'll not stick it. It's hard-going out there. There's many a man came back.'

'I'll stick it alright.'

'You'll not, you know. Come out with me and I'll put you on the tools. I'll give you all the shuttering you want.'

'For fuck's sake, look at that …' English shouted from behind us, before I could answer. 'Ah, would you look at that.' And we turned around to see a replay of Liam Brady, missing a penalty in the European Cup Winners Cup Final.

'Fuck him anyhow.'

10

WE WERE TO MEET LONESOME TOM IN THE ADAM THAT LAST Friday evening. I had to lie low after the kerb job finished at the Airport. Murphy, I knew, would be as good as his word, and he would cherish the grudge for a long time. So I went to work on the fabled M25. It was, like all the big construction jobs, a defining moment in the lives of anyone who worked on it. Defining in that men would always refer to it. Even though I only spent two weeks there that's something I share with hundreds. Even so, it was like being back out at Heathrow with Dunne that first day — there was nothing to do. All the heavy work being done by machinery. Tom was again the ganger. There were twenty-four of us on the section between Slough and Staines. From where we were we could watch the approach of an agent or foreman in a van from miles away. About us were piled tonnes of sand and aggregate — at the sight of any fast-moving cloud of dust we'd jump to our feet and begin hoking the ground. The sun beat down relentlessly. There was a pub in the trees behind us and there were always eight of us in it.

Tom confessed to me that he believed any man who spent long enough there would forget how to work. It was exactly what I felt. I had no head for drinking during the day in that weather. The beer made me listless and I struggled through the heat like it were sludge. I was glad when Diffley suggested we skip work for the last week.

We spent the last few days instead traversing London. One night we wound up in The Dove along the river in Hammersmith, where we got into conversation with a group of Americans. One of them told us her name was Chi Chi, how she was a Buddhist and claimed Irish ancestry. That was how we came to spend the following evening at a Buddhist meeting. There were about twelve people there, who began to chant, a deep incantation. After a while some of them began to move rhythmically with the sound of it. I realised I was the only person there whose eyes weren't shut. I glanced across at Diffley, eyes clamped tight and chanting with the best of them. He had a trace of a grin on his face. I padded to the door and made my way to the nearest pub. Diffley, Chi Chi and two others joined me a while later. My absence wasn't remarked upon. I could hear Chi Chi telling Diffley there was nothing like entering New York harbour on a boat. I could hear him begin to romanticise the sea. She eventually asked him would he come to another meeting?

'There are no second acts in Irish lives,' he said. 'We don't get two gos at anything.'

'That's very good,' she said, shaking her head. 'Who said that?'

'Fitzgerald,' he said, nodding in my direction.

'You said that?' she asked.

'No, he said that,' I said.

She turned back to him.

'It's our tragedy,' Diffley added.

Our last night the Adam was unusually full, as if the word had spread about us leaving. It wasn't that, though it was to prove to be one of those nights I would never forget. There was no particular reason to go to the Adam, other than to get our week-in-hand from Tom and perhaps to say goodbye to him, more than anyone else. There was Irish music there that night, for the first time. A fiddle player behind the door who I knew to see round the place. His name was Meehan and he was playing on his own. His hands were swollen with work — they were like shovels, dwarfing the fiddle. But he played with great verve and rhythm. His music was usually all drive but that evening, as we entered, he was playing some slow, mournful piece that sounded almost like classical music. It had gained some kind of purchase on the men. They were actually listening to him, raptly. I was told to shush when I asked for two light & lagers.

In the corner I saw the Rocking Horse on his own. He was clutching a pint against his chest. It was well-known that the Rocking Horse was barred in every pub on the High Road. Some men thought he was simple. The most I ever got out of him was that he had a plan. Having watched him over the past eighteen months I thought I knew what it was. He'd sidle into a pub and look for a barman who didn't know him. Then he'd buy a pint. When there was a mouthful left, he'd show himself to one of his persecutors. The glass would be lifted from his hands and he'd be escorted to the door. He'd begin to make noises then and the barman would reimburse him the price of the drink. He'd disappear up the road on the lookout for someone else who didn't know him. Later that night he might reappear in the same place, once it had got busy, and try the same trick again. Such was his plan that he was able to drink all night for the price of a pint.

Eventually Meehan drew to the end of the slow air. He put the fiddle down and drew his sleeve across his forehead. Then he blinked and grinned — as if he'd noticed us all there for the first time. Everybody started to laugh and any tension there might have been in the place dissipated. In that manner the music set the tone for the rest of the evening.

At that point the Rocking Horse showed himself and Chris the publican shot out from behind the bar and grabbed him by the elbow.

'Hold on there a minute,' someone said, 'that poor devil's harmless. Here I'll buy him a drink.'

There was a murmur of assent and Chris relented. By now Meehan had the fiddle in his hands again and had already launched into the "Dingle Regatta", a tune that has in it the bounce of boats on an undulating sea. Immediately the Rocking Horse took up the rhythm, hunkering down and rising to his feet in time with the music. A couple of men sniggered but within seconds others had started to copy him. On the other side of the bar men were moving in a counter rhythm — falling and rising in time with the rise and dip of Meehan's bow. The fiddler then too got to his feet and joined in. He seemed to prolong the tune, to drag it out until everyone was breathless, yet at the same time lost in the motion of it all, as he began to play faster and faster. The two English barmaids were by now also moving in time with the music. Only Chris was on his own, standing at the jump, wearing those old-fashioned armbands men used to wear to keep their shirt sleeves pulled up.

I have had to tell myself many times since then that those weren't children in the Adam that night. They weren't young men either. Rather they were men off buildings sites at the end of a very hot day, encased in sweat and dust, moving like marionettes to a Kerry tune played by a Donegal fiddle player. Meehan played until everyone was out of breath, then finished abruptly, bouncing the bow off the strings twice, then lurching backwards and sitting down again. He put the fiddle back in its case, drained his pint, slipped the case backwards into the crook of his arm and exited the building. There was a brief silence as men looked about at each other, grinning ruefully, followed by a surge to get to the bar. And nobody mentioned what had happened for the rest of the night.

There were men I didn't know asking me about Germany, pressing their addresses or phone numbers on me in case things worked out. Others were making the expected predictions, that we'd be back in a week. I remember the faces lined up along the bar. Yeller Dunne was there and by the end of the night was the worst for wear, his head nodding like one of those novelty dogs in the back of a car. He bought drink for everyone. 'Buying company,' Tom called it, asking 'What's he doing here?' I said I didn't know: he just called in. But Dunne was oblivious to us all. When he started to tell me about the pub back in Cavan, I pulled away from him. He had his elbows resting on the bar, his clothing as usual looking too big for him, the cuffs of his trousers puddled up about his boots. I left him lost in a miasma, nodding to himself like the victim of some great cosmic indiscretion.

It was a warm night and the light was a long time dying. The street lights eventually reflecting through the windows and prolonging its effects. The faces along the bar were lined and tanned by all weathers, their features taking on a sepia glow. I had so much drink taken I began to feel there was something unearthly about it all. As time wore on various faces began to disappear, one by one — as they would from my life — their great thirsts slaked. Diffley had long gone to see his Buddhist and I was on my own amidst all these people I knew. The Full-Back for the County was blundering about the place and T-Bone was going up and down the bar winding people up. He told me that he'd heard Hoppy the manhole expert had died back yonder at Christmas. Somewhere the far side of Belmullet, he said, getting a bucket of water from the well. Keeled over, the auld ticker, he said. But all of that seemed to pass me by, though I think I nodded, as if my assent were needed.

There were so many men there whose stories I knew, even
if only vaguely. There was Martin Lynch from Connemara,
an old Long-Distance Kiddie, who slept rough even though
he owned two houses. Martin Lynch, who when once asked,
condescendingly, where he'd spent the previous night,
replied, 'With John Smith.'

'Which John Smith?'

'John Smith. Born 1882. Died 1915.'

There was Jervis Fullerton whose son was doing time for
Jervis's mistake. Jervis had several lorries and had seen, in his
travels, a great pile of top soil just beyond the boundary of the
Airport. He marked it and even told us all of his intent, one
night in the Adam. There was no talking to Jervis. He sent a
man up there one Saturday morning with a digger and began
to load it up onto one of his lorries. Within minutes the
machine man was surrounded by armed police. The pile of
top soil was more than just a careless arrangement, and what
had looked like a traffic cone on top of it was really a beacon
vital to air traffic control. The son did the time. Jervis
meanwhile had two machines on the M25. He was looking
forward to four years' hire on day-work. It was said he'd
stolen them in the North of England. He had the same aim
as Dunne, except his pub turned out to be located in some
fastness on the Fermanagh-Leitrim border.

I looked around at the others, men there with their
children, skinheads, Teds or punks, and I felt I would never
see these things again — not in the same way. I always
thought that the most any of us could ask for was a degree
of education, plus some surety about where we came from.
But for most of those men there was no indemnity. Most of
them had few enough things they could tabulate in their
favour apart from the ability to work blindly. I looked at
their sons and the odd daughter and wondered what was in
it for them as their fathers and mothers assembled bits and
pieces of different counties to make a history of sorts? At

times like this it felt to me that they were living in a fugue
state — a place where to be Irish was no advantage. A place
where others emerged from their parents' pasts and planted
bombs amongst them: our history continually impinging
on them.

I eventually went up to Lonesome Tom and said sorry.
He thought I was talking about not turning up on Monday.
He said it was no odds, both myself and Diffley had
graduated to the status of dead men anyway. Maybe there
was a future for him in the M25. This work thing was
overrated.

It wasn't what I meant and I told him that, but I couldn't
tell him what I did mean. I couldn't find words. He was
leaving and I went outside with him. He shook hands with
me.

'You'll be alright anyhow,' he said, 'sure you're a prime
boy.' He laughed and went off up the road shaking his head,
his looping shadow dancing about the lamp-posts.

I made my way across London that night in a reverie —
from Kentish Town to Acton. The streets were quiet and an
occasional taxi whizzed past me before I could gather
enough resolution to flag one down. The shadows along the
road had begun to dissipate by the time I caught sight of the
bridge at the top of the road where I lived. I could still hear
the buzz of the pub, the "Dingle Regatta" going round and
round in my head like carnival music. Yet when I turned
into my own road, it was as if I'd walked off a bustling,
neon-lit sea-front onto a quiet beach where the light was
now playing itself out, pallid, bleached and disinterested —
indifferent to what passed beneath it. I knew then that I had
no indemnity either. That there was no going back. I knew
that like I was learning a lesson.

A matter of hours later I phoned my mother from
Liverpool Street Station, minutes before the Harwich train
left for the Hook of Holland. She said she thought I'd left the

week before. What was I at? It might have been better if I'd married that Sligo woman. She might have made something of me.

11

I ARRIVED WITH DIFFLEY INTO HANNOVER HAUPTBAHNHOF at two o'clock in the morning. The place was thronged with whores and Turkish *Gastarbeiters*. As I watched the Turks, it struck me again how close men on the move stuck to their belongings — their battered suitcases. The Turks reminded me of those Irishmen at Euston Station or photos of older generations of Irish people at places like Cobh or Holyhead. Mostly men without women, on the move from one job to another. Wary and ill at ease, wearing old fashioned suits, the Turks seemed like moustached, shuffling anachronisms in that train station, standing out against the billboard of a half-naked woman advertising a tabloid newspaper. Their eyes were fixed ahead of them, and now and then a foot would snake out and brush against a cardboard case, tied up with twine or a leather belt, reassuring them that it was still there.

Germany was as alien to them as it was to me. Whereas when I had gone to London in the mid-Seventies I had already evoked a sense of the place. I had watched their football on television, I knew their politics, I'd listened to John Peel on a rickety transistor beneath the bed-clothes — after that it was only a matter of scale or the individual tics that are found in any not altogether familiar place. The sound of a tube shunting fast through underground tunnels, the vibration of dub music on Electric Avenue in Brixton, the smell of Indian food in Southall, the murmur of prayer from a mosque, the realisation when I spoke that mine was sometimes the only Irish accent in a room — all that together with the overwhelming forward momentum of any big city. It was a matter of accent more than anything else, the language was the same.

But in the hubbub of noise in Hannover train station there was little that familiar. For a few brief minutes there I was the other. I thought I was the only one with that feeling as I looked about, half in awe, half in expectation, but Diffley described the same experience to me years later. He said it was a feeling we could never repeat, the dissonance of it all: the babble of language, the smell of bratwursts cooking, the billboard of the half-naked woman, the advertisements in a language we could only grasp at. And our first rudimentary efforts in that language, 'Sprechen Sie Englisch?' Fumbling back again to the familiar, 'Where is the Hotel Roma?'

The next day we got a train south to the town of Einbeck. We even managed to divine that there was no train station in Einbeck — instead we got off in a place called Salzderhelden and got a taxi. The taxi took us to a hotel on a hill. The hotel was called Der Heldenberg, or the Mountain of the Heroes. We went into the bar and ordered two beers. The bar was dark and timbered, lit only from a room beyond it that appeared flooded with light. There was one other customer, sitting by that doorway, reading a newspaper in the shafts of falling sunlight. He glanced up, then ignored us. I was surprised when I was introduced to him later. I'd thought he was German but his name was Mick Coen and he was from Galway. He sat there for a while, no doubt listening to us. I was looking down, trying to read what might as well have been hieroglyphics on a beer-mat, when the light suddenly dimmed, as if a cloud had moved across the sun outside. Diffley nudged me and I glanced up to see Coen blocking the doorway. He had a glass of beer to his mouth which he downed in one. He was big, all of a piece, with little fat on him. He moved off towards the stairway, favouring his left side, as if afraid the world was going to pitch up against him from the opposite direction.

Our first week was spent out of work, but since we had phoned the agent — one of the few German agents — from London, he eventually agreed to pay us for our trouble. This was a new experience, getting paid for not working — an experience that was to prove illusory in the long term. We had the start for the following Monday so we had to buy tools. At some stage during the week we'd been introduced to Coen. When Diffley asked him where in Galway he was from, he either didn't hear or chose not to answer. He waited a while and then asked were we carpenters. We looked at each other. That would have been enough for him, but then I started to go on about how we had no tools with us. That all you needed to shutter was a hammer, saw and auger. It was a well-practised patter, although I hadn't tried it out on anyone up to that. Still I was uncomfortably conscious of where I'd lifted it from. Diffley was nudging me. All but telling me I was making a fool of myself. Coen said nothing. He refused our offer of another drink. When he rose to go he turned to me and said, 'I'm two years in this country now and I never saw an auger yet. Forget about the auger, will you?'

When he'd gone Diffley asked me why I went on like that? It makes no difference to him, he said.

We had to buy the hammers then. We decided that

Saturday morning would be the best time to go looking for
them. It wasn't like it was a problem, buying a hammer. We
walked into Einbeck that Saturday. It was scorching hot. The
land about the town glimmered in the heat. Vast fields of
crops, undulating gently as far as the eye could see. The
Heldenberg was the only hill for miles in any direction.
Einbeck itself was our first German town. It was a
Wimbledon Saturday. Diffley had brought a phrase book
with him from London. He bought two ice-creams, *Zwei Eis,
bitte*, using it. Now, he said to me, it's your turn. 'I even
found the word for you,' he said, gesturing at the book.
Hammer, *Hummer*. '*Zwei Hummer, bitte*. That's all you have
to say.' I wasn't so sure. In any case my attention had been
distracted by the television display in a shop window. For a
while we stood about watching McEnroe destroy some
hapless opponent. There was no avoiding the issue.

'You're not getting off the hook,' Diffley said.

'I'm not trying to.'

'Look,' he says, 'there's a tool shop over there. We passed
it on the way down.'

We walked back up to the tool shop and looked in the
window. Mostly it was full of electrical tools, Skilsaws and the
likes. The only thing that approximated a hammer didn't look
right. It had one long prong like an ice-pick. There was
obviously a grove for pulling nails between that and the short
prong. The back of it — the hammer-head itself — looked
flat, sawn-off almost. It looked like a cheap tool with a gaudy
yellow handle. It also looked like an ice-pick.

'That's never a hammer,' I said.

'Why not? What else could it be?' he responded. But I
knew from his tone that he was less than convinced.

'It could be an ice-pick,' I said at last.

'What would they be selling ice-picks for in July?' He was
looking down at his melting ice-cream. Neither of us said
anything. Then Diffley said, 'Of course a man would be

wrong to get any ideas about another country. You wouldn't know what they'd be at. Maybe they do sell ice-picks in July.'

I said he'd taken the words out of my mouth.

'There's only one way to find out,' he said. 'In you go.'

The shop was almost empty. What customers there were were away from the main counter at the front. I seized my chance. Looking again for reassurance in the phrase book I approached the sales assistant.

'*Zwei Hummer*,' I said.

'*Bitte schön?*'

'*Zwei Hummer, bitte*,' I amended.

'*Bitte?*' he said again.

'*Zwei Hummer bitte*,' I said again, a good deal louder.

The sales assistant turned around to hide a smile.

Here, I said, thrusting the phrase book towards Diffley. You try it. By this stage the three or four people in the shop had made their way to the front. They'd been called there by our friend the sales assistant.

'*Zwei Hummer, bitte*,' Diffley said.

Everybody broke into uproarious laughter. At that stage I crossed to the window, grabbed the nearest two ice-picks and placed them on the counter. We paid and left, the Germans laughter still ringing in our ears. It was most disconcerting because Germans weren't supposed to have a sense of humour. And, of course, it's less than reassuring to have people laugh at you for what you believe to be no good reason.

It was almost a year later before we were any wiser. I was working in a town called Vechta, in the north of the country. Diffley was off in Berlin. I came home from work one Monday evening, tired out both from the weekend's excesses and the day's work. There was a message for me to phone a Berlin number. I guessed who it was and wondered what he was at, phoning that early in the evening. When I rang the number a woman answered. I took her to be a barmaid from the commotion I could hear going on in the background. She got Diffley for me.

'What's up?' I asked.

'Do you remember the hummers?' he said. As I hadn't altogether forgotten, I said I did.

'Well,' he says, 'I solved the problem.'

I waited and he went on.

'What's a hammer in German?'

'A hammer's a *hammer*,' I said.

'Exactly. That auld phrase book was written for English people: you know, it was written phonetically, the way they have trouble with a's and u's?'

'And?'

'And … well, I was in a restaurant last night — a fish restaurant — and *hummers* were on the menu. A *hummer's* a lobster.'

We spent our first few months in that country oddly disconcerted. There was little of the immediate sense of otherness we'd felt on our first night in Hannover Bahnhof. If I had been infected by Diffley's pursuit of the novel, the novel proved to be a let-down. We were in a hotel on a hill, about five kilometres from the nearest town and even the nearest town was a place where little ever happened — that despite the fact it had 25,000 inhabitants. The hotel surveyed the countryside about as far as the eye could see. We waited in vain for anything as heroic as a valkyrie to come swooping down out of the skies to rescue us from our torpor.

A gang was already ensconced in the hotel when we arrived and they proved the first disappointment. They were young, if slightly older than I, mostly squaddies who'd been discharged from the British Army, yet had nothing to return home to. It was the first time I'd come across men like them. I didn't realise then that the country was full of them — like the windblown detritus from a series of insignificant skirmishes. I was still infected with the notion of work as some form of poetry, but here were men who were intent on its avoidance at all costs. Avoidance at any time other than when they picked up their pay cheques. They were also bent on inflicting a reign of terror on the town. On our first weekend there they succeeded in getting barred from the last pub that would serve them drink. It was immediately apparent that they were running out of options. They told us of other places they'd been in. Places we learned, in time, to avoid — Bielefeld, Paderborn and Osnabruck: squaddie towns. They spoke of these places with yearning, their futures already seemingly immured in the pasts they were trying to escape. Their lives lacking definition without the drill sergeant's bark. A Geordie called Billy was their self-appointed leader. Billy spoke more than any of the rest of them, but, in truth, their leader was whoever appeared the most volatile in any situation. Billy tried to be emollient, apologising, often in advance, for what they did. I disliked him more for that. More because he lacked the authority to tell them to stop. Usually, by the time he'd finished apologising, they'd singled out their next target. There were anything between eight and twelve of them, depending on how many were off scamming somewhere else.

One morning at breakfast — which was prepared the night before and consisted of black bread and cornflakes with flasks of milk and coffee — myself and Diffley came down late to find one of the milk flasks filled with urine. Diffley was in the act of pouring it over his cornflakes. He looked up, his face reddening.

'Why don't you fuckers just re-enlist?' he said.

There was an awkward silence. Broken when one of them, Wolfie, who was from Liverpool, laughed and accused us of being two thick Paddies who couldn't take a joke. There were overtones of what was happening in Northern Ireland in what he was saying, as there was in most of what he said. Wolfie had served there, as they all had, except that Wolfie had lost his best mate, or so Billy told us. Wolfie had a scalloped and beaten face, bent inward like a dented tin can. His front teeth protruded and there was always a skein of saliva hanging from them. He also carried a heavy air of menace.

'Fuck you too,' I said.

I had no romantic notions about fighting fair and was ready to crown him with one of the heavy flasks. We started towards each other, but I don't suppose either one of us truly needed the fight and we were easily dissuaded. That was as well because there were six of them. Eventually they left the room, still laughing at us. Billy's head came back round the door. 'He doesn't mean anything by it lads,' he said. 'Don't take it personal like.'

'It was him did it then?' I said.

But Billy was gone.

Diffley said we should avoid them at all costs but in fact it was Diffley who was sucked into their orbit.

The following Saturday he went with them to another town where they were as yet unknown. I stayed in the hotel bedroom, reading. When he came back he was unsteady on his feet. It was the early hours in the morning. He woke me up to tell me they weren't as bad as he thought.

'What does that mean?' I said.

'Maybe,' he said, 'if you'd got up off your arse and come with us you'd have seen for yourself.' Reminding me that the invitation had been extended to me as well.

'I don't trust them,' I said.

'Well, you don't have to go hunting bear with them. It's only a few pints and a bit of crack. All they're after is drink and women. Anyways, they think you have a mad head on you from the other day, when you were ready to fight Wolfie.'

'They think what?'

'They think you're mad. They think you're up for a fight.'

'Do they now? Well they might as well know I am. I'm

not scared of any of that lot. I'd love to pull that bastard by the ears.'

'Well,' Diffley said, 'they'll not back down if it comes to it.'

Then he added, as if an afterthought, 'You'd want to get that auld fighting out of you. You're an awful man for it.'

'There's only one way to get it out,' I said.

'You're a right bollocks, at times,' he said.

I turned over. It took me a long time to get back to sleep. I could hear him chuckling to himself.

12

THE FOLLOWING MONDAY THERE WAS A PHONECALL FROM
the agent we were working for. He wanted one of us to go to
a job in Alfeld — in the paper factory he said. Travel today,
start tomorrow. He would pay ten hours for travelling. At
that time we were working on the building of a school. By the
time we'd started on it the job was drawing to a close. We
were detailed to strike shutters and remove nails — the
German equivalent to following a brush. I had never been in
a paper factory. I jumped at the chance. That was how I got
hooked up, briefly, with Paddy Carn — who wasn't really
called Paddy Carn. He said he was from somewhere like
Moville or Inishowen, Swatragh or Limavaddy. One of those
places we've all heard off that are way off in some distant
geographical sphere, not real places like Einbeck or Alfeld or
Vechta or Bergisch Gladbach. In fact Paddy was from
Willesden. His parents were obviously Irish, his accent a
Londoner's approximation of an Irish accent.

I met him in a bar in the town of Alfeld. 'Johnny Black,'
he said and he reached across the counter and pulled the

barman towards him. 'Johnny Black *schnell!*' Then he caught
me looking at him and let go of the hapless German, who fell
back against the drinks display. 'Your German's not so good
then?' I said. 'You Irish?' he asked. I nodded and he threw
back his head and laughed.

There were about twenty of us working in the
Papierfabrik, two to a small tent you could push along the
ground. One of those tents with red stripes that tells everyone
to avoid it. Inside we were jackhammering up the floor. The
tents were meant to keep the dust down, away from the
factory machinery. Inside it was like a dust storm. There were
soft drink machines all over the place — someone said that
Coca-Cola owned the factory — but every so often, one of us
would stage the other and we'd sneak out and cross the road
for a beer. That was how I met Paddy. As he was talking to
me I could see the barman pouring the whiskey. His hands
were shaking.

'Don't mind him,' Paddy said, 'he's well used to me. Isn't
that right Fritz? *Donner und Blitzen.*' The barman nodded
uncertainly.

Paddy told me he was going for the straight twenty-four.

'How could you work twenty-four hours?' I asked.

'*Sure* that's nothing,' he said, exaggerating the sure in that
way he had. '*Sure* I've done forty-eight.'

He told me he was a cooper. Imagine that, a man in his
twenties who'd served his time making barrels? If you
could make a barrel you could make anything. 'Carpentry
be fucked,' he said. He was, he said, 'Only in the jackhammering for the money. The long shifts. What was the
point in doing shite work if you weren't raking it in?'

There was something in what he was saying.

'So what are you at?' I asked, because it was obvious he
was on something. His glittering eyes recessed in his head,
darting around the bar.

'Speed,' he told me.

Speed to me was what happened with three English brickies on a scaffolding outside Hannover.

'What do you do?' I said. 'You send a fat boy to the chemist?'

He told me this wasn't the stuff you could buy across the counter in an *Apotheke*, provided you could convince the chemist you needed to loose weight. This was the real thing. I told him about the brickies and the way they built up the wall, the corners plumbed and everything looking good — until we realised there were no openings for windows. He laughed.

'No, this stuff's not like that.'

'What is it then?'

'This is the good gear.'

Indeed this was the good gear. Speed. The perfect drug for a country that was on the move relentlessly. Where there was always noise, a deep subterranean thrum. Even in the middle of nowhere you could hear crickets nattering. Speed meant movement. It ate you up, unlacing you from the inside. There was never much thought or thought of thought. Rather it left you shaking, with no co-ordination, frazzled, clammy-skinned, tongue swollen as if your mouth was clogged with dust. Oblivious to the forward momentum of work. The jackhammer was like a Coke bottle in my hands. The echo of disco music constantly in my head. Funkytown.

We worked through two weekends, rarely eating and hardly sleeping. When sleep came, it was interrupted by vivid nightmares. They seemed to last a long time but, when I'd turn to look at the clock beside the bed, I'd realise I'd only drifted off for a few minutes. It became so I was afraid to sleep. I was losing weight. I remember the third weekend. How myself and Paddy clocked out all the Germans who'd clocked in that Saturday morning. We were laughing, thinking of the confusion we'd cause. We were by now in the same tent. But then we decided to really go for it. We said we'd split up — that way we'd make better headway. I went off to the far side of the factory and looked back at him. Paddy grinned.

'Paddy's motorbike,' he said as he revved up the jackhammer. '*Breaking rocks in the hot sun*,' he was singing, '*Needed money coz I had none …*'

There were red channels marked out on the floor, like tramlines for us to follow. But we veered off them. We made our own tracks, eating up the factory floor, so that by Monday morning the place was a labyrinth of trenches that went nowhere. Circling about and folded back in amongst themselves. Runnels of dust ran up the sides of the machinery where we'd cast aside the tents. The shiny floor was splotched with water and sweat, spilled soft drinks and beer. Everything had an exaggerated look to it, scabs of rust standing out on the machinery. None of the rest of the workers who'd had the weekend off said anything when they came in. The Germans returned to their huts and opened their sandwiches early. The English sat about on the machinery, looking at each other. I looked across at Paddy. I could only see his eyes, his face crusted with grey dust. He looked like an old man but he was grinning. We sat like spent marionettes amidst the wreckage of our weekend. The German *Bauführer* came in and stood in the middle of the havoc. He looked about him and began to jump up and down, screaming. Everywhere he went he seemed to stumble on an empty beer bottle. This was all — for once — happening in slow motion. Nothing he said made any sense. It all had a muffled far-away quality to it — all I could hear was the vibrations of the jackhammers still in the air and Paddy singing quietly to himself, almost under his breath.

We quit that morning. We had no choice but to quit. We were unemployable. I went back to the hotel in Einbeck, convinced I'd sleep and sleep I did. I felt as if I were an LP slowing down — wah, wah-ing inarticulately. My stomach was in revolt and my breath seemed to hiss like steam escaping from me. I remember Paddy rattling on about poor Mammy who was dead and gone now. I remember waking that evening with a start. From a dream I was in a forest full of fireflies and couldn't work my way out. It was twelve hours later and I got out of the bed, went to the toilet and had a drink of water. When I got back into the bed I had the sensation that I was falling towards the centre of it. As if it were a sort of sump, full of grit and dust and flakes of skin. I hauled myself out of the depression with difficulty and rolled over to the far side of the mattress. After a while I rolled back into the centre again, where I found myself scratching to get the dirt and dust off me. Eventually I got up and turned on the light. I pulled back the duvet. There was nothing wrong with the bed. Then I got dressed.

I went down to the hotel bar. Mick Coen was there. Coen was a steady man, or so I thought then, before I got to know him. He didn't talk to anyone which was just as well because I didn't trust myself to talk. He was older than the rest of us, in his mid-thirties. He had a small beer in front of him, the froth gone off it as if it had been there a long time. He nodded towards me. 'Steady man,' I said, 'steady man.' But the steady man was just as much reassurance for myself. I ordered a taxi. There was a kind of dance going on in the room behind me. Old people gliding across the floor. As I waited for the taxi I watched them. They looked like they were on rollers, propelled by sticks across a stage to the sound of German oom-pah music — like the devilish birth of disco itself.

I must have walked every street of the town that night and drank in every bar. There was a fine, misty rain, not so much falling as hanging in the air. I couldn't stay in one place. I felt penned in. In the small places I felt paranoid, the shadows accumulating about me. In the busy places the dissonance seemed to follow me back out onto the streets. I had to shield my eyes from the glare of the streetlamps. My feet seemed to be moving independently of me along the glistening pavement. The skin on my face felt taut and dry. I went into Puzzles Bar and ordered soup. After four or five spoonfuls my shrunken stomach seemed full. I was afraid I was going to throw up and made my way out again. I sat on a wet doorstep and Puzzle, the owner, followed me outside. He sat beside me and put his arm round my shoulder. He spoke quietly into my ear, asking if I needed a doctor. I shrugged off his attention and started moving again, lurching up the street.

I wound up in a whorehouse for the drink. That was where I saw Paddy again. He was entertaining two women at a table, buying them Piccolos, pink champagne, at fifty marks a throw. I strained to hear what he was saying, at the same time drawing back so that he wouldn't see me. I couldn't hear anything. All the noise had the quality of a mangled tape. Paddy was smiling. The smile on him was like the smile on a Dresden doll. He looked as if his face might crack and I felt something like a premonition, shivering, not knowing whether it was for me or for him. I had never noticed he had such delicate features. That smile was a trial for him.

Paddy Carn lit out after that. He didn't so much disappear as we went our separate ways. I'd meet some boys on a job somewhere and they'd mention they'd heard of me. There'd be a slight pause in the conversation then, as if we were broaching something insurmountable.

'Didn't you work with that madman London Paddy?'

And I'd say aye, taking on old familiar speech patterns. 'What's he at now?' I'd ask. And they'd look at me. 'Still on the white powder?' I'd say. Once, one man, a Scotsman, just crossed himself.

But that wasn't the end of Paddy. Some fifteen years after that I was running a pub in North London. I was, at the time, trying to work out the logic of alcohol, not knowing it was

imposing its own logic on me. It was a Monday night —
rather a Tuesday morning in the early hours. I was locking up
on my own when I saw a shape through the stained glass
windows, sheltering from the rain in the doorway. That it was
a rough night wasn't entirely the reason I went to the door. I
don't know the reason. It wasn't characteristic behaviour — to
open the door to a stranger with a house full of money and
drink behind me. Anyhow, I only half-recognised Paddy but
still I let him in. He sort of sidled past me like a djinn or a
wraith, something with its own volition. At least that's what
I thought, as there appeared to be so little of him in it. But
he was flesh and blood alright, for he shivered. The two of us
spent the night huddled up against a radiator for warmth. I
asked him if he wanted food. He asked me if I had cocoa and
bread and butter. I found some hot chocolate and he sat with
a mug of it between his hands, willing them to stop shaking.
When the drink cooled he dipped the bread into it,
slobbering as he ate. He had seven mugs of hot chocolate that
night. 'Isn't it wonderful,' he said to me several times. 'Isn't it
wonderful what something like this'll remind you of?'

We talked a fair bit that night, though in a sense there
wasn't much to be said. The fifteen years were never filled in.
We talked about the work we'd done. He said that the world
was different now and it was good to meet someone from the
old days, just to prove it had all happened. We talked about
the men and the separate ways we'd all gone. Much of it was,
as I remember, perfunctory talk, wishful thinking even. 'Sure
he's likely married now, your man, with a big family of
childer.'

The lights were all turned down except for the dim glow
of the till and fridges. The hum of the cooler filled the air.
Now and then a car sloshed by on the wet streets of Kentish
Town, the arc of its lights circling the pub walls. In that half-
light I'd catch a glimpse of him now and again, wrapped in
his overcoat, huddling back against the radiator. When he'd

notice me he'd look away and I'd think how grey he looked and aged. We were about the one age I'd tell myself.

He asked me if there was a pool table. I said it wasn't worth the hassle, pool tables only attracted trouble. He nodded. Music then, he said, traditional music. Have you that Cooley album? The one the auld lad was always playing at home? I was going to tell him I didn't know his father but there seemed little point. I knew what he was talking about. I put the album on. Coming from the speakers above us, the music sounded almost distilled, far away. The part recorded in the pub in America still goes round and round in my head. That percussive playing and the yelping as Cooley accelerated the pace of the music, and the hum of voices in the background making it feel as if it were coming from a room a way off. Perhaps around the corner where I could just distinguish the glow of the cigarette machine.

Before Paddy left I asked him where he was for. He said he had a gaff up in Hendon. He was going fixing steel. His hands seemed to flex involuntarily, as if he were clutching tying nips. I asked him if he needed money. No, he said, he was well-enough fixed. I called him a cab, and as I put him into it, I said, 'At least give me your phone number?' He laughed and fleetingly his delicate features lit up. 'Ah Jasus,' he says, 'men like us doesn't have phones.' He told me I'd done well for myself. I didn't for an instant believe that, but neither did I correct him. It seemed a peculiarly old-fashioned thing to say. A throwback to a time when being a publican was a respectable thing.

Maybe it was the weather that night or the way the lights were turned down. Or the fact there were only the two of us alone in the early hours — or maybe even the fact that I was feeling jittery anyway — but the following morning any recall of what had happened more or less eluded me, at first, at any rate. Right enough I felt disconcerted, as if there were something spectral lurking in the peripheries of what I could see. Then bit by bit I began to recover the memory while simultaneously doubting it.

I had to work the afternoon shift. I tried to get out of it but couldn't. I had the mirrors set up in that pub so I could stand behind the bar and see into every corner of it. That dated back to when the drug dealers used the place. Back to before I'd thrown them out. The mirrors looked like a normal part of the furniture but I could see clearly the long table they'd used. All afternoon my eyes flickered over and back to it. It was the table myself and Paddy had sat at by the radiator, at angles to each other. For the better part of that afternoon, a door banging or a sudden comment from one of the customers would cause me to start. By the evening time I was in a state of apprehension. That was when the cleaner came in for his drink before going home to bed.

'You were on the cocoa,' he said.

'What?'

'I said you were on the cocoa.'

I didn't know what to say. The cleaner didn't like me. He doubted my virtue. He was continually comparing me unfavourably to the previous landlord. The one who had let the drug dealers in.

'It's that when I came in here, at seven this morning,' he said, 'there were crusts and cups of cocoa over at that radiator yonder. You wouldn't know nothing about that?'

I shook my head. The gesture was for myself.

'It must have been the ghost of Malden Road then,' he said.

The other customers were laughing along with him. I wasn't listening to them. I clearly remembered asking Paddy before he left how he knew I was there. He said he'd heard it off someone in the Welsh Harp or the Hop Poles, one of them places. Except, of course, I knew the Welsh Harp and the Hop Poles were no longer there. The place I was in used to be called after a famous witch — the Mother Shipton. It was still marked as that on the London transport bus route. It was a far better name than the one it had now. All those English pubs with Irish names and what seemed like the flotsam of a parish priest's backyard hanging from the ceiling. That's why, I told myself, there was no significance in his naming of those places. It was just one of those places renamed. But still I had the feeling that the night before had never happened. Or if it had happened it had happened in a parallel sphere — like purloined time.

If Alfeld came to an end on the floor of the paper factory, in another sense it never finished. Rather Alfeld was another place where I'd left a part of myself as collateral. By the time I got to view the place in the rear-view mirror I felt as if I was leaving purgatory — but truly I was only on remission. Back in the Heldenberg the squaddies had gone. They hadn't left together as they might have wished, but had dissipated gradually, in ones and twos, finding there was no more work for them in that part of Germany. They had also disappeared with two hundred pounds in travellers cheques belonging to Diffley. Billy had remained behind. Diffley, with his indefatigable belief in the best intentions of his fellow man, told me Billy wasn't the worst of them. He was easily led, he said. His indefatigability was increasingly unnerving me.

The woman who ran the hotel asked me for my passport. She said it was their policy now to hold passports as security against the bill. *Die Englischen Soldaten* had gone off without paying.

'*Ich bin kein Engländer,*' I said. I said it ruefully because I knew what was coming. Those were amongst the first words of German I had learned. I was tired. For what it was worth I was glad to be back there, but I knew what was coming. She shrugged and shook her head sadly. Inferring I was missing the point.

'*Iss ja egal,*' she said and held out her hand.

I handed her my passport.

After the squaddies departed things settled down in the Heldenberg. A whole range of people we'd only caught glimpses of began to appear from the dark stairwells and the multiple corridors of the place. English people who'd give you to understand that the North of England was being sacked by the Tory Government. Men who put a price on their labour, whose work was their culture. Who came from defunct shipyards and steelworks and abandoned coalmines. There were many empty rooms in the hotel, and over the next few weeks more men arrived. The Heldenberg was ideally located for work, near the autobahn between several big towns. It was relatively inexpensive. But mostly it was the empty rooms, a big attraction for men who were used to having to share with the next stranger who came along.

13

BILLY, THE SQUADDIE WHO STAYED, BOUGHT A VOLKSWAGEN Variant. He used it to take us on tours when we finished work on Saturdays. I was reticent, only half-trusting him. I couldn't understand his need to please, how he glided effortlessly from one company to another, but Diffley continued to believe the best of him. So I'd sit tight-lipped as we journeyed around the Harz Mountains, Billy reminding us interminably that this was where the World War II Dam Busters had brought destruction. The old dams looked like great monoliths in the wan autumn sunshine; overgrown and stained by history, they'd taken on something of the sheen of the surrounding countryside. Once when on our travels we stopped for a drink, I got into conversation with an old man. It was a stilted conversation and I turned to Diffley for help as his German was already far better than mine. But even then the conversation was stymied by Billy, who kept interrupting, throwing in phrases he'd learned, mostly from Diffley. Phrases that were of no consequence to the conversation, things like you hit the nail right on the head, a stitch in time saves nine or you've fallen between two stools. The old German was growing visibly irritated by all this. But then I made the obvious point that there was a lot of concrete in those dams. The old man nodded his head slowly. There are plenty of Russians also, he said. They shot them where they fell from exhaustion and tumbled the bodies into the concrete.

The biggest difference between London and Germany was the younger age profile of the men there. I was barely out of my teens in a place where somebody in their thirties was considered old. There was, I suppose, little wisdom amongst us all and we were competitive about what we did know. We were also all prone to exaggeration so you never knew what was the truth of what you were hearing. That was perhaps why when Philip who was in his early fifties, appeared we were all taken aback.

I was having a drink in the hotel bar with Les, a Yorkshire man, and one of the newer arrivals at the hotel. Both Les and his wife Lynn were staying in the hotel. We were talking about football when Philip came in, carrying an old canvas rucksack with a Tricolour stitched onto the back of it. We watched him walk up to the bar and order a beer uncertainly, before he turned to us and asked if he was in the right place.

'What place are you looking for?'

'The Helden-something,' he said.

'The Heldenberg,' I said, 'that's it. That's where you are.' Then I asked him where he was from.

'Redhills,' he said.

Les laughed. 'Is he a Yank or what?' he said. 'Redhills, that's in America.'

'Redhills,' I said, 'is in Cavan.'

'And where's Cavan?' he asked.

That was in a way the crux of the matter. That is, there's a kind of ambivalence between Cavan and Monaghan — one that exists between a few neighbouring counties. A Cavan man once told me that what in snooker is usually known as "an English" — the kind of sideways cut that's put on a ball, hit at an angle — was known as "a Monaghan" around Belturbet. I still don't know whether I should've taken that as a compliment — that's what I mean by ambivalence.

Philip, it turned out, wasn't a man who had much to say for himself. Yet what he did say was considered — and emerged after a period of thought. We never found out what he was doing there. It wasn't wanderlust because he suffered greatly from homesickness, and after a few pints he would grow lyrical about where he came from, and about how you could shoot your dinner from the skies or take a fishing rod and head for a lake. Those few occasions apart he had little to say. The English lads thought he was slow and I had a job explaining to them that he came from a place where silences were expected. After all, I could well remember conversations punctuated by long silences where I grew up — a place where a single word could sum up a whole argument.

We were on our way back from work one evening, passing a stretch of water outside the town of Northeim, when Philip turned round to me and said, 'Do you miss them auld lakes?'

I nodded. It was a Saturday, two weeks later, before I located a pair of rods. All I had to do was hand him one.

'Tomorrow?' he said. Lynn, Les's wife, wanted to know how we did that — without talking.

'Did you know each other before? You must have talked about it, at least,' she said.

'No,' I said, 'I hardly know the man.'

'How then?'

I couldn't explain it. 'You'd just know,' I said.

Anyhow, we went fishing that Sunday. The water in the reservoir was hardly stirring and there was no place to shelter from the sun, beating down. It was the last good day of the year and already felt like a breath of air from another time. The shore was crowded with Germans — all of them with good equipment — many with sun-shades. I always felt that what you need for fishing was silence and space — time to get into the rhythm of casting and trawling; becoming a part of it so that each slight sound would be accentuated: the plop of tackle, the shifting of reeds.

That Sunday I worked my way round the shore of the reservoir. The weather was bad for fishing, overcast skies and shade are the best things. It was too hot and my casting was reflexive, overworked and anxious. From time to time I'd glance over at Philip — who never moved from the one spot. There were few fish caught that day and most of them were caught by him — small, spiny perch. 'Yokes,' he said later, 'you wouldn't be seen dead with at home.'

By time I'd circled the reservoir, there were a crowd of Germans gathered in a semi-circle about him. He wasn't talking to them — he was completely absorbed with his own intent. His casting was languid, unhurried. He was able to cast great distances and seemed capable of suspending the tackle over the water for a fraction, so that when it descended it caused little dissonance — sent out few ripples. One of the Germans asked me did I know him? Or where did we come from?

'Redhills,' I said. He looked at me blankly.

'Ireland,' I added, though I felt that too was inadequate. But the German nodded — as if it explained everything.

Later we went for a drink. Philip said it was as good a day as he'd had for a while. 'You can't get away from it, no matter where you go,' he said. I nodded and sipped my beer.

Back at the hotel we'd arrived at a kind of a stasis where everyone seemed to be getting on with each other. Though the trees outside had begun to lose their leaves, the weather had stayed balmy and it hadn't rained for weeks. Yet we all seemed to sense that there was something false about it. That the odds on it continuing like that were lengthening.

Diffley and myself were working with Mick Coen on a

regular basis. Coen was initially suspicious of me. He knew what had gone on at the *Papierfabrik* with Paddy Carn, and saw me as a hard-line drug user. He questioned me about it obliquely, as was his way, and I tried to assuage his fears, implying that it was a phase I'd gone through. Coen had spent half of his life away from home, but drugs weren't something he'd experienced, even indirectly. They were something he equated with being English. Still I meant what I said. My time on amphetamines had shaken me and I secretly feared that I hadn't yet faced the full consequences of what I'd done. This nagging intuition was coupled with mild insomnia and what I took to be a series of flashbacks. These last were like watching a television where there is interference, the ascending horizontal lines on the screen creating the effect of a looped experience. I had the feeling that Coen didn't believe me, that he saw in me some inherent recidivist trait. But there was no way to score speed with Paddy Carn off the scene, even if I'd wanted. After a few weeks what suspicions Coen had appeared to be allayed, at least temporarily. In fact he had reached the stage where he tolerated me more than he did most people.

One night we sat listening to Billy telling anybody who would listen about the amount of amphetamines he'd taken. He said he'd used it to stay awake on sentry duty. He was less than convincing. Yet now and again he'd glance up at me conspiratorially. I was trying to switch him off, knowing if I said anything it would flow from me, harsh and percussive and endlessly. I also knew that nobody believed a word he said. Coen must have seen my anxiety, for he bought me a drink.

'What does Diffley see in that bollocks?' he asked.

I shook my head.

Diffley got on well with everyone. He withheld nothing of himself — which led to him running interference for Billy. All the men thought that if Diffley felt he was alright they

should give him the benefit of the doubt. That was apparent
to everyone except Billy.

Unfortunately Norman had no one to run interference for
him. Norman was from Cleveland in Hartlepool on the
northeast coast of England. His troubles began with a group
of Mancunians who'd arrived in the hotel. They used to go
about humming a song, 'Nobody wants to dance except me
and my monkey.' Norman would blush and stare into his
beer as they sniggered. One night somebody asked them what
the joke was. Back during the Napoleonic Wars, they said, a
French ship had been wrecked off the coast of Hartlepool.
The only survivor was a monkey who may or may not have
been dressed in a French *matelot*'s uniform. In any case the
locals, having never seen a Frenchman, supposedly tried the
monkey and hung it. Which is why they've been known since
as Monkey Hangers.

Norman told us he was a refractory bricklayer. A
specialist in brickwork that was resistant to heat — which
could well have described his nature too. He'd served his
time building factory chimneys, but with the loss of
Britain's traditional industries, his trade appeared as arcane
as Paddy Carn's coopering. In any case Norman became the
butt of everyone's jokes. He had that vague, stop-start
nature, as if he hadn't quite finished. Always half-a-beat off
the tempo of things, he'd contribute to a conversation some
time after the subject had been changed. The best advice he
could have got was to say nothing. Everything he said was
laughed at. He had a police record he told us. Maybe he was
trying to impress us. He'd got it in London. London, he
added, he'd only been in once. He was on the underground.
He had no ticket. Getting off the train he was approached
by an inspector. Instead of bluffing his way, he ran. He got
wrapped about a barrier when he tried to jump it, ending
up with a broken ankle and a fine.

Over the years I've thought of us, living on that hill —
drinking and working in a place none of us expressed any
affection for. I've thought of that as an excuse for the way
we treated Norman. It doesn't wash. We made his life a
misery.

The dope meantime appeared with the Mancunians. It
didn't materialise so much as it was sourced. Diffley once
said to me that dopeheads are amongst those that have an
unerring sense for things: the way serious dope smokers
always seem to recognise each other. He said if they were
stuck on the Antarctic you could bet they'd be approached
by an Admiral Penguin who dealt grass. The smoking
began in secret, in bedrooms upstairs, and for a time it
divided the hotel as neatly as any class war might have.
There were those who knew what was going on and those
who didn't, and those who didn't were severely
disconcerted to find a group of men descending for dinner
who were likely to start giggling over the most trivial of
matters. At times they sat at the table in silence, seemingly
absorbed in the colours of the pasta bows on their plates,
waiting on one of their number to speak. The tension
would build. Then someone would cough indicating he
wished to speak. He'd mutter something about needing a
haircut. Nobody would say anything — as if stupefied at
the lack of profundity in what had been said. Forced to
qualify himself, the speaker might mutter something about
a long back and sides. With that, the rest of them would
shudder with laughter, literally falling out of their seats.
The rest of us sat at the other tables, watching, both
confounded and intrigued, unaware at the beginning of
what they had been up to upstairs. To us there appeared to
be some form of cryptic etiquette at work here. The
laughter would eventually subside, only to begin again,
unprovoked. Erupting like mortar fire about the place.

When Diffley told me what was going on, I was surprised. I reminded him of the time, a couple of months previously, when we'd been working on another paper factory. We had a small deck to concrete. It was a Saturday morning and we were held up, waiting on the concrete wagon to arrive. There were three of us at work, Scots Willie the third. Willie lit up a pipe. I refused it. Diffley, who'd told me how he'd tried dope and it hadn't done *anything* — he'd emphasised the anything — for him, took a long draw. The deck was on an overhang, cantilevered over the face of a cliff with a sixty-foot drop on one side. The German foreman had Willie off striking shuttering somewhere when the concrete arrived. Diffley had been explaining to me how good it was, not to be working and having it recognised that there was nothing to do, with no concrete. Not having to hide. The skip swung overhead on the crane and as I jumped up and pulled the lever down to open it, I saw Diffley look back over the side and his face blanch. He froze where he was. I had to lead him in off the deck, talking to him like you would a child, telling him everything was alright. I finished the deck myself while he looked on, occasionally apologising, and telling me he felt he was going to throw up. I was putting the finishing touches to it when the foreman came round.

'What's wrong with him?' he asked, pointing to Diffley.

'*Krank*,' I said, the word for sick.

He asked had he been drinking.

'No,' I protested, 'he's sick.' And I pointed out, as best I could, that the job was done and could we go home? Please.

Diffley swore, after that, that he would never touch dope again. But when I reminded him of this at the hotel, he said it was different this time. Moralistic as I was, I wondered aloud how many times I'd heard that used as an excuse. He told me to get my head out of my arse and reminded me about my own recent experiences. 'And this is nothing like that,' he said.

We were in a place called Luthe when the snows came. Luthe was a sewage treatment plant not far from Hannover. We were living in the *Buden* — or huts — on site. The huts were like something from a Second World War film. There was an electric hob, a fridge, a table and four sets of bunk beds with a coal stove in the middle of the hut. We were lucky in that there were only three of us sharing. Most of the men on the Luthe site were from Yugoslavia. If we saw Yugoslavia as a monolith, they were quick to point out they were Croatians. They all seemed to drive Mercedes. The first weekend we were there Diffley and Coen left on Friday for the Heldenberg. I stayed on the site, going into Hannover to spend Sunday in the Mickey Mouse Bar. It was freezing that Sunday and there was a high wind-chill factor. When I got back to the site a group of Croatians were standing outside one of their huts, looking up at the skies. The sky had the colour of a well-scoured pot. Snow, they told me. Some of them had already begun to move gear into the boots of their cars. 'We go home,' they said. Home to Croatia.

I awoke the following morning to profound silence. It was, at first, perturbing. Usually I was awakened by the noise of the cranes, already manoeuvring the vast shutters into position. Machinery should have been clattering to life. Instead there was an air of expectancy about the place. I could see my breath in the cold air in the hut. I got up and filled the stove with coal. Then I went out. There was a foot of new, unmarked snow on the ground. There was even more snow in drifts in the lee of the huts opposite where I stood. There were a few men stomping about here and there. There was no sign of Coen or Diffley. Some of the English boys were back though. They told me everyone was waiting for the word to work. Some of them — the Germans — didn't want to start. They'll have to though, they said, it's only the 28th. It was the 28th of October. I wasn't aware of the significance of the date — but I wasn't letting on either. The Englishmen hadn't been in Germany as long as I had — even though that was less than four months.

We began work just after nine o'clock. There was still no sign of Coen or Diffley. I reasoned they were trapped on the hill in the snow. We were divided into sections for work purposes and the sections were based on language. Coen was the boss of our gang. The three of us and five Englishmen. We were working on the top of the building, four floors up — on the *Treppenhaus* — the stairwell. There were three cranes on the job and all the gangs were in competition for lifts. I wanted to get started early, even without Coen. To get a head-start in shifting some of the four big shutters we needed that day into position.

At the start there had been maybe some merit in protesting that you couldn't speak German — but only for a short time. A hammer was a hammer and the nails looked the same and the job was the same job in any country or language. I was also glad to be in Luthe. Happy because for the first time since we'd got to Germany here was real work — not just pulling nails out of someone else's. I knew the Englishmen weren't carpenters. We used to call ourselves shuttering carpenters to distinguish ourselves from joiners. What we were distinguishing ourselves from was tradesmen. Coen, who was a joiner and a fine tradesman, described shuttering as glorified labouring with a hammer. I knew the Englishmen knew less than I did because one of them had asked me, what is shuttering? I explained that essentially it involved constructing big boxes from timber, then placing a steel cage of reinforcing within them — this was done by steel-fixers, another entity entirely. Then they were filled with concrete. When the concrete had dried the box was taken away — or, as we said, you struck the shutters.

'That sounds easy,' they might say, or in one case — 'I can do that. I saw it done from the window of the post office in Cambridge where I was working.' But then that was said by one of two brothers who smoked too much dope and finally got sacked, not because they were useless, but for committing the greatest of sins: they stole the Germans' beer. They were what we derisively referred to — not far beyond that evolutionary phase ourselves — as cowboys.

Shuttering isn't easy. It's hard, physical work — manoeuvring vast structures into place — even with the help of a crane. And German crane drivers were notorious; alone for long stretches of time in their cabs, they often drank to excess. You always had to be aware that a shutter might be dropped at speed on top of you. That it could catch in the wind and twist like a whirlwind. That it could bounce off something else, deflect towards you, sweeping you off your feet and over the edge of a deck — plunging you downwards to serious injury or death.

And even then when they were in place, they had to be propped with heavy strong-backs and Akros, a telescopic metal support, because they would move from the weight of the concrete that was poured into them. And because there was no division of labour in Germany you would have to pour the concrete — either from a pump or from a skip attached to a crane that opened on one end. And that, on one occasion, because it hadn't been closed properly, opened in mid-air over our heads, sending us diving for cover and a Turk to hospital with concussion. Then it had to be vibrated so that it moved into every corner of the shutter. If it didn't there were honeycombs when you struck — the pure sign of a cowboy — and everyone would stand about going *buzzzz*, *buzzzz*.

After you poured the concrete — usually the following day because the Germans were always in a hurry — the shutters were struck — which was alright if you knew who you were working with, and they knew what they were doing. But if you were dealing with green concrete — concrete that hadn't gone off — you had to be careful. Easing the shutters away, with steam rising from the edifice, and that distinctive, near-chemical smell that smelt like something fresh and new-born.

I had never seen the Germans as they were that day. We appeared to be the only gang making any effort. We located the first of the shutters and I nailed four-by-twos across the back of it, for propping the Akros off. Then I went to find a crane driver. The three of them were standing in a knot, drinking Apfel Schnapps from the neck of a bottle. I pointed upwards and they laughed. After a time I eventually cajoled one of them into giving me a lift. I had to promise it was only one lift. Still I was filled with foreboding as I watched him climb up the ladder towards his cab, clutching a full bottle in one hand and moving with no great urgency. He stopped to get his bearing every few rungs, swaying over and back, more intent on the safety of the bottle than anything else. When he reached the top he began to address his comrades below. Shouting down in what we called *Baustelle Deutsch* — building-site German. It was a language I was almost perfectly conversant in. It comprised a vocabulary of about 200 words — half of them work related — the rest a series of repetitive and unimaginative swearwords. The lift was a long time coming

The worst thing about having to work with the Englishmen was knowing how little they knew. The shutter we needed was far below us on the ground. The best I could hope for was that the crane would get it in an approximate position. We would then have to let it take the weight while we wedged and manhandled it forward, getting a couple of Akros up against it as fast as possible. The shutter was twelve-foot wide and twenty-foot high. I couldn't trust anyone to sling it safely on the crane so I had to go below, put the hooks on it and make my way back to the top as fast as possible. By the time I'd got there I'd heard the shutter twanging off the side of the building twice. I knew it would have built up considerable velocity. In fact it was spinning above the Englishmen's heads like a vast drill bore. They were watching it, unsure of whether to run or attempt to bring it under control. One of them made a grasp at a length of rope that was trailing from its bottom. As he caught it, the shutter swung out over the edge of the building, dragging him in its wake. He let go just in time. Before I could say anything, one of the German foremen drew me aside by the arm.

'Do you want to get killed?' he asked me in English.

'The crane driver is drunk,' I said.

'We do no more work,' he said, 'the work it is finished now.' He spoke to the driver on a walkie-talkie. After the shutter was taken back down he sent the Englishmen to unhook it. 'They have to begin to learn,' he said, laughing at me.

'Come, we will drink.' He took me back down into his office and gave me a mug of hot rum. He re-filled a saucepan on his hob from a bottle on his desk, showing me three more bottles he had beneath it.

He was right, dying was something I didn't consider. Though I'd had a couple of close calls. The time I'd fallen off the scaffolding in Vechta onto another level of staging. I might have landed in the street with a broken back. Or in Bracknell, almost two years before, when we were digging the hole, and I'd been banking the muck-skip out of it. The muck-skip was slung on a crane whose driver was too far above us to have a proper view over the edge of the scaffolding. So Hoppy was positioned across the road while I perched on a scaffold tube. I could see the skip, Hoppy could see me and the crane driver could see Hoppy. So Hoppy's job was to relay my signals upwards. We were half in awe of crane drivers — as if you'd need to be stone mad to spend your day alone at a great height looking down on everyone else. That type of silence might shatter you. There were many crane drivers who were odd in their own way, though probably no odder than the multitude of us. This one was new which meant we didn't altogether trust him. Hauling the skip out blind was a dangerous job. Perhaps more importantly, though it didn't cross our minds, he might not have trusted us.

I was clenching and unclenching my fist — the signal to take the weight. I could see Hoppy grinning at me and I smiled back. I felt a sudden lurch then as the skip caught on the side of the scaffolding below me. I was signalling frantically to Hoppy to get the driver to ease off the weight. I started to panic then and shouted as the skip bounced back off the scaffold. In moments like those — which we think of as split-seconds — time in fact seems to expand. Things happen in slow motion. Indeed you can stand transfixed by the enormity of it all. I could see the skip swinging towards me like a pendulum. It was certainly heavy enough to have knocked me off the scaffold. Or it could have pinned me up against it — either way it could have killed me. Instinctively I reached for the tubes above my head and pulled myself upwards, hauling my legs out of the way. When the skip hit the scaffold though, the shock of the collision made me lose my grip. I fell onto the top of the skip, holding on for dear life to the crane's hook as it swung over and back. Every time it struck the scaffold it bent it further until the framework began to crumble. At this stage Lonesome Tom had come out of the hole and was roaring at the crane driver. However events were beyond the driver's control. The skip had built up its own momentum and I had to ride it out. When it eventually cleared the scaffold it began to spiral wildly. That was the first the driver knew of my predicament — the first time he'd seen me — and there was still nothing he could do. He lowered the skip to just above the ground. I couldn't jump because I was dizzy from the speed I had been spiralling at. At this stage the whole site was looking on. Eventually its natural momentum wore out and he lowered the skip wholly to the ground. I climbed down from the bucket. My teeth were chattering.

Diffley and Coen arrived that evening. They had been snow bound. Diffley was in raptures about the way the Germans had cleared the roads. 'If that was at home now …' he said. But Coen pointed out that nine out of ten German winters had heavy snow.

'What does heavy snow mean?' I asked.

'Snow,' he said, 'that'll not go away till well into next year.' Then he explained why the date was important. 'From now until Wednesday they'll do nothing. On Thursday they'll go back home when the *Schlechtwetter* begins. They get paid most of their wages for not working between the first of November and the last day in February. If they do work, they get an extra payment on top. But they won't work. Not in this weather.'

'And what'll happen to us?'

'I'd say we'll stay here with them until Wednesday and they'll tell us they won't need us until it thaws — or until March. What were they like today?' he asked.

'They were like pigs in shit,' I said.

'Wouldn't you be, if you were getting paid for doing nothing for four months?' Diffley said. 'That's us fucked then.'

It was true. I'd spent the day under the shutters smoking cigarettes and talking about reincarnation, amongst other things, with the Englishmen. After my mug of rum I went back out into the cold. I had begun to sweat, the alcohol coming through my skin and freezing into crystals on it. My fingers were sore from where I'd touched the metal on my hammer that morning. From where they'd stuck to it. The Germans were in and out of the huts all day — heating spirits and sweating them back out. The Croatians appeared to have finished loading up their Mercedes with booty. They were merry and offered me drink. Later that night I went back out onto the site alone. I moved away from the huts where I could hear raucous laughter and occasional spats amongst the card players. Fists hammering down on tables. Steam issuing from the heavily condensed windows. The sounds of bottles clinking. Way down the site it was deathly quiet apart from the groaning noises made as the metal in the strongbacks supporting the shutters expanded. I checked the barometer outside the foreman's hut. It was 15° C below and still dropping. My fingers had actually stuck to the metal on the hammer. You couldn't work in that weather. There was a real feeling of the end of the year about it, even if we were still two months off Christmas. And it was snowing again. The snowfall was so heavy it seemed to obliterate everything, but for the white light it generated itself.

14

WE WENT BACK TO THE HELDENBERG AND THERE IT BEGAN — what we referred to afterwards as the time that time forgot. It was like sitting in a room, listening obsessively to a clock tick-tocking while the hands refused to move, and it lasted for six weeks. I once sat, years later, in a bar on the Liverpool docks and heard two men talk of Germany and the times they'd had there. One man described to the other a period he'd been stranded in a hotel on the top of a hill in the snow with ten other men. He swore he couldn't even remember the name of the place. He couldn't because he hadn't been there. By the following summer those six weeks had become a byword for Germany for all eight of us, and the story had already begun to grow in the telling.

It began with Diffley and Mick Coen examining the contracts we'd signed. They discovered that Claus, our German employer, was legally obliged to pay us if we weren't working. It was a minor clause, but it had escaped Claus when he was drawing the contracts up. He wasn't pleased to have it drawn to his attention and although both Diffley and

Coen argued that it would be better for all of us if he fronted
us the money, he insisted if we wanted it, we would have to
stay in Einbeck. So we got our hotel bill paid and six hundred
marks a week.

The view from the Heldenberg was across a plain as far as
the eye could see in all directions. It continued to snow
irregularly for a week, deadening all the sound about us. The
roads were kept clear, but across the plain it was said the snow
had drifted three and four metres deep. All the natural
landmarks that marked the view from the hotel were buried.
Only the rail line far below us was kept cleared, where the
train plied from Hannover to Kassel and onward. Yet it was
so distant it felt as if we were positioned in the middle of a
toy railway, being interminably circumnavigated by
miniature trains. Rather than the clock marking the passage
of time, we came to rely on the fading light and the railway
timetable. Hours were defined by the prevalence of goods
trains over passenger trains or the number of express trains
that flickered past the window in the bar. From time to time
Elizabeth, the hotel owner, or Ute who worked there,
appeared with food. That too marked the passing hours.

Rising late, we began to drink steadily from early
afternoon. Everybody was smoking dope except Mick Coen,
who was blessed with an ability to sleep for longer than
anyone else. When he was awake he plied between the town
where he disappeared for the afternoon and the hotel bar
where he stopped to refuel — or that was the impression I
was gradually coming to. Meanwhile the rest of us played
incessant, soporific card games and wondered that Elizabeth
hadn't noticed our dope smoking or sometimes — lucidly —
whether she had and chose to ignore it. Our dealer trekked
up the hill every evening. He was a seventeen-year-old,
leather-trousers-wearing student. We christened him Ralphie
and argued about his get-up. The Mancunians said no man
should wear leather trousers unless he was Phil Lynott.

Charlie, an old hippie from Hull, insisted that Jim Morrison, who he'd seen with the Doors in London, was a better role model. Ralphie sat impassive as we played cards. He was listening to every word. I watched him keep time with his finger as two of the Manchester boys talked, then heard him repeat the conversation word for word, to himself, as he prepared to make his way back down the hill. His accent was almost perfect. He told us he'd gone to the top of his English class, although his teacher questioned some of his vocabulary. 'Not Oxford English,' he added defiantly, getting that accent right also. Like the food, Ralphie's visits were a welcome diversion. We'd run out of things to say to each other. It was as if we all knew each other's histories so well that conversation was superfluous. We were in a permanent torpor.

It was then that Elizabeth found a cache of *Readers Digest*s that dated back to the 1950s. They belonged to the man who owned the hotel before she'd bought it, she told us. There was also a hard-backed notebook which Diffley took. It contained a series of German expressions translated into English. The man was obviously trying to learn the language. Some of the expressions were highly technical, seemingly compiled by someone who had an advanced knowledge of physics. Charlie said the man was obviously a war criminal hiding out on the hill. The *Readers Digest*s proved much more useful and they were taken up voraciously. For the next few days every joke in them was recounted energetically. We argued over who had what magazine in an effort to uncover stories before each other, then recounted them as if they were our own. The range of obscure information that passed between us seemed almost hallucinogenic. We were experts in the history of the Hudson Bay Company, Adenauer, the rise of Kemal Atatürk, Nansen of the North, the plant life of Lapland, the wiles of the sabre-toothed tiger and the sexual proclivities of the South Sea Islanders — or how they were seen in the early

1950s. Every conversation had an arcane quality to it. But as
the *Digests* were exhausted, stories began to be recycled and
we argued over details. Nansen was never in the Middle East,
that had been Atatürk because of the Byzantine Empire. No,
someone else would argue, not Byzantine, it was called
something else. Byzantine was just the conversation. Then it
became that to start one of the stories brought yawns of
boredom or apprehension from the audience. We began
playing cards again, silently.

On Sundays someone used to travel to the nearest big
town to pick up the English papers, but that had stopped. We
also stopped listening to British Forces radio and the BBC
World Service. There was a world out there we were ignoring.
We didn't even follow the football results anymore. I phoned
home every Friday regardless, but I did so with an increasing,
unspoken belief that the calls were serving to shore up a
mooring I was slipping far beyond. Sometimes they had the
quality of communication with a place much farther away —
as if the signal was being deflected off a satellite somewhere.
Static built up on the line — the static of things left unsaid.
The price of heating oil was going up. Or there would have
to be an election, a new Taoiseach. My pulse quickened. I
shared my mother's love of elections. But there were parts of
the conversation missing, silences which enveloped what was
said. Was I coming home for Christmas? 'I didn't know,' I
said. 'Well there was the snow, see,' I said, which I couldn't
explain. Made little effort to explain. It began to seem we
were having the same conversation every week, as if, in some
Einsteinian way, time had flattened out and caught up with
itself and everything was being repeated over and over. I went
back to the card game. Hearts was the trump card — wasn't
hearts always the trump card? There was no sound except for
feet shuffling and the flutter of a card onto the table.

Who is the Taoiseach anyway? I asked Diffley.

A deep sense of ennui pervaded the place, infecting some

of us more than others. Norman, who had a fitful interest in things at the best of times, was drawn increasingly to the window, humming disco tunes to himself. He too was smoking dope, mostly in his room on his own. He took to disappearing for long periods of time. But we passed no remarks of this. There were whole areas of that hotel which we'd never explored. It seemed like a great nineteenth-century folly, all nooks and crannies and hidden rooms, almost impossible to heat. There was a turret no one had been in. And the floor above where we slept was unused. We used to joke that it was haunted. There came to be something self-fulfilling about this as we ran out of things to speculate on. Men talked about noises up there, footsteps. We said it was heating pipes expanding and contracting. There was a plumber among us. He nodded, it might be. We said it was the sound of the upper limbs of the trees outside battering against the building. Our unease grew proportionately. One morning I woke earlier than usual and made my way up the rickety staircase. The air up there was rank, damp and musty. In places it had another sulphurous smell, not quite that of boiled cabbage. Its labyrinthine corridors were in bad repair: there was no heating and many of the light bulbs clicked uselessly; wallpaper peeled off the walls, the plumbing gurgled and groaned. Rounding a corner I bumped into someone. I fell over backwards onto the floor, tearing my wrist on a nail on the floorboards. I looked upwards to see Norman's concerned face peering down at me, looking mottled and poached in the pallid light. I tried to hide my shock in an Oh-This-is-a-Surprise kind of way as he helped me upward. I asked him what he was doing there. His look gave me to understand that it was none of my business. There was something proprietorial in it — as if to say, what was *I* doing there? He broke eye contact then and looked beyond me, like he was waiting on someone or something to materialise. I asked him who he was looking for. He didn't answer me. I led him back downstairs, nursing my smarting wrist. The card game was just beginning. He took his place at the window.

'What time is it now Norm?' someone asked. For once I didn't join in the general laughter. Even though I'd solved the mystery of the footsteps I kept that knowledge to myself for the time being.

Men began to talk of leaving, or of other men they knew, mates who'd gone home and phoned them. But all this talk petered out into uncertainty. There were only two weeks of our six weeks' grace left and yet we couldn't struggle beyond inertia. We resented those who tried.

Diffley had stopped smoking. He retreated to his room with the physicist's phrase book. He said he was going to master grammar. Then, one afternoon, he appeared during a card game. Obviously energised, he started to go on about walks — about walking. Nobody said anything. He was trying to inject life into us. He stopped, then started again about wonderful ice crystals, nature and the icicles that were hanging off the rooftop outside his window. He was let finish.

'It's getting to him,' someone said.

'Nah, he's just stoned.'

'Don't we go out at night?' someone asked him.

Diffley stormed out of the room. The slammed door resounded in his wake.

'What's up with him?' Billy asked me.

I shrugged.

'Roll another J. Whose turn is it to deal anyway?'

We settled back to the cards. Waiting on the gloom to gather outside so we could emerge, blinking, like crepuscular things.

Diffley returned about four hours later. The card game was winding down. Some of the men had already made excuses and drifted off to their rooms, saying stuff like they wanted to get ready for dinner. There were the usual ribald suggestions as to their true purpose, and they were reminded that formal dress wasn't required in the Heldenberg.

'Where were you Diff?' someone asked. The inquiry seemed genuine. There was a palpable urge to find some news of what passed beyond where we were — transient and all as that urge may have been.

'Cinema,' he answered.

'See anything good?' But Diffley pushed past us on his way to his room. I made some excuse about getting the beer in before dinner and followed him. Upstairs Mick Coen's door was open. Coen was out but Charlie was in his room, sitting in his chair. He had headphones on and was plugged into the stereo. His long hair was flailing about the place as he sang along, out loud, to a record.

Hey Lord, won't you buy me a Mercedes Benz ...

I knocked on Diffley's door and pushed it open. He was sitting on the bed with his hands wrapped about a cup of coffee.

'Well,' I said, 'what did you see?'

He got up and threw open the window. Freezing air rushed into the room.

'That's what it's like outside,' he said, 'if you want to know. This central heating is killing us, can't you feel your blood thicken?'

I wanted to point out to him that it wasn't the central heating. Moreover his rebellion was having no effect — they were all too stoned anyway. Instead I changed the subject. I closed the window and asked him about the film again. He relented and began to laugh. It wasn't, he said, that he didn't want to talk about it. It was just that it was an odd film to see. Jack Nicholson was in it. He was in a hotel, in the middle of nowhere in the snow. He ended up going mad with an axe.

We both laughed. Diffley poured me out a cup of coffee. He was worried about Norman, he said, about the way we treated him, calling him Normal and fucking him around.

'Look at the way he stares out the window? And all that smoking on his own — all joking apart — all that smoking on his own's doing him no good.'

I told him about finding him upstairs.

'That's it,' Diffley said, 'we'll go and talk to him. Dinner should be there by now.'

Norman was sitting at a small table on his own. We took our plates off the big table and joined him. There were some comments passed. Norman didn't look up as we took our places opposite him. It took him a few seconds to register our presence. He blinked when Diffley started to talk. Diffley leaned across the table towards him. I tugged at his sleeve. Diffley's whole stance implied urgency. Norman looked startled. Eventually he told us he was going to leave. The way he said it the thought might just have occurred to him, but he grew excited and his resolve seemed to fasten. He said he thought he'd never get away. He had no contact with home. Really he had no one to be in contact with. He was afraid it would never thaw and we'd be stuck there forever. Even if the weather changed, well, that could be a long time away.

'The thing is,' Diffley said, 'if you want to leave you'll have to do something about it. You can't be waiting on anyone else. On any of these boys here. You should just up and go. How would you get back anyway?'

Norman said he could get a train to Rotterdam and get the boat from there to Hull. After that he'd be fine.

We were all grinning by now. I went and bought three beers. We had a plan. It's always good to have a plan.

It was several days after before Norman did get away. By that time the Englishmen were growing even more uneasy about our situation. They'd discovered a new enthusiasm for Second World War films, particularly those set in POW camps. They talked about wooden horses and escape tunnels, wire cutters and fences. All their jokes were about the war. They pranged Lancasters and shot down the Hun. There were Jerries at 11 o'clock and at 12 o'clock. There were Jerries twenty-four hours a day. Norman mentioned he was leaving several times. He said it matter of factly, yet every time there was a silence. The men laughed at him. I saw Diffley drawing Billy aside: they talked and looked in Norman's direction. I got the impression that he was trying to arrange a lift. Diffley was a kind of a transitional man among all of us. He was the only person whose attempt to escape wasn't resented. Still, nothing happened with Norman. Then, one afternoon, he appeared with his bags packed. He shook hands earnestly with each of us individually. Everyone was too taken aback to make a joke of it. But then a taxi failed to materialise. He said he would get the next train. We shook hands again. This time jokes were cracked. He went off only to reappear half-an-hour later, having forgotten his glasses. Finally he was gone and for the rest of the afternoon, every time a train passed, it was Norman, going round Germany in circles. Not knowing where to get off. We laughed inanely.

That was the night we finally got thrown out of the Tanzbar. At nine every night three cabs arrived and transported us into Einbeck where we drank copiously. Our usual diversion was avoiding Norman, going into a bar, ordering a round and disappearing out the back door, leaving him with the bill. Now we had no Norman to divert us and in his absence he was the subject of much speculation. He'd gone and done something and confounded us all. There was some grudging admiration for him. After the bar shut we made our way unsteadily, sliding on the frozen pavements, to the Tanzbar.

Every German town had at least one Tanzbar. The Tanzbar was a disco and we all professed to hate disco music — the true beat of Germany. Inside the Germans were lined up, dancing as usual. Disco rhythms had some hold over them — some strange appeal. We used to joke about automatons until Billy pointed out pedantically that disco

was based on the polka and what could be more German than
that? It was something he'd no doubt heard from Diffley who
worried about these things. Still, it explained a lot. In the first
place it explained why the Germans did a polka on the disco
dance floor. A very fast polka while the music beat out
incessantly: *D.I.S.C.O. … D.I.S.C.O.*

It didn't explain though why they dressed the same —
both men and women — with those peg-leg trousers and
pointy shoes and ridiculous blousey shirts. Two or three of
the Mancunians had come through punk. They knew Joy
Division and The Buzzcocks and harked back to those halcyon days which disco had done much to destroy. They were
the ones who took the floor in the first place and did the
Dead Fly. The Dead Fly entailed lying on their backs on the
floor and wiggling their legs and arms about in the air,
frantically. When they began the Hawaii Five-O the other
four Englishmen joined in. I stood with Diffley and Coen
watching. Coen was perturbed. He hadn't reckoned on this
when he'd agreed, belatedly, to come out with us for a change.
The Hawaii Five-O meant forming a line on the floor on their
hunkers and rowing in time with the music, switching the
imaginary oar from left to right after each stroke. There was
consternation on the dance-floor, with some of the Germans
seeing the funny side of it and others obviously angry. This
was all before the Blue Max. To do the Blue Max you had to
join forefinger and thumb into a goggles-shape over the eyes
and run around the dance-floor with elbows sticking out like
wings. At this stage the dumbfounded Germans had had
enough. We were asked to leave. Coen protested. There were
comments about *Scheissengländer*. Coen tried without avail to
say we weren't English. We hadn't even been dancing for
God's sake. We were all escorted to the door. He was disgusted
but beyond him there was general euphoria. A victory of sorts
had been won. The impassive Germans had been routed. It
was one-nil for the Escape Committee.

When we got back to the hotel I joined Diffley in his room. We were still laughing at what had happened. It wasn't, he suggested, that bad a day. We'd achieved something, even if we had to get Norman to do it for us.

The euphoria was still around the following day, but it wore off sharpish when we saw a *Polizei* car pull up outside. Obviously the Germans would have to take it a step too far. But they weren't there because of what had happened in the Tanzbar. We should have known why they were there. All the signs were in place, the hints that something was amiss. Elizabeth had found Norman's passport when she was cleaning his room. We all laughed at that. It was typical Norman. He'd be back. It was suggested it proved we couldn't escape the place. We were like airmen caught in civvies in the middle of France. But the policeman put an end to the laughter. 'Someone — an *Engländer* — had fallen,' he shook his head when he said this, 'an *Engländer* had perhaps fallen in front of a train in Hannover.' Most of us got what he was saying but we asked him to say it again. We asked Diffley to translate. He said the *Engländer* had no identification on him. They only suspected he was English because of the labels on his clothes. That was all he had on him — that and a receipt from the Heldenberg. What they needed was someone to identify the body.

Coen and Diffley went to Hannover. Diffley was very matter of fact about it. He said Norman hadn't been difficult to identify. His face was alright. The train though had cut him in two. 'Why did he do it?' he asked. One of us said we didn't know he did it in the first place. 'It could have been an accident.' None of us said anything to that. 'Well it could have,' he repeated indignantly. We'd seen Coen's car coming in the distance and had gone out to meet them. Now we were standing at the entrance to the hotel in silence.

'Do you know what the worst thing was?' Diffley said. 'It was when they asked us about next of kin and all we knew was where he came from. Nothing else about the man.'

We'd left the massive Bastille doors of the hotel open. The wind had changed and was now astringent. Creaking noises came from behind us as if the roof were about to lift off the place. Snow was falling again. It had begun to flurry and was already building into a drift at the side of Coen's car. You could see patches of it here and there that were stained with soot. The afternoon was flooded with sunlight.

15

I LEFT THEN. WE ALL MOVED. DECAMPED. ALL EXCEPT COEN and Diffley. Diffley said he was going to winter out. Those were his words. I got a lift with two of the boys to Hull and I hotfooted it down the Motorway to London. Two days later I was in the back bar of The White Hart on Fulham Broadway. Raymond Roland, Roger Sherlock and Liam Farrell were playing music. It was like I'd never left. Outside London was lit up for Christmas. The streets looked decorous after the great white plain of Northern Germany. This was as near to home as it got.

I stayed the night with Brian, a friend of mine from Northern Ireland. Brian was an electrician but he'd given up working. He was studying to become an astrologer, he told me. I was sceptical but he persevered. The problem was he'd been cursed by a witch up at the Royal Astrological Lodge. There were all sorts of people in the Lodge apparently. He described her as a big woman dressed in flowing robes, who spoke in a grandiose manner.

'And how are the stars over Ireland?' she demanded.

Brian looked up at her.

'Same fucking sky,' he said.

After that, what he called his small household gods began to conspire against him. He said that was how these things worked, nothing grandiloquent, rather a series of small disasters he could neither prevent nor reverse. A key broke off in the lock, his bath was infested by spiders, lights flickered on and off, a fox pelt he owned took off around the room of its own volition.

'What, like a real fox?' I said.

'No,' he said, 'more like a shadow across the wall.'

'What you're saying is the place is haunted?'

It was, he agreed, and he had to get out for a few weeks. He was going back to Ireland. The rent was low but I was unsure. He could see my indecision. 'Look at it this way,' he forced a laugh, 'if you move in here you'll never have to read fiction again.'

The following day I went up to Fleet Street. I could have gone back with Lonesome Tom but I felt that if I did I might as well forget about Germany. There was unfinished business there. I didn't even ring to tell him I was in town. In those days Fleet Street — before an Australian press baron, the British Prime Minister and what was termed new technology conspired to make the place an irrelevance — was where you went for work, specifically the art-deco offices of the *Daily Express*, the Black *Lubiyanka* as it was called. That was where the *Evening Standard* first saw the light of day, paradoxically at eleven o'clock in the morning. The *Standard* contained all the advertisements for building work. We called going there the Fleet Street Shuffle. It called for speed off the mark, as there were times when there were more men there than jobs advertised. I was lucky that morning and got work over the river from Battersea, underpinning on the King's Road.

The work was a shock to my system after six weeks' inactivity. Underpinning involved shoring up the foundations of an old building from beneath. There were three of us and we were expected to fill five skips a day. I was wondering what was going on. We were excavating an area the size of a small semi-detached house, when all we needed to do was dig out the sections of the building that needed to be underpinned. And it was all hand-digging, heavy-going. The house was on an L bend on the road and a machine would have stopped the traffic. The two other men introduced themselves to me. There was a man who called himself Speedy, ironically as it transpired, and Tommy who said he was from Tipperary. Tommy had a head of hair the colour and texture of steel wool and a face like a battered crisp bag, as if it had been flattened in different directions. Tommy and myself dug — or I dug in the bottom of the hole, with Tommy on a stage above me shovelling the spoil into the barrows which Speedy then emptied into the skip. We worked without pause. The agent stood above us for the whole of the first day, his hands clasped behind his back and his belly protruding over his belt. Once or twice we pulled up and grabbed a roll-up as the skips were being changed over. Work was, Tipperary Tommy gave me to understand, at a premium. It was heads-down time. Christmas was coming, he informed me needlessly. The shadow of the agent hovered over us again. Tommy ground the roll-up under his boot and was already shovelling.

There were also two Cockneys on the job, two boys from south of the river. Something had passed between them and Tommy the morning I'd started, a nod or a half-glance. I got the impression that they believed they'd see how I worked out. There were two ways of keeping a job, the first was an ability to do it in the first place. Secondly, your face had to fit in and often that was the more important consideration. Although I couldn't find out exactly what the Cockneys were doing there since they never joined us in the hole, I could see that they believed they had the agent's ear. It was ten days until Christmas. I still had money from Germany but I needed to keep working. I needed to get the Heldenberg out of my system.

For the next few days I dug like a metronome. I asked no questions and watched everything. It didn't take long to find a rhythm again. I could pace Tommy easily. Several times on the first two days he tried to burn me off. He'd begin by shouting something, some encouragement to himself or an admonishment to Speedy, then he'd start to shovel frantically. I remembered what Lonesome Tom used to say about always keeping a gear, working within yourself. My upper body was sinewy, ropy with muscle. I knew how to lean into the aches and pains, absorbing them into the rhythm of what I was doing. Tommy shovelled as fast as he could, glancing down at me from time to time. Those were glances he couldn't afford. I effortlessly filled the stage with spoil, which built up about his feet so that the area he had to work in became smaller and smaller. As his motion became circumscribed, he ran out of steam and stopped to wipe the sweat off his brow. I was below him, grinning to myself. Like that, a hierarchy was formed. He knew I could have him, just as surely as I knew that someday somebody younger might well turn me over. It contributed to the tension between us. But by Friday, although the agent hadn't said a word to me, I knew I was in.

The first time he talked to me was in the Cross Keys that same day. We looked out of place amidst the lunchtime drinkers and the Bohemian crowd that the pub attracted. The landlord welcomed us just the same. He knew there was a big job around the corner and that meant men with money to spend. The agent told me it was a wine cellar we were digging out. The job was for a rich man who'd made his money in advertising. I was astonished to hear that there were fortunes to be made in helping people to sell things. The agent said he'd gone through fifteen men to get me. I was a great worker. I had it all in front of me: it could only get better for me. He said he looked after his men and he had plenty of work. I was wary of this talk. I'd heard it all before. I could see Tommy was listening and I knew, without him saying anything, that he shared my cynicism.

We got drunk that Friday. When the pub shut at three o'clock we went back to the site and tidied the tools away. I had the shift for the following morning and we only had one skip to fill. I walked up the road with Speedy to the bus stop. Feeling that kind of daze that comes from midday drinking, the feeling we'd done something unnatural. My head felt light as Speedy told me about all the insurance claims he'd made. How he was hit by a car on the zebra crossing on Abbey Road that the Beatles had used for an album cover — that was five grand, he said. 'You'd want to give me a clear berth. I haven't had a claim for a while now.' And this, I told myself, was the man who was wheeling barrows over my head all day.

I went home for Christmas. I had money in my pocket. My mother was trying to formulate a way of telling me that I should have, by now, got a proper job. She found it difficult to say this and I didn't help her. There were one or two references to gallivanting just the same. The last series of phone calls from Germany had unnerved her. She thought there was something amiss. Still, here was I in good health and obviously still working. There was a part of her that settled for that.

In the new year we were back in the hole in the snow. For a while it had reminded me of the excavation myself and Diffley had dug at Heathrow. I remembered Diffley and his Greek mythology and the thought of a job that would never end but we did finish, the second week in January. It was an impressive feat accomplished without a machine. It was apparent that for the agent that had been part of the attraction. He joined us with a crate of pint bottles of Courage Light Ale as myself and Tommy finished the bottoming out. The Last of the Heavy Diggers, he called us.

In truth the work was only beginning. We had a roof now over our heads, as we were working within the walls of the existing building. It froze hard and snow flurried outside — blowing in on top of us as we poured a concrete base and began to shutter a spine wall to take the weight of what would be built above us. The snow fell heaviest the day we poured the wall. We again barrowed the concrete in from the road — crossing rickety scaffold boards spread across bandstands or trestles. It was the first day I'd seen the Cockneys working. One of them slid, with a barrow of concrete, off the walkway and broke his arm. It was late in the evening when we finished. I stopped for a few pints in the Northcote just above Clapham Junction. I was wearing a German Army parka which was splashed with the wash of the concrete. The pub was full of working men who hadn't been out since before Christmas. They were curious as to where I was coming from. I knew no one, spoke to no one.

The two Cockneys were called Tel and Del. Tel, the one with the broken arm, came back to work. The agent made him a tea-boy. He decided we needed a canteen for the shackle-up. That was a word I hadn't heard used for a long time. The pace of the job had eased considerably as it often does when there is no showcase piece of work to be accomplished. Nothing that progress can be dramatically measured against. We sat for longer-than-usual breaks in the new canteen. The snow was thawing and there was already an inchoate feeling of spring in the air. The Cockneys looked like they were unused to daylight: their skin had the blanched look of tubers dug up from far beneath the earth. I wasn't surprised to learn that they'd done time. What did surprise me was the way they boasted about it. 'Bird,' they called it, like it was something out of an old-fashioned movie. Tel was a petty thief, Del was out on bail for mugging old-age pensioners and Tipperary Tommy — it turned out — had several convictions for robbery with violence. Bookies' shops, he told me, liberating his own money. Their talk was peppered with prison jargon and they jokingly divided the day as it would have been in the prison yard. We slopped out early in the morning, lights out was when we finished work and they rolled their cigarettes competitively, seeing who could get the most out of a few strands of tobacco — a pure sign that they'd done time. I thought little enough of them. They'd preyed on their own. If they were any good, had any intelligence, they wouldn't get caught. It was like the myth of the fighting man. The way we shied away from the man with scars when in fact the really good fighters didn't get scarred. Still for all I disliked them, they were unavoidable and I fell in with them on occasion. I even found myself giving futile advice to Del, who was the younger of them. Even as I felt they wouldn't be long separated from a life they were clearly nostalgic for.

They drank in a pub just south of the river, on Falcon Road. There is no great geographical division between wealth and poverty in London. The City of London ended up snarled up in the hucksters and sweat-shops down in Tower Hamlets; the King's Road gave way to the Falcon Road and that pub in the perpetual shadow of the tower blocks. Salubrious areas petered into modern slums, the parkland and expensive shops and restaurants of Hampstead were bordered by the high-rise flats behind Chalk Farm where teenagers chased the dragon. The Tory Government had promised much to their parents. They had the right to buy their council properties but the real conspiracy was to move them on — to make way for a series of acronyms that weren't quite yet current — the Dinkies and the Yuppies. But these people weren't for moving. A journey north of the river was a trial for many of them. They were only familiar with the streets of the particular fastness they grew up in. They were white and English and working-class with generations of lost Irish married into them. They mention ancestors from places like Wicklow or Roscommon with the same bafflement they reserved for Rochdale or Islington.

I was well-aware that I was in that pub on sufferance. And even though I wasn't afraid of anybody in there, as I would have been when I came to London first, I felt there was something millennial in the atmosphere there, as if its customers were preparing an assault on what they believed was their birthright across the river. In fact the assault would be low-key — would amount only to a few isolated shoplifting sprees. They were a rag-bag army on a forgotten salient — nobody had told them the battle was lost. Conversation quelled when I entered the pub, the paranoia almost palpable. But as they saw the company I was with, talk resumed, nods were exchanged and solitary men returned to their pints, mollified. Everybody was smoking, their cigarettes cupped, guarded like prized possessions. There was horses on the telly, the bar lined with betting slips and the stubs of pencils. It was Saturday afternoon.

Outside I saw a man, watched by a group of others, urge his pit-bull terrier to jump in the air, like something electric, and clamp its jaw onto the lower branches of a wizened tree. It hung there, obedient, like a vampire bat until he batted it over the head and it fell, cowering at his feet as he laughed. Inside there were two customers surreptitiously dealing hash in the corner and beyond them a group of young women with children in a variety of hues, a pall of glutinous, sickly smoke about their table. Seeing me glance in their direction, the landlord lumbered from his stool behind the bar, crushed his cigarette into an ashtray, lifted a dirty dishrag and began to wipe a spigot. He glowered from beneath his brows, a look he divided between me and the group of women. At last he bellowed, 'Take your facking rugrats out of here. Take the facking lot of 'em out.'

There was a titter of laughter as the women took their joints and disappeared through a source of light somewhere far at the back. The men with the dog then came in. One of them high-fived Del. He joined them in a conspiratorial huddle at a table, the pit-bull by now salivating at their feet. They nodded cryptically. The owner reached down from time to time and patted the dog's head, whispering melancholically in its ear. I gathered its name was Lucifer.

Tel bought the first round. 'Don't look now,' he said, gesturing to the group at the table. 'Computers,' he told me, 'the next big thing.' It was in that pub I first heard computers referred to as "the next big thing". I mentioned the salivating dog.

'I know,' he said, 'beauts aren't they?'

I told him I didn't like them. I'd never seen a dog like that before either. He looked at me askance.

'Don't like them? *Blacks* don't like them.'

For an instance I thought I'd be safer closer to the Junction or in Brixton, the way he said the word blacks with contempt. His fear and the Black man's fear of the dog.

'Your average pit-bull,' he said. 'He'll growl at yer. You got a chance. Yer average Alsatian, if you stand still, he won't attack. But yer average Rottweiler — yer average Rottweiler attacks without warning.' He spoke admiringly. Meanwhile the pit-bull struggled to its feet. Its owner leaned over and nuzzled it. It lay back down again. Unnoticed, the group of women had begun to reassemble in one and twos.

All those dogs were becoming the new status symbol. They said their owner was a bad bastard and if he didn't do you, the dog would. Perhaps your man couldn't afford a BMW, I thought, or a Capri even, jacked up off the ground with customised wheels. I was even to become used to those dogs as they became briefly popular, owned by drug dealers and body-builders. I worked with a hod-carrier once, so pumped up on steroids he couldn't climb a ladder — in itself a kind of contradiction in terms — who kept two pit-bulls in the back of a Transit van while he worked. The van had an air of febrile menace but the dogs grew frustrated. It began to reek of undigested meat and faeces and quaked from side to side as they turned on each other at first in sexual congress, and eventually at each other's throats. The non-climbing hoddie soon got sent up the road. It was over a year later when I came across a story in the tabloids about two pit-bulls who'd savaged a body-builder in one of those towns beyond the far end of the District Line, Stapleford Tawney or Botany Bay or Hades even. I could put two and two together as good as any man.

That day wore on meaninglessly. I was guzzling large amounts of generic, fizzy beer which passed through me like daylight through a window pane. It tasted insipid and could well have been concocted as some sort of an experiment by the landlord in a cellar like a chemical lab — an advanced version of the bromide the two boys swore they were fed in the Scrubs perhaps. I pissed like a horse and looked at myself, bleary-eyed in the toilet mirror, reminding myself that my situation was precarious. I had a premonition that some act of unspeakable violence was about to take place. But the shutters were down on the windows back in the bar, a haze of smoke enveloped everything and the earlier edgier atmosphere seemed to have evaporated, replaced with an air of *bonhomie*. I had been accepted. At the back of my mind I knew this too was transient and I would be looked upon with suspicion again the following morning. A lifetime would not be enough to gain acceptance in that pub. Still I got involved in a variety of conversations, with people who appeared to be trying to impart something urgent and doubtlessly cogent in a language that was beyond me. In truth we were all beyond language, communicating more through grunts and swear words, gestures and slaps on the back. The women in the corner had long since made a tactical withdrawal. Del and myself had sworn fealty several times and closing time was long gone when I staggered from the bar, partly supported by a woman I'd spent the last two hours talking to. At some point in the conversation — in which I was trying to impress on her how the Specials' 'Ghost Town' was far superior to anything in the charts — I briefly sobered up and realised where this was going. Del leant over and whispered in my ear: 'She's a sort.'

I began pawing at her in the lift but she pushed me off and rearranged her clothes. There were proprieties. She raised her finger to her lips as she led me into a darkened bedroom, up-lit from below by the streetlights which reflected off the ceiling through gaps in the heavy curtains. I remember her body and swollen nipples and the way she rose over me in the bed. She wasn't standing on ceremony and knew exactly what she wanted. She rode me like a succubus. I might not have been there indeed. She came before me, moaned and collapsed across me, muttering something to herself before she fell into a deep sleep. Eventually I eased her hard little body off me and fell into a stupor.

I woke early with the vague sense of a child crying somewhere in the distance. My eyes were melded together and I blinked several times to be sure of what I was seeing. I stood up and began to remember how I'd got there. There was a child in a cot in the corner of the room. The child had pulled itself upright against the bars of the cot. It was wearing a jump-suit of some sort. Its arms were stretched out towards me. I went back to the bed and shook the woman. She stirred fitfully. The pillow was saliva stained in the bow shape of her lips. She reached across towards where I had been lying. I shook her again. The child resumed crying. I could hear the tinny sound of music coming from somewhere. Somebody banged on the adjoining wall. I drew the curtains. From the window you could see way up beyond the turn in the river. You could see pebble beaches and then mud flats. For some reason, for an instance, each appeared like an entirely separate universe. Ones I would have preferred to be in. I got dressed

and legged it. The lift was slow coming. I took the stairs,
down and down, two at a time, with increasing velocity —
until I lost my footing, went over on one side and twisted my
ankle. I was confounded and breathless when I hobbled away
from the flats. My head throbbed and pulsed like something
mechanical. I realised I'd left my watch behind. It was Sunday
morning. It must have been early because I was the only one
on the streets. A bus was slow in coming.

I was still hobbling two weeks later when we began to
demolish the building about us. It was March already. Del
had been picked up for violating his parole. And Tel's brief
told him he too was facing a long sentence. Tel was on to
me about going to Germany. I tried to mollify him. I said
he should do his time. I knew if I was going to go it would
have to be soon. We took the roof off the existing building
early in the week. It began to rain and we sheltered, looking
up through the spars at leaden skies. The agent came out
and told us to finish early for the day. We began the
demolition on a Friday and worked through the weekend.
Tipperary Tommy started on one end, myself on the other.
We were four floors up, without a scaffolding, standing on
a thirteen-inch wall. The walls were made up of old
Flettons — a notoriously hard brick — plastered with a
sand-and-cement render that had withstood more than a
hundred years. They were like the walls of a medieval castle
and took our weight easily. We worked towards each other,
laboriously knocking the building, one course of bricks
after another, with sledge hammers. Every blow was
predicated on maintaining our balance. We knocked out
the bricks between our legs, then sent the ones we had been
standing on skittering downwards. The bricks exploded
loose in great chunks, toppling downward end over end.
We stopped every hour or so and sat on the remainder of
the wall with our legs swinging, smoking. The sun had
begun to shine. Spores of ancient dust danced in the light.

We told ourselves it wasn't the worst work imaginable —
neither was it. I took off my shirt. I could feel the heat on
my back and shoulders. There was a sheen of sweat on me
and a light coating of dust began to harden on my skin like
a resin. We were laughing at the four men below us trying
to sort the bricks out, to scavenge the stocks that could be
re-used, skipping the rest. We threatened to start work
again, to send more debris down on top of them. We
watched them scatter as we thumped the wall with the butts
of our sledge hammers.

'Are you going to hang around?' Tommy asked.

I didn't answer him.

'It's just,' he said, 'that the agent told me he has a big
demolition job coming up at the Elephant and Castle. He
says we could have it on a price, the two of us. What do you
say? It could be a handy few bob.'

'I doubt I'll be around,' I said.

'So you are going back to Germany then.'

I nodded.

'It's just if you're going back to Germany, well I might go
with you. How'd you feel about that?'

I took out my tobacco. I knew what was coming. There
had been a truce between myself and Tommy. He'd come to
the realisation that I wasn't interested in being what he called,
given his problem with authority, the Bull Elephant.
Although I said little and dissembled frequently it was
obvious I had been waiting for the weather to change.

What I didn't know was that so had Tommy, for entirely
different reasons. In the gaps between work that day he told
me he was minded to take to the roads again. He was
wistful. He'd spent the last few years sleeping rough in the
summer, migrating between Shepherd's Bush Green and
Furnival Gardens, down on the river in Hammersmith. If
the sun was shining, all he wanted was the price of a few
flagons, he said. People sleeping rough, even teenagers, were

becoming highly visible in London about then, but that
wasn't what Tommy intended. His was a life-style choice, if
you like. He was a class of a cuckoo tramp, drawn to the
long acre when the weather was good. His problem however
was that he'd taken up with a woman. He was living with
her in the White City. He'd bought her a big telly, he said,
but that wasn't enough. He had little experience of women.
Not that type of woman, at any rate, he added dolefully.
The type that would want you to stay.

Of course I should have once again realised all of this —
which became more obvious after he'd told me he had
skippered out. I should have known from the way he dressed
if nothing else, his mismatched clothing could only have been
acquired in a charity shop, track-suit bottoms and a line of
antique Ben Sherman shirts with wide, 1960s' Day-Glo
stripes. Still he was incapable of passing a wing mirror — or
a puddle even — without stopping, unselfconsciously, to
adjust his appearence. There was also his permanent dosser's
suntan. He'd even once shown up late for work, after an
interview with the DHSS — 'a man,' he would say, 'had to
look after his rightful gratuity' — wearing a pin-striped suit
with flared trousers, a kipper tie and a pair of engraved
cufflinks on his frayed cuffs.

I told him about Germany. I told him it wasn't easy —
that he would be considered old there. I tried to discourage
him. 'Look,' I said, 'there's no point in going now anyway.
They'll just be gone back to work after the winter break. You
were better to wait a month or more even.'

'Later in the year then you're saying.'

'Yeah, later.'

But I did end up giving him the number of the
Heldenberg.

By Monday morning the building was gone. A group of
locals gathered on the road. Somebody from the residents'
group enquired what we'd done. Somebody said she was an

artist of some renown — like that would make the slightest difference to us.

'Where's it gone?' Tommy said. 'Where do you think it's gone? It's out in the dump in Mortlake or in a landfill somewhere else. It's not coming back, that's for sure. Mind you,' he said, winding up for the pitch big time by this stage, 'we sold what we could of her. Didn't we lads? You could never say we missed an opportunity like that.'

They went off to consult the notice for Planning Permission which was tied to a nearby lamp-post. 'It says,' they said, 'superficial structural repairs.' Pointing out that the whole building was gone. Tommy told them that we were mere agents of destruction. We just did what we were told. Otherwise we wouldn't get paid. Then he told them about the demolition of a listed, historic building he'd been involved in. Took in a JCB of a Friday, he said, when everyone was gone home and levelled the whole thing with the bucket. Not a thing anyone could do. 'Where were you all weekend? Did you not hear us?'

Tommy was only making them more agitated.

'Look,' someone enquired, 'the man who owns this property will have to live next door to us ... we're his neighbours. I mean, this is hardly the best way to start. What is he building here? We were told it was a dwelling house. Do you know?'

'A dwelling you were told? Well that's a good one so it is,' said Tommy grinning. 'And I was told it was a home for retarded Arab boys. He's a rich Arab, isn't he?'

There was consternation at this news. The agent spent the rest of the day fielding phone-calls. He had to assure everybody that any rumours about Arabs were untrue. It was a dwelling house. He ended up having to agree that we would heed the provision of a little-used council by-law. There would be no work on site — work being defined as anything that involved the use of power tools or any noise indeed —

after five o'clock in the evening or before eight o'clock in the mornings. None at all after twelve o'clock on a Saturday.

'That's us truly fucked!' Tommy said when he found out. 'It's the job in the Elephant or the doss on Shepherd's Bush Green then.'

It was but I had somewhere else to go.

16

WHEN I GOT BACK TO THE HELDENBERG EVERYBODY WAS already back working. Snow still lay in sheltered spots along the roadside. Part of the plain in front of the hotel was flooded and all the rivers were in full spate. It would be months before the snows completely melted. Coen and Diffley were back in the *Papierfabrik* in Alfeld. Diffley told me that life had a lot of the elements of Greek tragedy, and revisiting Alfeld was chief amongst them. He said whatever else happened he would never spend another winter in Germany: it had almost driven him insane, the monotony of it. Claus the agent had an initial week's work for me, buttressing a railway bridge near Northeim. It was the coldest I've ever been. We worked exposed on the plain in the east wind: my ears hurt, my eyes stung and, by evening time, my jaw felt frozen in position. The Germans were philosophical. They looked in the direction the wind blew from, shrugged and talked of *Russki* weather. Anything that came from the East appeared to evoke bad memories but it was something that would pass. At the end of the week

Claus had no more work for me. As I hadn't signed a contract I got on the phone.

Two days later I travelled north to Bremerhaven. I had a job on the docks constructing a big sea-wall. I was working for Boma, one of the Dutch agents. The Dutch had a bad name. Their agents could disappear owing men money. But Boma was a big concern and well-established. I wasn't worried. The agent talked to me in German. I passed myself off, speaking my best *Baustelle Deutsch*. An extra mark an hour, he told me on the phone, and I was in charge of the gang. I'd meet them in the hotel up there.

The Bremerhaven gang was relatively small and there were a couple of faces I recognised when I entered the bar in the hotel. One of them I'd seen around the town of Göttingen the year before, where he used to hang around with a strange-looking Spanish woman. I remembered asking him what he was going to do for the winter. Something will turn up, he'd said. So when I saw him in the bar I joined him, though I only knew him vaguely, our acquaintance not far beyond nodding. I couldn't remember his name. I knew he went by a nickname and then I remembered it — how he'd introduced himself to me, holding out his hand in a foppish parody of old-fashioned manners. The nickname was Road-Kill and he was from Limerick. Tree surgeon, I thought, that's what he'd been and I remembered also that he had a reputation for liking drugs. Road-Kill had a gaunt look to him, sepulchral even, his skin a pallid colour that defied even the strongest sun. He always wore his shirts sleeves down, a skein of greasy hair tied back behind his head. Men used to joke that he was rarely seen in daylight. He was glad to see me that night in Bremerhaven. He had never worked on a site before. He said he couldn't stick the trees any longer and he needed to get money together. India, once he had enough to get to India, he was off. He was into all that Eastern religion stuff, he said.

'What were you at all winter?' I asked. 'And what happened to the Spanish one?'

'Don't remind me about that,' he said. I noticed how a couple of other men in the bar had stopped talking and were listening intently. I had the impression from the way they were grinning at each other that they'd heard the story before but believed it was worth hearing again.

'You were right,' he told me, 'nothing turned up. I was trying to shake off the Spanish one. She's a jeweller you know. The weather turned very cold there for a while. Jasus sure, I spent Christmas Day on the steps of the Cathedral. Only for Frieda I'd a starved. You know Frieda the German one? She brought me two tins of sardines.'

'Two tins of sardines on Christmas day? I thought you had a few bob?'

'A few bob? I had a few bob sure. You know what I did? I gave it to your woman. She says she could get us work in Spain where the sun was shining. Off she took.'

'You gave her all your money?'

'The most of it. Do you know what I called her? Cyclops. I called her Cyclops.'

'And you didn't hear from her?'

'That's right. By Christmas week I was getting worried. The only thing I had was an address for her. She forgot she gave me that. So I took off after her. Down through France and across the Pyrenees. It was cold, I can tell you it was fucking cold and all I could think of was your one. It was Granada I was heading for. When you think of it — I didn't know it was that far. Me and Cyclops in the Gardens of the Alhambra.'

'She was there — was she?'

'She was. She thought I was going to kill her. I would've too, but by the time I got there I was knackered. I nearly froze crossing the Pyrenees and Madrid was well below zero. I wound up washing dishes and was glad to get it. I met

Cyclops alright but it wasn't at the address she gave me. You should have seen her — she was shaking and thought I was going to bust her — but I was glad enough to meet her in the wind-up. I had no work, nor no Spanish neither.'

'So you hitched up with her again?'

'No I didn't!' he said indignantly. '"Money," she says, "I get you money," an' she took off again. I caught up with her farther south. I remember it was freezing down by the sea and the only thing I got out of her was a screw down on the beach. She had one of them cloaks and I pulled it up over her head so as I couldn't see her when I was doing it. Three minutes' pleasure and three months of pain. She left me this though,' Road-Kill said. 'Just took it out and gave it to me when we finished screwing. She says "I give it to you. You keep. I bring money." That was the last I saw of her.'

Everybody crowded round the table. We'd begun to attract the attention of the barman. Road-Kill held out his fist out in front of him and opened it slowly. A glass eye sat in the middle of his palm — staring, unblinkingly, up at us.

'She'll not go far without that — the one-eyed cunt,' he said.

We fell in with a Donegal man that night. He told us to call him Ready-Mix. 'Say no more sir,' he said. He didn't need to. It was obvious from talking to him that he knew what he was doing. He'd been around the year before as well. He'd teamed up with someone he termed a right greenhorn. A fella called Fogarty from London. Another narrowback, he said, meaning Fogarty was London-Irish. I had a hazy memory of Fogarty from the winter I'd spent on the hill. I had to share a room with him one night that he passed through. He'd joined us, playing cards and smoking dope. He wore a hat and I remembered he did a very good impression of Benny from the cartoon *Top Cat*. I also remembered waking to find the bedroom window wide open. I got up to close it and saw him

outside on his hands and knees on the flat roof, eating snow.
I asked him what he was at?

'Eating snow,' he said.

'I can see that. Why are you eating snow?'

He said he was thirsty.

That was our gang and we began work the following
morning. Both Fogarty and Road-Kill had shiny new
hammers which wasn't a good idea. Fogarty was twirling his
about like a gun, drawing even more attention to himself. I
told him to stop. He made some comment and I told him to
shut the fuck up. I intended to be there for more than one
day. It was too late though, he'd been spotted. Our first job
was to lever a shutter into position and put the shuttering
bolts through it, fastening them into position, nailed against
a length of timber. I was amazed when Ready-Mix lifted the
shutter and walked it into place by himself. He had a centre
of gravity somewhere about his ankles and was incredibly
strong. We were being watched but had got off to a good
start. Then the problems began. Fogarty couldn't get a piece
of four-by-four in place. It slipped and swung loose, held only
by the one nail he'd managed to sink into it. He panicked and
tried to bat it with his hammer. It fell and hit him on the side
of the head, knocking him head-over-heels onto the
scaffolding. He got up gingerly but the German foreman had
spotted him. It had taken less than fifteen minutes. He came
up on the scaffolding, lifted the four-by-four and drove the
three-inch nail through it with three blows of his hammer. He
started to speak to Fogarty, then realised he wasn't being
understood. Instead he tapped a nail into position and
indicated that Fogarty was to drive it home. He was holding
the four-by-four in place. Fogarty swung and missed. His
swing narrowly missed the foreman's hand. The foreman then
drove the nail home himself. He tapped in another one. This
time he rook a red crayon and marked the head of the nail.
Fogarty missed with six swings. The foreman took off his

glasses and gave them to Fogarty who put them on. Eventually he did manage to hit the nail but bent it sideways. Most of the workers on the site were watching what was going on, watching and laughing. The foreman took the shiny hammer off Fogarty and led him down the ladder. He threw the hammer away and gave him a shovel. He sent him down into a trench and called me over, telling me to tell him to bottom it out. 'Sixteen Marks,' he said, 'that's all we'll pay him.' I told Fogarty this. It was as good as he was going to get. He accepted the offer.

We worked on the shutters for most of the rest of the day. Road-Kill at least managed to make himself scarce. I sent him round the back where he couldn't be seen. Occasionally I glanced downward to see how Fogarty was progressing. The trench he was supposed to be bottoming out looked considerably worse than it had before he started. He had become absorbed in the minutiae of what he was doing. He'd climb out to see if the bottom looked level from above and every time he got back in he knocked part of the sides in after him. The trench was filling with spoil in his wake. Still, I consoled myself, he might well last. The trench was becoming a place of pilgrimage for the whole job. The Germans were laughing at his efforts. At least he was entertaining them and because of that his future was probably secure.

Despite all, we settled in well. The Germans knew that Road-Kill didn't know what he was up to, but they let it go as long as we carried him. Meanwhile they tried to keep Fogarty as far away from any important work as possible. The only difficulty was the antagonism that had developed between Fogarty and Ready-Mix. They went into the town on one occasion and returned separately. Ready-Mix said he would never drink with him again. I asked why and he said it was women. Fogarty would get you in trouble. He wouldn't say any more. As for Road-Kill, he had little to do with the rest of us. He obsessed about India and meditation, all the while taking a shortcut to Nirvana by smoking copious amounts of hash. If the rest of us went for a drink he'd remain in his room, joining us later in a blissed-out state, hovering beyond communication, as if subject to siren calls inaudible to everyone else.

The Germans as usual worked their thirty-seven-and-a-half-hour week: they wouldn't work Saturdays. Saturdays were the days we struck and cleaned shuttering. The shutters beneath a deck were left up longest. A deck was a concrete floor that was made by setting up rows of Akros with lengths of timber — headers — running across the top of them. Sheets of plywood were then nailed across the headers and steel laid on top of that. The concrete was poured and levelled then. When the concrete had dried — gone off — the shutters were struck, leaving the finished floor in position. When we struck the shutters we were meant to do so gradually, basically a sheet of ply at a time. We had to denail the timber and stack it and the Akros in piles so they could be moved to the next place where they were needed. When the Germans were there this was what we did. When they weren't, we did it our way. Our way usually meant staying back after the last of them had left on a Friday evening. Then we'd ease off all the Akros except for a few we left, strategically placed, usually at the corners of the deck. Then we'd pull those and drop the whole structure together. It was dangerous work — jumping clear at the last minute as we dropped tons of metal, timber and plywood virtually on our heads.

One Friday, myself and Ready-Mix pulled down the last of the big decks. We went back to the hotel to let the dust settle until the morning. That Friday night, as usual, we had a skinful of drink. Early the next morning Ready-Mix pulled me from the bed. He had a struggle to get the other two up, who, if anything, were in worse condition. On our way down to the docks we saw Road-Kill lob an empty soft-drink can across his shoulder, hearing it clatter behind us, dead-centre into a rubbish bin. We'd only begun to jeer him when he tossed another blindly backwards. We turned to see it follow the first can into the rubbish bin. By now Road-Kill was high-fiving Fogarty, doing a little dance across the road on his toes.

'He has,' Ready-Mix said, 'a fierce streak of luck, that man.'

In fact he was really referring to what had happened when we'd struck the shutters the evening before. How Road-Kill had stayed standing in the middle of the deck, the only sheet of ply that hadn't fallen was the one above his head. He could have been killed — yet he just stood there unfazed, zoned-out, oblivious to how close he'd come to being skulled by a strongback or guillotined by a sheet of ply.

When we got to the site that Saturday morning we were surprised to see some Germans there before us. They were loading some of the storage huts onto lorries, using a crane. It was a sure sign the job was coming to an end. It was, I said to Ready-Mix, time to get on the phone again. Meanwhile the deck we'd struck the previous evening looked like a tornado had hit it. There was ply, strongbacks, Akros and timber piled helter-skelter from floor to ceiling. It was a forbidding sight. Ready-Mix and myself began at one end, Fogarty and Road-Kill at the other. The work was repetitive and boring and it was a couple of hours before we'd made any noticeable headway. We stopped and I went for coffee. Ready-Mix said he would check on the other two boys. When I returned he said they had done little or nothing. He said he'd given out to them, told them we weren't going to carry them this time. We worked on until we heard the church bells ring for midday. We could see an end in sight — at least an end to our half of the deck. But by now we should have seen the other two. We both went to check on them this time. There was no sign of them anywhere, apart from their nail-bars and hammers lying on the ground. 'They're in the pub, I bet you they're in the pub,' I said. 'I'll fucking kill them.' That was when we heard the shouting coming from above.

Road-Kill told us later what had happened. He blamed Fogarty. He said it was Fogarty who said if they had a smoke they'd work better. 'We were dying,' Road-Kill said, 'so we went off to the toilets. You know the way the toilets are,' he said, 'with that little gap beneath the cubicles? Well I skinned up and had a couple of draws. We were passing the joint over and back under the gap. You know the gap, the one they used to write *Beware of Limbo Dancers* over? Anyhow Fogarty passed the joint back to me, saying he was getting car-sick. I said how could you get car-sick in the toilets and he said it was because we were moving. I said we weren't moving. "I know it's good dope," I said, "but we're not moving." But then he said to look at the door handle. I did and I couldn't believe it … it was moving back and forth, from side-to-side like. So what did I do? I got up. I could feel the floor shifting and I had to hold onto the walls to get to the door. Anyhow, I opened the door. I thought I was going to be sick. I don't know what stopped me — but I stopped and I looked down and there we were about fifty foot up in the air over the docks. Only you boys heard us shouting … I could've stepped out when I think of it …'

We had got the crane driver to lower them back to the ground. After which Ready-Mix lost his temper. He told them that only for us they wouldn't have lasted a day on the job. We'd carried them. The chances were that the firm had now had enough of the lot of us. We'd all be for the road the next week. It was our bad luck to be associated with them. They would have to finish cleaning the shuttering by themselves. Our part was done.

Surprisingly it worked. They both looked admonished. They said they would finish up if we promised to tell nobody about what had happened with the toilets. We agreed readily enough. We packed our tools, got changed and walked off the site, leaving the two boys still working. Ready-Mix was still seething. He said he was going to go back to London. All the work the Dutchman had was in the south. He wasn't going to travel south. 'I'm leaving sir,' he said, 'I've enough of working with wankers. All them fuckers are good for is slam-dunking beer-cans.' He drained the can of beer he was holding and threw it across his shoulder in an arc. It hit the edge of the pavement and clattered into the road.

'Fucking jammy bastard,' he said. I looked at him and laughed. He blinked, then laughed himself. When we got back to the bar at the hotel I ordered two beers as Ready-Mix's money rattled through the telephone box beside us. 'Wait until you hear what happened to us this morning, sir,' I could hear him saying. 'Wait until I tell you about these two boys …'

There were a couple of weeks work left in Bremerhaven. Like Ready-Mix I didn't want to go south either. I liked the North, the occasional weekend back in the Heldenberg. I phoned the hotel. They were all still working for Claus. Diffley told me there was a big run of work coming up on a nuclear power station. Nuclear power stations were big news in Germany then. They were something I disagreed with. I said that to him. 'What about all your student friends in Göttingen — the *Atomkraft, Nein Danke* brigade?' I said. 'What they don't know won't hurt them,' he said. 'We're talking a long run of work here — all the hours a man can work.' I said I would think about it.

The following weekend Ready-Mix left for London. He said he was going for a holiday. To see what the lie of the land was and he mightn't come back. That was the weekend I had to sub Fogarty the price of his hotel bill. We got paid on Friday and he disappeared that night. The following morning he was broke. I told him he'd been paid the same as the rest of us and shouldn't have been stuck for money. He pointed out that he wasn't: it was just that he'd spent his money on two whores in Hamburg. At least he thought he'd spent his week's wages on two whores in Hamburg. He remembered going up to the room with them. He remembered them starting a floor-show and himself spraying champagne over them. All he remembered after that was arriving in the Hamburg train station broke and having to hitch a lift to Bremerhaven.

Ready-Mix used to say he wouldn't let Fogarty within the postal code. He looked upon him as something louche and priapal, a rutting bull loosed amongst the lot of us. Whereas the truth of Fogarty was much more prosaic: customs men at Heathrow Airport searched his bag later that year and found it half-filled with women's knickers, used women's knickers it goes without saying. Much later he became a success of sorts, training as an accountant. I heard he worked on the Barings Bank audit.

17

A WEEK LATER DIFFLEY PHONED. SOMEONE HAD BEEN ON looking for me, he said. A Scotsman named Alex. A big talker, he said. I phoned Alex. He talked big alright. He wanted to meet me in Bremen the following Saturday. It was my first job interview ever. I met him in a hotel. He questioned me about where I'd been and what I'd done. He was singing the familiar refrain: he looked after his men, he only wanted good men working for him — tradesmen, he said. That must have hit a nerve because after a while I'd had enough of it. I told him you could either do the job or you couldn't. 'Don't be so touchy,' he said before asking me could I grow a beard.

'A beard?' I asked in dismay.

'Aye,' he said, 'you'll need to look older.' He offered me twenty marks an hour — a mythical sum — exceeding even the Berlin rate. Which was how I ended up in the sleepy town of Vechta in the north of Germany with a beard.

Vechta felt farther from home than anywhere else. It was easy to lose touch. Ireland, which was rarely out of the headlines in England, hardly ever made them in Germany. We got an occasional Sunday broadsheet but they were English: full of news about the implosion of the Labour Party and the advent of the Gang of Three. There was nothing about Irish sport or indeed day-to-day life in Ireland. I had spent the Sunday of the 1980 All-Ireland hurling final the previous summer in a bar in Cologne full of Galway men. Everyone said the Galway hurlers were cursed and the men in the bar discussed the various explanations for the curse before the game started. A few years before I'd seen Irishmen on Overstone Road at the back of Hammersmith Broadway standing with transistor radios about telegraph poles. The poles acted as impromptu aerials. The reception was surprisingly good. There were no telegraph poles in that Cologne bar so when the game started the barman, who was from Kerry, phoned his brother in Killorglin and had him hold the phone against the radio. We took turns listening to what was happening in Dublin and relayed it to those about us — third-hand. Galway got off to a good start and were two goals up after ten minutes. In the second half Limerick came back at them and ran them close at the final whistle. Men elbowed each other out of the way to get at the phone. We heard John Connolly's speech and Joe McDonagh sang "The West's Awake" down the phone to a packed bar in Cologne.

That could only happen once. What other news we got was relayed on the phone or came from the *Bild Zeitung* — a German paper that looked like a broadsheet but was pure tabloid by inclination. It had a dubious — even to us — political subtext, along with the Kaiser Franz Beckenbauer as its soccer analyst, plenty of scantily clad women, horoscopes and problem pages. Mostly though it had big headlines that were easy to understand: *PAPST ERMORDET*. Ronald Regan too was *ermordet* that summer — but the headline that stood out for me was one that was printed the last week of the job in

Bremerhaven: *BOBBY SANDS IST TOT*. There was also a grainy — and very familiar — front-page shot of a vehicle ablaze.

That was what was on my mind when I arrived, on Saturday evening, in the somnolent town of Vechta. It reminded me of an Irish town because it was in the middle of good agricultural land with cattle belly-deep in grass in the fields that stretched beyond the town's boundaries. There was no traffic on the main street. What I noticed most though was the job we were going too — it was also on the main street. I knew to look at it that there wasn't work for fifteen men. Rather it was the type of job the Germans would have expected to build in two months' maximum with a gang of six.

That was how it turned out too. The Vechta gang were all from Sheffield, many of them had served their time in various capacities in the steelworks. They'd never shuttered, they told me. It wasn't something they should worry too much about, I told them. I was thinking of Fogarty. If they could hammer a nail straight and were willing to work they'd be fine. Fogarty had disappeared. When he heard about the Vechta job he thought I should bring him along but I'd had enough of him. I didn't say that. I said there was already a gang there. Road-Kill realised what was going on. He said he didn't blame me. He went back to Göttingen and then I heard he was staying in the Heldenberg. He got a start with Claus.

I didn't have to tell the Sheffield men the situation: they knew something was amiss within ten minutes of us walking onto the job. From that moment relations between us began to go wrong. Most of them had never been in Germany before. They'd come over on a bus from Victoria Station in London. They were all older than me, a lot of them married with people depending on the money they'd send home. That first day they congregated in groups, discussing what they could do about their position. I genuinely felt for them. They looked so out of place. They all had tool belts and the best of

tools, English hammers, saws that had been sharpened and
oiled, sets of chisels — tools they would never have got to use
in any case. All a shutterer needed was a hammer, a nail-bar
and a fistful of nails.

So I sat down with them that night. I said I would talk to
Alex the Scotsman. I would talk to Horst, the German
contractor whose site it was. I said if the worst happened
there were other jobs. I had a book of numbers. I'd talk to
Boma, I'd phone the Heldenberg for them. There was plenty
of work in Germany. They shouldn't panic. My words made
little impact. They stirred the food around on their plates and
looked at me suspiciously.

They had a right to their suspicions and I was worried. I
spoke to Horst the next morning. He wasn't exactly
forthcoming. I was left with the impression that he had
deliberately looked for a big gang so he could pick and choose
the men he wanted. He was a big man, corpulent and
abrasive. He brushed a lank strand of hair from his forehead
and held up nine fingers and then five. Nine men only would
be needed from Friday, four only two weeks later. That's what
I understood. I phoned Alex who was unimpressed. 'I have a
contract with him for fourteen men and you', he said. A
contract, I argued, wasn't worth the paper it was written on.
We were illegal, none of us had work permits. Nothing Alex
told me reassured me. If the German wanted nine men then
he would only pay for nine men — was Alex likely to pay for
the other five out of his own resources? Was Alex any better
than the fly-by-night Dutchmen, whose phone numbers
changed constantly, who weren't above catching hundreds of
men for a week's wages, or more? I kept my anxieties to
myself and phoned the Heldenberg. All I had was a series of
questions: was there room, never mind work, for nine men
there? The Sheffielders had heard all the stories about big
money and, worse, they had believed them. I tried to deflate
these notions. I told them that money was based on the

number of hours worked. I told them about Diffley and the
gang back in Einbeck, about how they earned less money
than we were earning — but maybe, I said, they're smarter.
At least they know the money is there every week. Claus lives
in the town. He's unlikely to rip them off. They were also all
legal and had health insurance. The best the Dutch would do
in the case of an accident was pay for a flight home. I could
see that what I was saying baffled them.

On Friday Horst wanted to know which five I was getting
rid off. I wanted him to pick the men. They were all good, all
willing to work and they all knew what they were about. I
gathered them around me at lunchtime and explained the
situation. I was looking for volunteers. They could go to the
Heldenberg, I told them; there would be work but it would
probably take a week or so. Alex was on about another job
starting up outside Munich. Two of the men said they would
go back to England sooner than be fucked around in
Germany. They were all angry: 'One goes we all go,' they said.
They gathered their tools and walked off the site. I had made
a fundamental error and I'd known I was making it. Men who
were being let go were never told what was happening until
the last moment. As much work as possible was wrung from
them. They were kept apart from each other, paid off and left
with no alternatives. There is no democracy on a building site
and I was acting like a social worker. It wasn't my job to look
for work for them.

They went back to the hotel to wait for Alex. I didn't
expect him to show up either. He surprised me. He came
down to the site and met with Horst. I could see the German
gesticulating fiercely. All the other Germans were listening to
the argument between the two men. Alex gave me my money.
'He's changed his mind again,' he said, 'he only wants five
men now — four and you.'

'What about that contract?' I asked.

'What about it?' he said.

He asked me to talk to the Englishmen. To see what I could salvage, if four of them would stay. I was thinking of avoiding them altogether. I dreaded meeting them that night. They'd been paid and had been drinking since lunchtime. They'd met what Alex had to say to them with a hostile, stunned silence — I didn't doubt they were waiting for me.

The hotel owner was working behind the bar. He saw me coming up the road and came out to the desk. He told me four of them had already left. He was nervous. As I made my way upstairs to my room someone raised their voice loud enough so I could hear: 'Paddy bastard, he'll have his mates down here next week.' There was a mumbled response. I heard someone say I was in the worst position. Anyone could see there was no work.

It was three hours later before I caught up with them. They'd moved on to another bar. By this time they'd begun to run out of steam. They didn't see me when I came in and I found a seat in the corner. The place, which was normally busy, was deserted. There was an air of menace as they stared morosely into their drinks. Two of them were trying to play pool. They were the ones who spotted me.

'What about that Hunger Strike?' one of them said. There was no mistaking whose benefit that was for. 'All those fucking Pats, killing each other. Fucking bastards, hope they all die.'

I didn't say anything. One by one they rose from their seats to sit on stools a few yards from where I was sitting on my own. The pool players had laid down their cues.

'I had a cousin killed by those murdering bastards,' the same man went on. The man beside him told him to take it easy. The barman had taken up a cloth and was anxiously wiping the counter top.

'I won't fucking shut up. Those Pats are all the same.' A murmur of assent greeted this assertion.

'What about you?' he said to me, 'I suppose you're one of them?'

I ignored him but he wasn't going to let it go.

'You're good enough at killing women and children. Would you fight a man?' he said. He got up, knocking his stool over. Blood was beginning to thunder in my ears.

'What's wrong with you?' I asked.

'You heard me,' he said, 'murdering Paddy bastard. I hope they all die, all starve themselves to death — save on bullets.'

'That's none of my concern,' I said. 'I came over here to work. To earn a few bob, not to sit around arguing about politics.'

'That's what you all say. You're all the same. Go on then, tell me they're wrong. Tell me they're murdering bastards.'

'Yeah go on,' one of his friends said, 'you tell our Bill they're murdering bastards and you want to see them all starve themselves to death. Tell him you don't agree with them. That you're on our side.'

By this stage Bill and two of his friends were on their own. The four others had pulled slightly apart from them and were conversing amongst themselves. If I had any sense of proportion I would have done what they'd asked but I knew it wouldn't be enough. There would always be something else. I also felt ambivalent enough about the Hunger Strike. I felt that whether I agreed with the men involved or not their bravery was beyond dispute. That after Sands died they had won their argument.

'I can't do that,' I said. 'It's not that simple.' I was trying to speak as quietly and as reasonably as possible. The barman came over.

'*Alles OK?*' he said.

I nodded.

'Fight me then, you Paddy cunt!' Bill shouted. His face was inches from mine. I shook my head. 'I'm fighting no one,' I said.

'You're afraid.'

'That's right,' I agreed, 'I am afraid. Anyway, what good would it do?'

The difference between fighting and not fighting in that situation in very small. I was afraid. Fear was pin-pricking my skin. I'd begun to sweat and could feel the nausea beginning to rise in my stomach. On the other hand there was somebody literally in my face. I could feel the heat of his body, smell his bilious breath. I had the urge to swing at him, to deck him on the spot. I'd begun to figure out the geometry of the fight. How many of them I could get before they overwhelmed me. It wouldn't be a long fight and I was going to have to take a beating. The events of the week were weighing on me. All sorts of things go through your mind in a few seconds like that. You can fight, you can run or perhaps you can talk your way out of it. Given that Bill had to wind himself up to fight, like schoolyard stuff: I will if you will. On the other hand there was enough drink involved to make the situation unpredictable. But it wasn't like one of those fights that come from nowhere, the first notice the sound of glass breaking, where it's all over in seconds.

What never occurred to me was to appeal to the other four, but it was their intervention that saved me. They got up from their stools and eased Bill back. They talked him down. It's only a job, they said. There'd be no fighting. 'And anyway,' one of them said, 'what has what's going on in Ireland got to do with us over here?'

It was a question I could have answered for him. I might never have felt that what was going on in Ireland should have had any impact on me — but it did, continually. And it was as unavoidable as daylight. But I said nothing that night. Why complicate an already complicated situation?

Vechta finished at the beginning of August. Alex had a job starting up outside Cologne. That was three weeks away. He had work in the meantime in Munich. I decided to go home.

I got a flight from Hannover to Heathrow and the boat back
to Dublin. The roads, from Slane northward, were bedecked
in black flags. There were caravans on the streets of all the
towns, canvassing support for the Hunger Strikers. The closer
I came to the border the greater the tumult was. In the first
days of August Kevin Lynch and Kieran Doherty died.
Doherty had been elected TD for Cavan-Monaghan. The day
I got back Thomas McElwee died. Before I left Micky Devine
died. It all had an intensity that overshadowed everything else
— a palpable feeling that history had a stranglehold on the
place. There were apocryphal stories circulating of British cars
being forced into ditches, English tourists turned away from
hotels. I went to the replay of the hurling semi-final between
Galway and Limerick. There were black flags outside Croke
Park: people were being asked to choose. There was little
room for ambiguity. For a brief ten minutes towards the end
of the game Galway hurled beyond themselves. The sun was
shining and it was possible to feel, sitting in the old Cusack
Stand, that you were in a different place altogether:
somewhere where summer was eternal and right always
prevailed. That weekend I saw a band called Moving Hearts
playing in the Baggot Inn. Their music was avowedly
political, more than anything else it marked the contrast
between Ireland and Germany. Ireland seemed to seethe with
ideas. There were accounts of young boys stowing away on
flights to America, of parishes struggling to field football
teams. Emigration had begun again. The country was
bleeding, it was being bled dry by the same people as ever, a
friend of mine told me in the Baggot that night. 'It needed
people to stay. If we all stayed,' she said, 'what would they do
then?' Behind her, on the stage, Christy Moore sweated in the
strobe lights: *This graveyard hides a million secrets, The trees
know more than they can tell. The ghosts of the saints and
scholars, Will haunt you in heaven and in hell.* The crowd
swayed while he sang, moving as one, like a juggernaut. For

my part, all I wanted to do was get away again. To escape. Even my mother, who hated militant Republicanism, was in tears for the young men who, she said, were needlessly dying. That was the peak of the Hunger Strike. Micky Devine from Derry was the last of those ten men to die. He died the day before I left. There was no message of sympathy from Dublin this time. The reaction in the North was muted. It had overwhelmed people, stunned them. The one question was when would it end? I often thought of Devine afterwards. Remembered the tumult of noise in Croke Park that Sunday and wondered what — specifically — he had died for?

If I thought I was escaping, I was in the short term escaping nothing. I was pulled in at Holyhead. My bag was turned upside down and relentlessly gone through. I was led into a room and left sitting alone at a table. After a little more than an hour two men came in and began to question me. They called me 'Pat' and asked about 'The Boys'. They said they knew all about my involvement. These were all words they laid stress on, *boys, involvement*. But their questioning seemed oddly half-hearted, perfunctory, dispirited even, as if they were fulfilling a quota of some sort. Clerks regulating the flow of goods inward and outward: the egress of souls. I had the feeling of two men about a job they weren't overly enamoured with. I did something stupid though. I decided to be intransigent when they asked me about how long I intended to stay in Britain: 'Over to sign on the dole, Pat, are we?' I finally told them I was passing through. That I'd never spent any time in the country. That could have been easily checked. I had a National Insurance Number after all. But they didn't check. I had the feeling that at some point they would half-apologise and release me. That this was a game we were playing and as long as I recognised my role in it — to remain obtuse, act puzzled but curb any indignation I felt — I would be alright.

And this was what effectively happened, they even

appeared solicitous when they let me go. They told me I'd
missed my train. I knew that. More seriously I'd also missed
my flight to Germany. I had to hang around Holyhead for six
hours for the next train, hardly an enlightening experience at
the best of times. I felt contemptible, like I'd been soiled in
some minor way. There wasn't a thing I could do about it. I
could hardly call it an interrogation. They hadn't even
removed my watch. They'd held me for seven hours and fifty
minutes, another ten minutes and I would have had to have
been charged, most likely under the Prevention of Terrorism
Act. For more than five hours of that time I was alone. All it
amounted to was an act of petty harassment — a fishing
expedition, on which they might occasionally get lucky. I
wasn't even an official statistic. I hadn't been charged. Let's
face it, though, in the world I was moving in any sort of
police interrogation lent cachet. I wasn't one of the countless
people with something to lose, a job where a phone call to
check a detail could have ramifications, or a nervous spouse
wondering where I was, waiting for a knock on the door. And
the PTA, which went unreported, which was renewed by
Governments of all hues without protest annually, did in fact
wreck lives. But there was no news value here, as there would
be when they slipped up and hauled in an occasional minor
celebrity, spurring the Irish Government into ritual,
unavailing protest. Being in turn ritually fisted by the Brits.

18

IT WAS SUNDAY WHEN I GOT BACK TO THE HELDENBERG. I had bought the *Evening Standard* in London, but ominously there were no jobs advertised. Then I went down to Victoria Station and boarded a bus for Njimegen. It was a cheap way of travelling. Dutch and British agents paid for the buses, which were a way of recruiting men. You got on the bus and the agent got you work. I played dumb, got off in Njimegen and made my own way from there.

The bar in the Heldenberg was packed, I might well never have left the place. Road-Kill spotted me. '*My papa told me there'd be days like these*, he sang, '*Ain't nothing shakin' but the leaves on the trees.*' He looked as spectral as ever. He'd also acquired a buckled top-hat and a frock coat from somewhere, making him look like a cross between one of the Muppets and an undertaker played by Robert Carradine in some black & white Western.

They were all stoned and playing cards. The Sunday Tea Dance meanwhile was going on in the next room, that devilish oom-pah music, elderly couples swirling round the floor like a confusion of falling leaves. There was a group of younger women amongst them — denizens of the whorehouse on the outskirts of the town out on a bit of Sunday afternoon R&R. The women were attracting attention, though one look at their louring minder was enough to defray any romantic notions. He danced with each of them individually, turning a cumbersome arc like an oil tanker in the middle of the dance-floor, as the elderly couples gave him plenty of space, both titillated and scandalised. The barman was under severe pressure to dispense with the Germanic custom of allowing the beer to settle for several minutes before it was topped up. Mick Coen was sitting on his own at the bar. He bought me a drink. Tradition, he said looking at the barman, is a great burden to these people. He said Ready-Mix was about somewhere. I told him about a start going in Cologne and he said he might be interested. He was in debt but that was between me and him. Mick had gone direct for the local German firm. What he earned would just about pay his bar bill. He needed money, he said, and he needed it last week. The problem with the Cologne job was that it was a week away. Coen had been having an affair with a married woman down the town. A big secret the year before, it now appeared to be open knowledge. It was the first time anyhow I'd heard him talk about it. He seemed wistful, talking about her as if she were already in the past tense. She was threatening to leave her husband and bring the kids with her. Coen didn't know what he wanted. I left him on his own at the bar. His eyes were already glowing — it was early in the evening and I knew he would drift in that state for some time. Shaking his head from time to time like some termite was gnawing at his brain.

Road-Kill meanwhile was so high and talking so fast he didn't seem to need oxygen. I remembered his previous lethargy in Bremerhaven. Something new was fuelling him

and I could guess what it was. He said he was prepared to be
magnanimous — he was going to forgive me for leaving him
high and dry on the dockside like a South American sailor.
Then he acknowledged that I might have been right. 'These
boys have looked after me,' he said. 'All I had to say was I was
a mate of yours — you're well got here,' he said.

I never knew why I took up with him that time. I had a
week before the job in Cologne started and I already had a
gang. I knew Coen and Ready-Mix were going south with
me. Alex had even agreed to pay for the week between jobs so
a trip to Amsterdam must have seemed like a diversion —
two days there and back. I was to meet Road-Kill *en route* in
the Bahnhof in Hannover on Wednesday.

I did meet him there but he was late to the train on the
following day. A group of Turks had already boarded, alerted
by the barely perceptible increase in the engine noise, just
before an apocalyptic voice boomed out over the tannoy,
listing stops and the destination. They were well used to
trains, the Turks. I saw Road-Kill coming through the crowd
towards me, rather I saw his top-hat over everyone else's
heads. 'Where the fuck were you?' I asked. Within minutes
he was asleep in the carriage. The last thing he said,
something that left me puzzled, was, 'Look, whatever you do,
don't call me Road-Kill until we're off this train.'

'Why?'

'Just don't. You'll see.'

I should have known then that it'd all go wrong. I should
have got off the train at the next stop and left him sleeping.
Sure, didn't I know well enough that it wasn't the Van Gogh
Museum we were going to see. I was thinking of him the
night before in the bar near the station in Hannover. It was
no different than the bars he'd favoured in Bremerhaven.
Places down on the docks, lost to geography. Neither in nor
out of the red-light districts. Dingy, crepuscular places stuffed
with narrow booths and battered furnishings, the bar scuffed

and gouged, the walls and floors splattered with people's blood and sweat. Another type of person — those who haven't a clue — might describe it all as character.

It was in such a place in Bremerhaven that he'd taken up with two Argentine sailors. Their boat had limped into port, an old-style tramp steamer that looked like it had been involved in every dodgy enterprise since Joseph Conrad had hove to within sight of the mouth of the River Thames. The Argentineans were intent on off-loading some undefined contraband and Road-Kill was willing to act as a conduit. Their English was perfunctory, his Spanish non-existent. It did stretch to calling them *amigos* though. The Argentineans were saturnine and taciturn but then they didn't need to speak, didn't get a chance. Road-Kill greeted them like revolutionary confrères, high-fiving and back-slapping and rattling on about Franco, Zapata and Pancho Villa. I became accessory to this. 'You speak Spanish don't you?' he said. My Spanish was like my German or my French indeed — I could find an ill-lit *bodega*, *bôite* or *Kneipe* in any town. I had gone along out of curiosity and dragged Ready-Mix with me — on a last-minute whim — as security. Muscle, Road-Kill called us. Not that we made much impression on the Argentineans. They were exasperated to see us and conferred amongst themselves. We left our drinks untouched, there were lipstick traces on my glass and the beer lay flat and dank, placid as a greasy puddle.

'See that shape in your man's trousers?' Ready-Mix said. 'Well, he's either hung like a donkey or he's carrying a machete.'

The Argentineans were reluctant to do business in front of witnesses. 'The merchandise,' Road-Kill said. 'We need to see the merchandise.'

One of them said something about women.

'Women,' Road-Kill said, 'we'll come across later. We can

have all the women we want — but this is later. Later understandee? Later?'

Ready-Mix said he was under the impression that women was what they were selling.

There was more conferring and the same man said 'Jiggy-jiggy?' He formed an O shape with his thumb and forefinger and thrust his other forefinger through it rapidly. His hips were buckling on the chair.

The other one turned to me and machine-gunned me with Spanish. The only words I picked up were *mujeres* — women and sex. Either he was deeply frustrated or Ready-Mix had got the drift of what they were about. They left — giving us to understand they would be back in thirty minutes. We bailed out, dragging Road-Kill reluctantly with us, accusing us of blowing his big chance. We could see their boat at anchor, listing slightly to one side, as we left the bar. There were no lights on board. It lay low in the water — like it could submerge at will back into the subterranean world it had come from. We heard later that it had sailed leaving one of the Argentineans behind. The Argentinean, a German told me, was looking for someone. The sailor gave, he said, a very good description of Road-Kill.

The incident that night before in the Hannover bar was relaxing compared to that experience. 'Two drinks,' Road-Kill said, 'that's all. I just have to check something out.'

'How do you find these places?' I asked. I was even more puzzled at how he found his way back to them. You might stumble into a place like that unawares, but your natural reaction would be to leave as quickly as possible and your memory — perhaps employing some atavistic survival technique — would forget where the place was. As if you would be doomed to lumber through such back-streets for an eternity otherwise.

Road-Kill made no response.

He said he had to meet some associates and left me at a table on my own, being eyed up as carrion by a coven of wrung-out whores. The two associates blended in with the décor. I could see them sitting alone in a corner, where the least amount of light might get to them — like twin cultures of some deadly virus being nurtured in the dark. It wasn't for nothing that the Germans sent Lenin on a sealed train through their own lines to the Finland Station. Anarchy ferments in the dark. I tried in vain to overhear their conversation, catching odd words of it. One of them put money in the jukebox and signalled for the barkeep to turn it up. Roy Orbison's "Pretty Woman" throbbed through the place. I saw a fat envelope cross the table. Road-Kill stuffed it into his crotch awkwardly. He bought them two beers. The drinks were never touched. One of them sat back in the shadows, his voice seemed to quaver hoarsely in time with the song. It looked like he might be singing along, except for he wasn't. Road-Kill nodded eagerly. The other one got up with Road-Kill and approached where I was sitting. He blocked out the light for an instant and then he bent over, offering his gnarled paw. The veins stood out on the back of it like a river delta on a school map. He crushed my hand.

'You know Abie for a long time?' he asked.

'What?' I said. 'Abie?'

'You know Abie for a long time?' he exaggerated every word.

Abie? I said nothing. I nodded.

'He is crazy — no?'

I nodded again and he went back to the table. Road-Kill gestured at his retreating back. 'Ex-Legionnaire,' he said — as if I was to draw what inference I wanted from that. The problem with Road-Kill was all his conversations had come to sound like something heard crackling over the radio in the back of a police car.

He awoke in the carriage, apparently refreshed, before I could fasten on any resolve to get off the train. He was feeling nostalgic and described for me his route through Europe, years before. France, Spain, Marrakesh. He told me how the hippy trail had ended for him when he'd had to cut his hair to get into Morocco. 'Standing there at the Moroccan border with a pair of shears in my hand, thinking of nothing but dope,' he said. I pushed him on his Limerick background but he seemed reluctant to talk about it. He mentioned his old man and said the best present he ever bought him was a scanner. The old man sat up in his room monitoring the police airwaves. It was, in its way, a telling image. Then he turned to London and the years he'd spent there. The train was by now trundling through the monotonous Dutch countryside. I felt we'd been somehow lucky — there had been no passport check. 'I hate the Cloggies,' he said, telling me how he'd lived with a Dutchwoman in a houseboat down on the Thames. When the tide receded the flotsam and jetsam of city life encroached, the stench of dead fish, old mattresses and rotting vegetation awash on the mud flats. They were living like bilge rats. The boat need caulking. She'd been beautiful, he said, that woman. Beautiful in that Dutch way, high cheekbones, healthy looking and all. The boat stank in the winter of dampness and mildew, and its planks secreted the same stink, concentrated, during the hot summer months. He was rarely there, always ducking and diving, on the scam. He bought her a Wurlitzer jukebox to mollify her. Everyone has a dream, he said. She dreamt of flashing lights. But the jukebox was too big to fit down the stairs into the cabin. It was worth some money that jukebox. It sat amidst the clutter on the deck through the rains that fell incessantly from autumn through winter and into spring. The Dutchwoman turned yellow, unhealthily jaundiced looking. She left and returned to her family. They were some strange religious sect, some cankerous off-growth of Protestantism. 'Not that it mattered,' he said, 'they had no time for me.' He fell asleep again, as Holland stretched like purgatory about us.

He disappeared once we arrived in Amsterdam, after we'd booked into the hotel. The receptionist asked for our passports as collateral against the bill, and I argued when Road-Kill paid for both of us in advance. 'A man needs to be able to get out quick,' he said. There were two American girls in the reception area. We overheard them giggling, commenting that one of the newcomers was a weirdo.

'That's you,' Road-Kill said. 'We'll tap that pair later.'

I stretched out on the bed, mumbling something about going out to eat later, and fell into a deep sleep. When I woke up he was gone. Passing traffic moved in shadows across the ceiling of the room. I went down to the bar. The receptionist was behind it. I tried my hand with her. She took it in good part but it was obvious that all she was going to do was flirt. Then the two Americans came in. I could hear them talking and bent to mask my laughter. One of them was going on about being up a grapefruit tree when her diaphragm slipped. 'Straight up, Rach,' she said, 'I nearly fell outa that tree.' I bought them a drink. The receptionist winked and made some comment about rich virgins. But when they joined me they told me they were broke. I was going to say I never saw any of nature's poor with Sony Walkmans, and what were they doing staying in a hotel if they were broke? But I forbore and bought them more drink. I ended up spending the better part of the night futilely groping one of them. The receptionist was obviously a better judge of character than I.

The following morning I woke up, muzzy-headed, in my own bed. For a few minutes the contours of the room appeared indistinct. Then it all wavered into view and I could hear Road-Kill — who was obviously back — ranting somewhere. I thought, hardly for the first time, that the man was inexorable.

'I did it man,' he said.

'You did what?'

'I fulfilled the fantasy of a lifetime. Do you know what it's

like to fulfil the fantasy of a lifetime? To have all your dreams
come true?'

'*Hey Mrs Dolan*,' he sang, '*your son, he isn't working*.'

'What do you mean the fantasy of a lifetime? What are you
going on about now? Jasus,' I said, 'will you give it a break.'

'Did you ride the Yanks?' he said. Then he laughed. 'No
you didn't ride the Yanks. If you rode the Yanks at least you'd
be in good form.'

'What are you on about?' I asked.

'I'll tell you what I did. I spent two hours with a whore
in a taxi. Two whole hours … nothing on her but suspenders
and a fur coat … not a stitch on under it … can you believe
it? And I never laid a hand on her. Is that kinky or what?'

'Jasus,' I said, 'you're for the birds. How much did that set
you back?'

He laughed. 'Look,' he said, 'I only came back to grab the
bag. I still have business.'

'What business? For fuck's sake will you tell me what
you're at?'

'I'll see you at the train,' he said. 'Don't be late.' With
those words he disappeared through the door.

He only showed up for the train at the last minute. Or so
I thought then. The same crowd of Turks were there. I was
breathing deeply, reminding myself that he wasn't my
responsibility. And I was watching the Turks: how they knew
when the train was about to move off, how close they stood
to their cases. They said that when the Turks came to
Germany first they were taken through reception centres
where they were treated like livestock, yet the only time they
protested was when their cases were taken away. I
remembered again how Lonesome Tom had told me to watch
the way men stood close to their suitcases. It marked a
particular type of man he said, a working man, and you
should never take away his case: it held the notion of home.
Even if that man was going round in circles like a pilgrim on

a relentless pilgrimage to a shrine that didn't even exist — the bag was all.

Maybe that was why Road-Kill slept, arms wrapped about his bag, in the carriage. He was completely deflated. I was in no mood to talk to him in any case. Still, I was wondering what he had in the bag and whether it could land us in trouble. But I drifted off and was myself asleep when the German Border Guards entered the carriage. I woke with a start and moved towards the bag. Road-Kill was still flat out.

'*Pass!*' the German demanded, his hand already out-stretched. I handed him my passport. '*Aha McBride*,' he said, making a desultory attempt to pronounce my name as he riffled through it, stopping to look at some of the stamps. The other guard meantime had pulled the bag from Road-Kill's grasp. I could hear my heart vaulting. He shook it out, upside down. A shirt and a British passport fell out on the floor. He nudged the shirt aside with his boot and bent to retrieve the passport. He looked at it and blinked and bent over towards Road-Kill.

'*Aha … Weintraub*,' he said, '*Weintraub*.'

Road-Kill stirred groggily. The guard bent forward and tilted his chin upwards. A skein of spew dribbled from Road-Kill's mouth onto the cuff of the guard's uniform. The guard let go his grip with alacrity.

'*Scheisshund!*' he said as he flung the passport onto the seat. Both of them left the carriage. I waited a few seconds before chancing a look into the corridor of the train. They were giving the Turks a hard time. They'd taken them out of the carriage. I hurriedly re-took my seat and reached for the British passport. Road-Kill was fully awake.

'Jasus,' I said, 'what are you at?'

'I thought that was a great touch with the sick,' he said.

'You were awake the whole time?'

He nodded.

'But Weintraub?' I said, 'Weintraub? You don't even look Jewish.'

He laughed. 'That's what's wrong with you, Your Eminence,' he said. 'No fucking sense of humour, no fucking imagination. All that matters is the picture. They don't ask to see down your fucking trousers, you know. You have to admit anyhow it's not a bad likeness?'

I looked at the passport again. He was right. It was just about imaginable to picture Road-Kill as a baroque figure, with ringlets — an Hassidic Jew. I didn't know what to say. Finally I said, 'Do you know what the worst of it was? I thought all the time you were smuggling drugs. I thought the bag was full of them. I wanted to get hold of the bag but I fell asleep.' I must have sounded relieved.

He moved across the carriage and sat beside me.

'Do you want to hear the truth?'

I nodded.

'I am smuggling drugs.'

He leant over me, took a paper bag from his pocket and tipped out the ashtray into it. He fished a small, tin-foil-wrapped square from the bag and held it up for me to see.

'There's four ashtrays to a carriage. The train's twenty-one-and-a-half carriages long. That's eighty-six ashtrays. As soon as the bastards leave, we'll start. Sure you might as well help me empty them now. I can't wait to see the faces on some of the auld ones on this train.'

I never really met Road-Kill much after that. He just kind of drifted off into his own sphere. I heard, a year or so later, that he'd cleaned up. That he'd run out of steam. That's what it was like there. You met somebody, took them for what they were at that moment and moved on. It didn't pay to get too close to anyone. They might be gone the next week. They might be gone with your wages or what they could lift from your room. Alliances were easily formed and just as easily

dissolved. It was the same with women. What was the point
in getting close to any woman when you could be moving on
to the next town the week after? I had known this woman in
Einbeck for the past three or four months but I kept her to
myself. I was like Mick Coen with the married woman, only
for different reasons. Annelisa was her name. She was very
good-looking, short, straight dark hair and big, querulous-
looking eyes. I had her in a separate hemisphere altogether. I
was intent on keeping her apart from everyone I knew. She
was suspicious of what I was at, but how could I have
explained to her the double standards I had? Say to her I
didn't think she could deal with the profanity. That she wasn't
the same as the rest of the women who circled about us. The
ones the men would say had had more abortions than hot
dinners. Whereas the Germans romanticised us, romanticised
the Irish in particular. This was largely Heinrich Böll's fault:
his *Irisches Tagebuch* had them all looking at us through bleary
1950s' lenses. As if the country hadn't moved on. Weren't we
scamming all the money we could off them through the
EEC? In this they were like the London-Irish kids, whose
memories of Ireland were those of their parents. And it was
disconcerting for those of us who had been in London to be
seen as figures of romance rather than as figures of suspicion.
The Germans loved our music, our history, our literature.
That we surfed through life. That we spent money like the
original existentialists. For them we were the last of the
spailpíns, a migratory people — we'd face anything except a
notion of tomorrow.

Annelisa had her own flat. I used to disappear there.
Another time she came up to meet me in Bremen. She
wanted to hear some different music, she said, so we went to
a place where there was a jazz band playing. It was very
serious music, dark music, music for listeners. Then, for no
reason, she got up on the floor on her own and began to
dance. She had real grace, a true dancer's poise. She was

inventive. She moved on her toes like a wraith, spirited by the music, sinuous and spiralling, melting into it. And the musicians, who were taken aback at first, responded to her. They clanked and honked like they'd fall apart. It grew wilder. It had its own volition: until it reached a crescendo and stopped abruptly and she fell to the floor, out of breath. And when she stood up it was like she hadn't known she was there — was unaware of what she'd done. She took the applause blinking like she'd just woken up to something.

Once we ran into Mick Coen. Off on one of his solo reconnaissance missions. 'You're the quiet one,' he said, 'keeping her to yourself. And I was wondering why you'd calmed down.'

She said all her friends said she had an Irish accent. She thought Coen did the right thing in taking a job with the local firm. I said he'd never last. She questioned that, questioning what I meant — was I talking about him or about myself? She said Coen was a gentleman — which indeed he largely was. She admired his grasp of Germans — the ways in which he was willing to bend towards them. I didn't tell her about the winter before, about how when the leaves fell and the grasses withered a mountain of vodka bottles became transparent in the denuded clump of weeds below his bedroom window. He remained for a time a paragon but turned out in the end to be a severe disappointment to her.

Though I never met up with Road-Kill again I didn't fully escape him. Four years later I got a phone-call in London. It was the middle of the night. I was living in Finsbury Park. There was a payphone at the far end of the house. I didn't give out the number and usually ignored its intermittent ring. It was the province of the dole scammers in the bottom flat. They gathered about it in convocation at all hours of the day or night, sparsely bearded anarchists and neo-punks —

nobody having pointed out to them that all that had ended back in '77. From what I knew of them they were orchestrating a vast fraud, signing on in different names all over the town. There didn't seem any great current of intelligence amongst the lot of them. But the phone was vital to their purpose and — from my perspective — was probably tapped. I kept well clear of them. I knew enough not to invite the police to kick my door in.

The phone had rung that morning at two o'clock. I cursed it, knowing that I had to be up at half-five for work and would be unable to get back to sleep. It rang off, then took up again, growing increasingly strident in the quiet house. Just as I got to it, it stopped. I cursed it again and turned to lumber, still half-asleep, back up the stairs. It jumped on the hook once more and I felt like I had caught it in mid-air. 'Yes!' I snapped.

No matter how I tried afterwards I never found out how she got my number. I'd lost contact with almost everyone I'd known in Germany and my progress, if it could be called that, over the past four years in London had been labyrinthine — Finsbury Park was my fourth change of address. She said her name was Gundula and that I didn't know her. She was the friend of a friend who had asked her to contact me if anything went wrong. I had been a difficult man to find, she said. I felt she was wondering on the other end of the phone if I would prove worth the trouble.

The details she gave me were sketchy but I had them confirmed over the next couple of days. Road-Kill had moved to Karlsruhe near the French border, where he had returned to his previous career as a tree surgeon. He had ended up in the university there, as a mature student. He was living the good life. He had even had a long-term relationship with this woman. And then he had fallen off a balcony. She told me she'd seen it happen. He'd stepped backwards, the rail on the balcony was lower than it should have been, some modernist design, and he'd struck against it and tumbled down four floors. He died instantly.

'Drugs?' I said.

There was a pause as if she had shook her head.

'Was he drinking?'

'You don't understand,' she said, 'he was doing nothing like that.' He couldn't drink. He could not use drugs. He had an addictive personality. He recognised that. He was doing so well. She was angry with me for suggesting otherwise.

Her initial problem was identifying the body. It was supposed to be next of kin. She wanted it released for burial or cremation. I said I wasn't next of kin and she said that he'd had a photograph of the two of us together. It had been taken somewhere there were ships in the background. I was the only person she knew of. The authorities would accept me as next of kin: they wanted rid of the body. It was apparent — from the photograph — that I had known him a long time. In any case, she said, he talked about you always.

'What about his family in Limerick?' I asked.

There was a pause.

'Do you want to help or not?' she said.

I was standing in the hallway in Finsbury Park, shivering.

'Give me your address,' I said. 'I'll be there later today.'

There was no doubt it was Road-Kill. Even if his hair was short and he'd got heavy. He had a little pot-belly but the same stick legs. In a way it suited him — even in death — he looked younger than I'd have expected. I nodded and they drew the sheets back over him. The doctor who did the autopsy told me he had initially looked in good enough physical condition for a man of his age. But this only proved how deceptive looks could be. Inside he had the organs of a man twenty or thirty years older than he was. It wasn't the fall that killed him. It was the shock of the fall. It was only a matter of time. He could have as easily turned over in his sleep and smothered on the pillow. His constitution was shot.

Then there was the question of what to do with the body. I brought up his family again. We were sitting in a restaurant. She was toying with her schnitzel, her eyes on her plate. I remembered the way he'd turned melancholy that time on the train to Amsterdam. I told her about his father and the scanner. I was re-living it. It was a reprisal of the man I'd known, a bleached-out, monochrome memory, of a train trundling through Holland. Evidently it had little bearing on her experience. She looked up from her plate. Her eyes were tear-filled, opaque — and in them I read that I was talking about the wrong man altogether. She shook her head.

'He liked to make up stories,' she said.

'He told me about a Dutch woman he lived with on a boat — are you saying that was a lie too?'

'Who knows,' she said. 'I never asked. I do know he wasn't Irish. He did very good accents. I think he may have worked in the antiques business with an Irishman in London. Perhaps that was it. *Ja, natürlich*, he did see himself as Irish. He said his mother was Irish. Perhaps he grew to be Irish?'

'Then what was he?'

She told me his real name was Weintraub. His family were in the garment business. He was originally from Whitechapel, in the East End of London. His mother died when he was young. She said his family were wealthy. He had taken her back to Whitechapel but there was nothing left there. All the Jews were gone. He had no connection with his family. He had been disowned years before. She didn't know why. He never said. As far as she could say he came from nowhere. Why wouldn't he claim to be Irish? She said those last words defiantly. I was too shocked to contradict her even if I'd wanted to.

'What about his family?' I said at last. 'Do they know?'

'I phoned them,' she said. 'He always had his brother's number. I told them. There was a silence on the line. It was, how would you say it, like a lead balloon? They didn't say anything. *Ja*, they had nice manners. I gave them the number here. That was two days before I phoned you. They never phoned back. That was why I phoned you. He talked about you all the time.'

We had him cremated. She'd got hold of some kind of a secular rabbi who said a few words. There were two or three tree surgeons there and some students who knew him from the university. One of the students read some poetry badly, that shit about having seen the best of our generation. There were flowers and things. The sun was shining. The whole thing had an air of unreality, of the surreal about it. We went back to a bar. I was in a daze, baffled. I could hear everybody talking about someone I hadn't known at all. Someone, the woman said, who had talked about me incessantly. Yet when I was asked how I knew him, I could only mutter that it was all a long time ago — like I was entering a plea of mitigation. It felt like a washing machine was going off in my ears all the time. I stood out amongst them all. I didn't even have what might have been called respectable clothes. I was wearing a T-shirt and black jeans, a battered Levi jacket and the same scuffed cowboy boots I'd worn on that train almost five years before. I used to think of them as lucky. The next day I went with her to the Black Forest and we shook his ashes loose from the urn. It was a windy day and they blew away deep into the trees.

19

AMSTERDAM AND WHAT HAD HAPPENED THERE I RELAYED TO
nobody. I had left Road-Kill back in Hannover to pick up
the pieces of his own life while I got the first train back to
Einbeck, thinking about picking up the pieces of mine.
This time I avoided the Heldenberg. It was Friday and I
had four days to kill, as the job in Cologne didn't start
until Tuesday. I went to Annelisa's flat in the town. I hadn't
seen her in a week, although she knew I wasn't working.
She acted like she wasn't surprised to see me. That it was
commonplace for people to come and go as they willed.
She tried to act as if nothing was amiss. I sensed something was. I couldn't face arguing with her. I felt sorry for
myself. I had spent a shift in Holyhead Police Station and
had narrowly avoided doing the same in two other
countries. Nothing I wanted to happen, I told myself, ever
happened the way it was supposed to. Yet if what I was
after was reassurance, I had come to the wrong place
entirely. She went into her bedroom to put on make-up.
I'd never seen her wearing make-up so that when she came

out she looked different, made-up for strobe lighting, for a stage. Made up for the night. We went out for something to eat.

Where had I been?

Amsterdam.

And who had I been with?

Road-Kill.

That set the bells ringing.

'And you were doing what?'

I wasn't going to tell her. I stabbed a *pomme-frite*.

'This and that,' I finally said. She let it go, for the time being only, I felt.

'The winter is coming,' she said. Right enough, it was raining outside but it was barely September. I knew what she was getting at. Where was I going to be for the winter?

'There's still a couple of months left,' I said. She looked up from her plate. Was I saying we had only two more months?

'Did you go for drugs or did you go for the bordellos?' she asked.

'Neither,' I told her. She didn't like drugs and it was true I hadn't touched anything like that since those six weeks in the Heldenberg before Christmas. I hadn't known her then but she'd heard about it. 'Neither,' I repeated. I told her I'd just gone along for the trip. Things had happened that I had no control over. That last part I just blurted out and I regretted it immediately.

'You were having trouble with the police?' She was playing with the food which had grown cold on her plate, rearranging it with her fork.

'No.'

'But you could have been having trouble with the police. You were lucky?'

I didn't answer her. She nodded to herself and called for the bill. When I tried to pay she pushed me away. Put her hand against my chest and pushed me backwards. 'You would say,' she said, 'it is only money — yes?'

We walked up the street in the fine, warm autumnal rain. There was about a yard between us, which was three times the distance, I thought ruefully, there had been on the way out to eat. There was a part of me wanted what she wanted in that moment. The possibility of an argument that might have proved cathartic — where I might have told her that I wasn't going to be around for much longer if the weather didn't hold. I could have told her that I liked her more than I could say. That I wanted nothing that wasn't also for her but that I was afraid. I was afraid of my own intent, my own inclinations, and that perhaps I had believed in something foolish too much and for too long. That I'd read too many books about travelling, that I was afraid of always vaguely planning and never taking off. That I was like this with everybody, dissembling and superficial, and that I was afraid that if I did change this, other parts of me that I valued would begin to fall off. That all I wanted to be was like those Turks with their suitcases in the Hauptbahnhof in Hannover — well, not quite like those Turks. Just to say I was afraid.

Instead things simmered between us. She stopped walking outside a shop and told me she had things to get. I offered to accompany her. She told me they were women's things.

'Look,' I said, 'I have to go. I have to go to Cologne. I have to be there for work on Monday.'

'Oh yes, Köln,' she said. 'That's very important. Work is very important. You would be a good German, I think.'

I flinched. I was looking down at the pavement. The rain had stopped and was steaming off the road, postponing any thoughts of winter.

'Anyway,' I said.

'Anyway,' she said, 'you must go Köln. You will go today?'

'Tomorrow.'

I reached over to kiss her. She stiffened. Her cheek was cold as a relic and I was left with a faint taste of make-up on my lips. I believed that in that instant she saw right through me. She saw me as someone who slid, skated about things, oblivious of anyone else, leaving the consequences floating like debris on water in my wake. She had seen into the soul of the person I'd invented and she disdained what she saw. I felt a shiver run down my spine. I felt very small. My heart ached and I had to get away from her, get away from her damnable bravery, the way she had lost herself to the jazz in Bremen. The way she held onto what was essential in herself. And the way she had just now drawn back into herself, completely.

I was thinking, above all else, of that jazz club in Bremen. But that's never the soundtrack you get. Life does that — it ends up like a bad song. A song that went on and on because I let it repeat itself. Like a bad song there's always a reprise. Like a bad song there's always a reconciliation.

'I'll phone,' I said.

'Yes,' she said, 'you'll phone.' And her mascara was running.

See, like a bad song there's a hook so insidious you'll never forget it.

I went back to the hotel so and shaved the beard off. I was a different person without it. I was much younger. When I went down to the bar the phone was ringing. It was for me. I was feeling shaken, burdened and light-headed when I picked it up. The voice was familiar.

'Is that you?' he said.

'It's me,' I replied, unsure of who I was talking to.

'It's me,' he said, 'Tipperary Tommy here. Where are you? Are you there? I'm coming to Germany. How do I get there?'

I began to give him directions. 'Train to Hannover. Train to Salzderhelden …'

He interrupted me. 'That's what it says on the sign,' he said and he began to spell it out. 'S … A … L … Z …'

'OK, OK,' I said. 'I see what you're at. I'll come down and get you.' I went down and brought him up from the train station at the bottom of the hill. He was in trouble, it didn't take much to work that out. 'What about Del?' I asked.

Del had got done for credit card fraud. It was a very complicated case. He pleaded not guilty and that didn't help matters. His brief was useless. It went on for three days. At the end of it the beak asked him if he had anything to say for himself. He stood up in the dock and said, 'Guilty, man.' The beak threw the book at him. Seven years he got. Maximum sentence. No appeal, it goes without saying.

We got back to the bar and I introduced him round. Coen was there and Diffley, Les and his wife Lynn, plus Ready-Mix and three of the Sheffield boys who'd got work with Claus the agent. There was also another crowd of Englishmen who I told myself I needn't bother with, not until I found out if they were going to be around for a while. I was in no mood for talking and left Tommy to make his own way. Diffley joined me and we talked about what was happening at home, about sport and politics. He knew there was something wrong though and it wasn't just with me.

'That boy', he said, looking at Tipperary Tommy, 'has a bit of an edge to him.' I could see where Tommy was sitting on his own at the bar — like you'd need a Geiger counter to approach him.

'He's alright, leave him alone. What about that Billy?' I said, the squaddie. 'Did you ever get the money you lent him back?' I of course knew he hadn't. I was having a dig at him for the sake of it. It was unworthy.

'Billy never came back,' Diffley said, 'you know that. What does it matter? It was only money, you know. I'd have spent it anyway. A man can do worse than help other people out.'

'You're talking shite. I wouldn't give them the steam off my piss.'

'I don't know what to think,' he said getting up. 'Whether

you're really turning out like this, or whether you're just letting on you are. You were never this bad, though.'

I watched him walk away, knowing I should apologise, but asking myself who would I really be apologising to?

At the bar the boys were arguing over where they were going to go later that night. When asked for my opinion I suggested we go somewhere else for a change, another town altogether. I was worried that I'd see Annelisa again. It was a subject I wanted to avoid, but then I ended up talking to Lynn who knew her. Lynn had got a job looking after the bar in the hotel when Les was out at work. She knew her way around the town and had met Annelisa several times for coffee. She wanted to know what my intentions were, gradually introducing the subject the way that women do — which is to say, relentlessly. She was telling how much she liked Annelisa. What a good woman she was. 'I thought she was a bit flash at first,' she said, 'but that was only me. My own prejudices.' I could see Tipperary Tommy at the bar talking to Coen. Coen was still moping about the married woman. He wasn't someone you crossed and I could see it coming. I got up and made my excuses to Lynn. As I did I saw Coen reach out and lift Tommy with one hand, by the throat, clean off his bar-stool.

'Put him down Mick. Put him down.' Coen looked at me and then slowly released his grip. Tommy fell back onto the stool, which skittered sideways, landing him on the floor. He made to get up but I held him back. I had never seen Coen involve himself in this way before.

'He's a fucking wanker,' he said, 'get him the fuck outa here.' I had never heard him swear either.

Diffley helped me drag Tommy from the bar.

'What did he do?' I asked.

'Oh, he started onto Coen about his woman. Jesus man, how did he know about that? He's only in the door. See, that's what I mean by trouble?'

Tommy was slumped between us. He was mumbling about doing the big bastard. I heard him going on about palming a horseshoe. When we got him back to the room I asked Diffley to leave me with him. Tommy was making small noises of exasperation. He began then to hyperventilate, swinging punches like a boxer at a heavy bag. I pinned him from behind.

'What the fuck's wrong with you?' I said. 'Never, never do that again — not to that man, not to any of them. Have you got that?' I said. 'Can you understand that? All them boys know each other. You say something to one of them, you might as well say it to all of them. English, Irish, Scots — it makes no difference here.'

I went back down to the bar, leaving him to sleep it off. I apologised to all of them. For what I wasn't sure, though I had brought him there. After the third attempt that day I had finally got to apologise. I could see Diffley looking askance at me — as if he knew part of the story was missing.

20

MYSELF COEN AND READY-MIX SPENT THE REST OF THE YEAR outside Cologne near the town of Bergische Gladbach. The man we were working for, Tomas Springer, was deeply political. He was to the right of Helmut Kohl who was elected *Bundeschancellor* that summer, breaking the hegemony of the Social Democrats under Brandt and Schmidt. Springer believed in Germany for the Germans. He likened the aversion younger Germans had to physical labour as similar to the conditions that led to the fall of the Roman Empire — a society too tired to do its own dirty work, importing instead an underclass. Springer spent all day, every day, on site with us. In the evenings, two or three times a week, he brought us for a drink. This behaviour was wholly new to us. We sat and argued with him as the summer came slowly to an end.

We were sitting one night outside a pub, looking down on Cologne in the distance. The cathedral rising like Excalibur through the mist that had begun to shroud the town. Springer was talking about the cathedral and how it

had survived the bombing of the city. It was the only time I
ever heard a German refer to the Allied bombing of their
country during the war. He said there was nothing standing
except the cathedral which the English claimed they'd
deliberately avoided flattening. You could still see shards of
metal imbedded in its pockmarked walls. 'Like,' he said,
'bombs knew what they were doing.'

He couldn't sit at rest. He was smoking a cigarette he'd
taken from my packet, without inhaling. Sweeping insects
that fell from the trees above us off the tabletops. He tried
to relax then, but he was like a mechanical toy whose mechanism has almost run out, yet it stutters onward. I asked him
if he'd been in Cologne back then. Reaching into his pocket,
he took something out and threw it across the table towards
me. I caught it.

'What's that?' he asked me.

It resembled a miniature cartwheel, with one spoke
protruding through the rim, although it wasn't exactly
symmetrical. There were eleven spokes in all. Somehow it
occurred to me what it was.

'A rosary,' I said. 'For praying.'

He nodded.

'Where did you get it?' I asked.

'Stalingrad,' he said.

'It was your father's?'

He laughed. 'No. It's mine.'

I was surprised. He looked much too young to have
fought in the Russian campaign. I told him so. Anton, his
foreman who was sitting beside me, half-asleep, started
forward.

'He was the youngest.'

'Anton was there too,' Springer said. He brought his fist
down hard on his cigarette box. 'That's what it was like,' he
said, 'we were like that.'

'Starving,' Anton said. 'Then they marched us back

through the snow. And Hitler parachuted in food. The food landed on the Russian side.' He told of men who defied Soviet fire to rescue a drop and found that all it contained were leaflets, imploring them to fight to the last man.

'They died for that. And we waited on them to die, so we could eat what little they had.'

'Or them,' Springer said wryly. He was staring myopically at the prayer wheel. Anton was staring into the gloom.

'It's hard to understand,' I said.

'There are some things you can never understand,' he said. 'Some things you can never know.'

He told us that night that he wanted us to come and work for him direct. He would look after us during the winter. He shivered involuntarily. 'It's going to be a very bad winter,' he said, 'snow in maybe ... three weeks. I know about these things.'

'You'd trust us not to take off next year when the work starts up again?' Coen asked. Springer nodded. It wasn't altogether altruistic he said. There would be no work around for us next year unless we worked direct. It was German jobs for Germans from now on. Kohl had said he would make it illegal for the unemployed to refuse more than a certain number of jobs. The *Arschlöcher* would have to work. Alex the Scotsman was finished, he added. The Dutchmen were finished.

At the time we didn't believe his words about the agents, though they did make us vaguely uneasy. We argued about his offer. It meant staying in Germany to get the full benefit from it. I was against it. The other two were undecided. Springer forced the issue on us. He offered us accommodation even. We told him we'd give him a decision in the *Kneipe* that evening. When we finished work we made our way up the main street of the town. He was waiting for us. He had four beers lined up on the counter. He looked up as we came in. Coen shook his head.

'No?' Springer said, obviously surprised.

'No.'

'A mistake, I think,' he said.

I offered him my hand. He shook hands with all of us. He said he was sorry and we said we were also sorry. It snowed two weeks later. In the end that Indian summer escaped as fast as a yelp from a beaten dog.

I hadn't learned anything. My position was worse than it had been twelve months before. There was snow on the ground and this time I didn't have six weeks' grace. Then Alex disappeared with our money — two weeks of it. We phoned frantically all over the place. Eventually his home number answered and a woman informed me dolefully that he was in jail. He'd been charged with tax evasion. He was in Stammheim Maximum Security Prison, with the Red Army faction and Baeder-Meinhof prisoners. Already Springer's words were prophetic. It appeared some sort of example was being made out of Alex.

I took the train through the snows to see him. He appeared to be in a deep depression. 'Do you know how many prisoners have topped themselves in this place?' he asked. 'All I did was avoid tax — why am I being held with terrorists?' He used to say he'd done well for a painter and decorator from Cowdenbeath. He had a red, new-series BMW, his girlfriend was a fashion model, his horse had won at Baden Baden that summer. The prison overalls he was wearing now dwarfed his frame. I wondered what had happened to the white suit he wore with an electric blue shirt, the collar of the shirt spread out over his lapels, the pallid skin of his narrow chest on display. He was wearing a kind of slipper now that dogged his steps, in place of the expensive Italian basket-weave shoes he'd favoured. His Travolta-style locks were shorn. As sure as anything, I thought, his future was largely behind him.

Somebody had grassed him. He was convinced of that,

obsessing on it. I tried to tell him he needed to get straight with his brief, enter a plea or something. He said the brief said he was looking at a ten stretch. There was a pub in Stuttgart — if I went there I was to ask for a man. 'How would the man know me?' I asked. He would know by the name I'd asked for. The man would have a key for a safety-deposit box. It was all he had that the police hadn't got their hands on. There were 60,000 DM in the box. I could take what we were owed and post the key to an address in Scotland — registered delivery. Alex stopped talking for a few seconds. He was chewing his fingernails. He was above board, he said. He could have got away without paying us. I had trusted him and now he had to trust me. Those DMs were all he had in the world, he said. I knew he was anxious and I promised him all I would do was take what we were owed. The warders stood him up to bring him back to his cell. He looked back at me over his shoulder.

'Tell me,' he said, 'none of us were in this for the money.'

I shrugged. His was a futile thought.

I stood in a room in the bank and counted to ten before I opened the box. I half-expected to wake up at any second, either that or the box would be empty. There was something chimerical about the whole exercise. The money was there. Alex might have been straight with us but he couldn't count — there was just over 100,000 DM in the box, about £25,000 sterling at the time, a considerable amount of money. It also contained some papers in German that looked like property deeds and a British passport in the name of Willie Jardine. Alex's photo was in it though. I counted out what we were owed into three separate stacks and returned the balance to the box. I locked it and put the key into an envelope which I later posted. It was his pension plan and he would be that bit nearer pension age before he got to see it.

All that was left was to decide what we were going to do for the winter — back to London again or onward elsewhere.

We went back to the Heldenberg. Most of the men in there were out of work. Diffley and those who had stuck with Claus were entitled to sign on for the winter. Coen also had enough time working direct to qualify for social security. All the work I'd done had been illegal — *Schwarzarbeit*. I said I was going to Israel. Tipperary Tommy wanted to know how you got there? Tommy had managed to fall out with everyone: he was isolated and barely tolerated. I left for Athens two days later — at the last moment Ready-Mix said he would come with me. I avoided the town those last few days. I hadn't spoken to Annelisa in weeks. There was no reason for this — no particular reason, at any rate. It was the way I did things, without definition, letting them drift of their own volition. I oscillated between lethargy and passion. Lethargy usually won out. The last time I saw her was in Göttingen. It was in Pegasus, the bar we usually drank in. We'd been there all day, drinking mulled wine, when I caught sight of her. She was sitting close to another man. She looked straight at me. I nodded. She made no gesture in return. She just looked right through me. I turned back to the company I was with. I told myself it was of no importance. By then I'd convinced myself it wasn't.

21

Myself and Ready-Mix came down off the autobahn, six months later, at a service station outside of Nuremberg. The bus, travelling from Athens to London, was obliged to let nobody off as it journeyed through wealthy Western Europe. That was the theory — and the bus avoided towns. Most of those travelling were Greek families, on their way to London, yet even the poor were entitled to use toilet facilities. Snow flurried about us as we slid down an embankment onto a service road. It was Good Friday. We had no money and the only food in our bags was a tin of corned-beef. I threw it away. We were back in the good times.

Within twelve hours we knew that Springer's warning the previous October had foundation. Phones were ringing out all across Germany and Holland, and the few answers we got were perfunctory — go home, there was no work. We were shivering in the thin clothes we'd being wearing for the past few months in the Negev Desert, yet we were about to begin a two-week odyssey up and down the autobahns. It was easier to get a lift alone so we split up, agreeing to meet in

Göttingen. My first lift took me from Nuremberg to Frankfurt and on to Bonn and Cologne, passing Wuppertal, Hagen, Essen and Dortmund and on to Hannover. It was an almost hallucinatory experience: driving through the industrial heartland of Germany at night, hungry, aware that the journey was probably futile, kilometre after kilometre of lights stretching in all directions above and below the autobahn to apparent infinity. Conversation with drivers was sparse and my head was full of the sound of unanswered telephones ringing out. From Hannover I switched trajectory southwards, coming off the autobahn near Northeim. I was dehydrated and walked into a bar and asked for a glass of water. The barman told me he'd call the *Polezei*. I walked to the Heldenberg. The hotel stood silhouetted against the night sky, dark and foreboding, like something from a fairy tale. It was closed. I curled into a ball in the shelter of the Bastille door and slept fitfully, till woken by the cold.

I got to Göttingen the next morning. It was snowing again and the temperature was below zero. There was no sign of Ready-Mix anywhere. I went to Road-Kill's flat, which was boarded up. I went looking for two Wicklowmen I knew and couldn't find them either. I slept that night, as much as I could, standing up in a telephone box, my clothes piled against the door to block the draught. The following afternoon Ready-Mix arrived in town, having taken more than twenty-four hours longer to do the same journey. We began trawling the bars. The Germans said everyone had left. There was no work anymore. Somebody however did say the Wicklowmen were still around and we eventually bumped into them on the street. We spent the night asleep on their floor — where at least it was warm. They were subsisting on minimum social-security payments. They told us about selling plasma. We went up to the hospital and joined a queue and got two hundred marks each. We bought food and took it back to the flat. The four of us ate ravenously. It was the first food I'd had in three days. The Wicklowmen said things could only get better. They said men weren't pulling together anymore. There was work but once someone heard of it they took off on their own. Yet all they had was rumours, some story of a long wall down the south. 'You could only keep hammering the phones,' they said, though their own had been disconnected.

We began phoning again. The results were the same. I phoned Springer who offered to take us on directly, under the same conditions as he'd offered before. We argued. Ready-Mix wanted to go straight there, whereas I wanted to give it a few more days at least. I didn't want to work direct.

Then I remembered a number Tipperary Tommy had given me: some woman he'd taken up with in Stuttgart, the cuckoo's nest he'd called it, only half-joking. I had met Tommy again in Israel. He passed me outside Beersheeba one day on a tractor. He had no money to get back from there. Myself and Ready-Mix pooled what we had and bought him a ticket from Haifa to Piraeus in Greece. The woman answered the phone. She hadn't seen or heard from Tommy in months. Where was he? She sounded desperate. I hung up. There was no work. There was only rumours of work. Germany was like that — there were always rumours of somewhere better, somewhere else to go, some Nirvana with more money, infinite hours, good prices and the best of men. If not Hy Brasil or Tír na Nóg, the Middle East, Libya, in time the Falklands — except you had to like sheep. There was a job in Belfast, the only problem was the Provos would shoot you. Or there was that wall near Stuttgart that went on forever. I would hear the same stories, years later, about what men were making painting Snow White's castle in Disneyland, Paris. It seemed apt somehow: Disneyland.

So Ready-Mix went south to Cologne and I headed west to Njimegen. We agreed we'd meet three days later again in Göttingen. Njimegen was a byword for work in those days.

Just inside the Dutch border it was a transit point for men travelling to Germany. The Dutch agents operated from there, bussing workers in from all over England every day. It was said at the height of the boom that the crippled walked again in Njimegen. But that April day it was a sombre place, like a triage station behind battle lines, with recumbent bodies everywhere. There was real desperation in the air, hundreds of men stumbled about the town, baffled that nobody had asked them to work. I stepped carefully amidst the sleeping bodies in the train station in an effort to recognise someone. In the end I lay down in a corner. I had no sleeping bag. The remains of the two hundred marks were stuffed down the front of my trousers.

Clearly I was in the wrong place. I remember a group of men gathered about a transistor radio. There was talk of an invasion fleet. They were all arguing about some war in a faraway place called the Falklands. Another group were standing near a kiosk trying to make their cups of coffee last. They were talking about work. A Scouser was going on about some big long wall, down near Düsseldorf. 'I swear mate, one big straight wall, miles long and all on a price, it'll go on for years.' 'Would you ever stop talking shite, you Scouse cunt,' an Irish voice answered. 'What are the Germans at? Re-partitioning the country is it, hah? North/South this time, hah? The best thing you could do is fuck off!' The Scouser struggled from his sleeping bag, but the murmur of assent that had followed what the Irishman said made him think better of it. After a while he bundled up the bag and moved on.

Then I met Geordie Colin who'd worked with Tipperary Tommy before Christmas. I'd met him before in Göttingen, the week before we'd left for Israel. I told him about phoning the woman down south.

'We should keep in touch with Tommy,' he said, 'ol' Tommy is lucky with work.'

So we rang the number again. Tommy was back but he

was laid up with a cold he'd caught while waiting for a lift in Austria on his way back from Greece. He had two new numbers. We promised to stay in contact.

By this time we were growing increasingly lethargic. Colin told me there was a gang of them skippering under a bridge near the town centre. We bought a bag of cheese rolls and a few bottles of beer and headed out there. It had begun to drizzle. There was a group of men there. Colin introduced me to a friend of his called Dog-Biscuits, a Scotsman he called Freddy the Frog and an Irishman whom he laughingly introduced as Fergus the Rocket Designer. They were sleeping under a sheet of plastic. They'd lit a fire with damp wood and acrid smoke billowed about us. Nobody slept. We could hear the traffic toil through the rain on the road above our heads. Dog-Biscuits told us he was a British Army deserter. He said he had a car.

'No you haven't,' I said.

'Have so,' he said.

'If you have a car,' I said, 'then why are we all sleeping out in the rain?'

There was uneasy laughter at what I'd said, as if our plight was making us ignore the very obvious.

Another Scotsman stumbled out of the gloom to join us. The boys seemed to know him, yet when he rolled out his sleeping bag all conversation stopped.

'Here there, move over,' he grumbled and squeezed himself between where I was lying and the fire. I could see his scarred face in the glow of the streetlights. Unshaven, he had a wild head of hair growing in all directions, like perverse foliage.

'You're new,' he said and he stuck out his hand. 'Feeney, they call me the Piranha.'

He settled back on his elbow and told us he'd been offered a job. Sixteen marks an hour,' he said. 'I told the Cloggie bastard to stuff it. I could get that at home.'

Silence greeted his assertion. No one believed him. We'd have all settled for a good deal less than that. There was nobody talking any more. I could hear bodies fumbling in the dark, trying to settle into some sort of sleep. The beer and cheese lay undigested in my stomach.

The next morning Colin said we should try Tommy's numbers. He said we should be clever about it. Let the men with good German do the talking. Let the agents make the running. Stop sounding desperate. Act as if we'd just come off a job. We all looked at Freddy the Frog when he mentioned good German. Freddy's mother was German and he spoke it like a native. Yet the first call came to nothing. It was a German agent and it was the same story, if a little more straightforward. No work and there would never be any more work — 'Go home, *Ausländer*,' he told us. We counted our money. There was a little left for food, enough perhaps to fill Dog-Biscuits car with petrol — for one journey. They were arguing about whether we should go home. Dog-Biscuits said he wasn't going back. I tried to tell him he could probably explain it away. He hadn't deserted in the face of the enemy. What could they do to him?

'What can they do?' he said. 'What can they do? They can shoot me.' There was a note of rising hysteria in his voice. There was, he said, going to be a war: hadn't the Argies invaded some place near Australia.

We were sitting in his car by then, listening to Brian Ferry sing "Avalon". The second of Tommy's numbers wasn't answering.

It was late that afternoon when it did answer. We were all grouped around the phone box — myself and Freddy the Frog inside. We'd all agreed: it was the last big effort. *Ja*, Freddy was saying in that mixture of English and German he'd come to speak. '*Six* men ... *ja, natürlich*, six *gute* men. *Keine zimmermen?* ... *Ja, ich bin ein* steel-fixer ... *Ich muss mit mein* colleague *sprechen* ... *Jawohl, er ist der beste* steel-fixer ... ?

Kein problem ... Alles klar ... Tschüss ... Mach's gut ... Mach's besser!'

'Why,' Fergus the Rocket Designer said, 'if you speak good German, were you talking like that?' Freddy said it was a Cloggie he had been talking to. 'Tell them nothing,' he said, 'don't let them know what we know.'

'And what do we know — what's the score anyway?' I said.

'He wants ten steel-fixers,' Freddy said. 'I told him you were a steel-fixer and you'd phone him back in five minutes. He's waiting for your call.'

That was how we got the job on the banks of the Rhine, in Karlsruhe, steel fixing. The four of them were ready to head directly there. All they had to do was get rid of Feeney. I had to go back to Göttingen. It was the only way I could make contact with Ready-Mix. It was too late for me to begin hitching, or so I thought. They were on about throwing Feeney a curve, saying that we should just take off without him. He wasn't trusted. He appeared volatile, incendiary, as if we were waiting on him to move precipitously. There was something of conversations overheard in a pub about his talk. He was unconvincing when he numbered the jobs he'd been on. There were small gaps in his knowledge of the places he'd claimed to have been in. He missed the nuances, things you couldn't get wrong, like the money you were on or what you were paying for a hotel. No one ever pressed him on these things. We hoped he'd go away but he'd attached himself to us. We'd lacked resolve to deal with him and consequently he'd come to rely on us. But that wasn't the way he'd see it. We were a gang as far as he was concerned.

I couldn't face another night with him under the bridge before I headed east so I headed back towards the train station. That morning had dawned cold and clear and bright after the rain and there was a frosty edge to the evening. I overheard a group of bricklayers talk morosely about muck frozen on spot-boards — as if it was something they might never see again. But I was in a euphoric daze — I had a job. I was in a reverie when I walked directly into Feeney.

'Come on,' he said, 'I have the price of a couple of beers. Are you up for it?'

We stood in a bar. He was garrulous, attacking every silence relentlessly. My feet were shuffling. All those half-lit pubs I'd spent so much time in seemed to have melded into the place we were in. We walked back towards the station. He was droning on about a new crowd that had moved into our pitch under the bridge. 'I'll run them,' he said. I could see his hooded eyes in the half-light, his splayed nose, his saliva-flecked, rosebud lips. His whole face seemed out of proportion. It was then a Dutch policeman approached and asked us for our passports, drawn no doubt by Feeney's animation. I half-remembered him telling me earlier his passport was in hock somewhere. I was preparing to reason with the policeman when Feeney reached for him, plucked him off the ground by his crotch. The policeman screamed and his hand grasped for his holster. Feeney wrenched his arm behind his back. There was a crack like ice snapping and Feeney bent towards him, as if to kiss him — only he bit him instead. Tore a chunk of flesh from his face. I could see Feeney spit onto the pavement. There was blood everywhere. I was already running. I could hear Feeney's lumbering footsteps disappearing in the opposite direction.

The following evening I arrived in Karlsruhe with Ready-Mix. We had pooled our money and taken the train south from Göttingen. It was Tuesday. The boys would have begun work that day. They were supposed to meet us in the Bahnhof. There was nobody there. There was nobody there the following morning either or the day after that. We had enough money for a loaf of bread. It was the cheapest bread there was, called toast because that was what it was meant for.

We bought Kit-Kats with what we had left and made sandwiches. The bread dried the saliva from our mouths. By the second day we realised no one was coming. Perhaps there was no job? Perhaps they had all forgotten us? We got soup from the Red Cross Station but what we needed was money. Enough money even to phone Tommy and find out where the job was. It was our lowest ebb over the two weeks. Somewhere there was work — where we didn't know. The Red Cross wouldn't give out money, only food. We discussed begging. But you needed a licence to beg in Germany. And then Ready-Mix remembered his cousin and a bar called Das Eiserne Kreuz in a town called Leonberg.

It was the day of my twenty-second birthday that we got lost in the Black Forest — Ready-Mix wanting to go right and me left and the sun blacked out by the trees so we couldn't even tell east from west. It was pure luck we emerged at all out onto the road and got the lift from the woman that left us at the bottom of the steps that led up the hill to the town of Leonberg and its famous Porsche factory. We were so weak and dizzy with the hunger that every so often we had to stop for breath — leaning on one another. '*Eiserne Kreuz*,' Ready-Mix kept repeating, more like an imprecation than a mantra, and in the years since then the number of those steps has grown in my mind — until they seem now as many as the islands in Clew Bay.

When we arrived, panting, in the bar, his cousin sat at the counter — a copy of the *Donegal Democrat* opened before him. 'Jasus lads,' he said, 'it was a fierce bad winter at home.'

22

EVENTUALLY WE FOUND THE JOB AT A HYDRO-POWER STATION on the banks of the Rhine in Karlsruhe. Within a week we were moved to the night shift. That first night we staggered over and back across a deck the size of two football pitches, burdened down by the weight of the seven-metre steel bars. Worse yet we were walking on steel. There is no give in steel. My feet were on fire, my legs leaden. The sound of voices filled the air. We had been working without stop for eighteen hours: there were six hours to go. The shift was from eight in the morning until eight the next morning. Voices carried from elsewhere on the site, interspersed with the sounds of steel clanging on steel and the whirr of cranes in constant motion. Clouds of midges gathered about our heads, attracted by the heat from the glower of the arc lights above us. Sweat glistened on my forehead and the midges stuck to it. Beyond the arc lights the early morning had turned cold and spumes of breath hung in the air. My leather jacket was ruined. It was scuffed and rust-stained from shouldering steel and the snagged lining had pulled free. Beneath it the shirt was stuck to my back with sweat. As soon as we laid down one seven-metre bar we returned to hump the next one.

Dog-Biscuits was wondering what we were building. We ignored him. We were wondering if we'd get paid. The day we came to work we were told we weren't needed. I didn't say anything to Ready-Mix. We both started to work anyway and for some reason we were kept. We slept in the changing hut. Dog-Biscuits was telling us that the majority of people died between the hours of two and five in the morning, when the night seemed the darkest. The human body, he said, reaches a natural low. It was like a bit of string was attaching you to the world and it comes loose. 'Like a balloon really,' he said. 'That string breaks and you float off, man.' I watched how Ready-Mix lifted the steel bar, then dropped it, glancing sideways so he could see it trap Dog-Biscuits' fingers. Dog-Biscuits squealed.

The seven-metre bars had to be then laid side-by-side to form an intricate lattice. They were tied in position and holes were left for the concrete, when poured, to be vibrated. The bars were an inch-and-a-half in diameter. They were very heavy. We hauled them in teams of three. Step up, lift the bar, walk forward, bend down, ease it into position, tie twice and repeat. It was repetitive work. The distance we were shifting the steel meant it wasn't worth shouldering. We held it at arms' length in front of us. We began with Dog-Biscuits on one end, Ready-Mix on the other and myself in the middle, where the weight was. It was up to the two men on the ends to remain aware of that and allow for it. To take more of the weight by hoisting the bar higher. But Dog-Biscuits wasn't doing this. I had to compensate by hoisting the middle higher and higher, gravitating towards his end. Ready-Mix tried to stage me but because he was smaller than I was it didn't really work. There were two other gangs working with us. They were cohesive. By the time we'd tied our bar they were already backed up behind us. We were being watched. Dog-Biscuits

said what we needed was some whiz — some speed. I
shuddered, remembering the paper factory. It seemed like a
long time ago. Ready-Mix told him to shut the fuck up.

Colin, Fergus, Freddy the Frog and Tipperary Tommy
were all on the deck but most of the gang were Italians. There
were over a hundred of them, all Sicilians. They were used to
working together. By comparison all our movements would
have looked ragged, corrugated. Seen from above we'd have
looked like a troupe of dancers who'd failed to master an
elementary step. I could hear Colin muttering about Dog-
Biscuits. This was rich — coming from the man who'd
brought him to Germany. Ready-Mix was getting
increasingly angry.

'Were you ever in Northern Ireland?' he asked.

'Was, man …'

'With a head like yours,' Ready-Mix said, 'it's a wonder
they missed you.'

Dog-Biscuits was impossible to rise. We put him in the
middle. That made things worse. He was blinded with sweat.
There was nowhere to hide. He stumbled on the steel, fell
and cut his knees. When we dropped the bar in position he
caught his fingers each time. He was wearing gloves. It was
almost impossible to manage tying nips while wearing gloves.
He fumbled. He wanted to wear them to carry the steel and
take them off before tying it. Ready-Mix pointed out that half
his ties were missing. Dog-Biscuits said who would notice.
Ready-Mix said that these things were checked on. That was
when Frodo joined us. Frodo was the overall foreman. He
began checking the ties.

Frodo went over to Freddy the Frog. He was
gesticulating, pointing over to the other side of the deck.
Freddy had the best German and whoever had the best
German was in charge. Moreover Freddy had ingratiated
himself with the Germans. He always got the handy
numbers. Once, when we couldn't get a lift from a crane, and

Frodo was standing nearby, Freddy had taken off his helmet and started banging it off the steel, shouting up at the crane driver who couldn't hear him. The Germans loved a show. They loved roaring and shouting. Frodo took the walkie-talkie hooked to his belt and spoke to the crane driver. Then he put his arm around Freddy and offered him a cigarette. The packet dropped onto the steel and when he bent to pick it up Freddy winked at the rest of us. The problem with Freddy was he didn't communicate with us. We didn't trust him, half-expecting to find ourselves up the road any day while he was kept on.

Frodo signalled that myself and Tommy along with Dog-Biscuits, Colin and Ready-Mix were to follow him. He took us across to where there was a four-metre gap in the steel between two sections of the deck, below which was a drop of six metres onto starter bars. Obviously we were to finish bridging the gap. And just as obviously a crane would have done the job in half-an-hour. Ready-Mix whispered to me that some of us would be gone in the morning. He looked over at Dog-Biscuits. I wasn't so sure. Either way, it was clear that Frodo intended to test our resolve, to sort us out.

There were a group of Italians standing on the other side of the gap. They didn't look impressed with us, as they stood talking amongst themselves, throwing the odd, disdainful look in our direction. Frodo detailed myself, Colin and Ready-Mix to bridge the gap. Tommy and Dog-Biscuits were to tie the steel in position. We hoisted the first of the seven-metre bars, which we had to swing across the divide to where the Italians would reach out, grasp it and pull it over. It meant that the three of us had to move in an arc, at the back of the bar, letting it run out into space. It also meant that only one man was in effective control of it — the man at the back. The other two had to let go. There wasn't space enough and three men couldn't work as of one mind. I was on the back. It was five o'clock in the morning and I'd been lifting steel relentlessly for twenty-one hours, we all had. My fingers seemed paralysed, my head throbbed mercilessly. At the end, on my own, I could feel the momentum of the bar drag me forward, careering towards the edge of the gap. I had to lean back while remaining in control of it. I was relying on the Italians' judgement and hoping they would trust me. Yet the only thing we had in common was a bad command of German.

It went better than I'd have imagined. We were losing few bars. Each time I sent one across there was another waiting. As we swung in a semi-circle, the two boys dove out of the way while I tottered towards the gap. Several times Colin and Ready-Mix offered to stage me but Frodo waved them back. My arms felt wrenched from their sockets, I could see a sheen of sweat on my jacket where I'd wiped the sweat of my forehead. This activity continued for two hours. There was no break, no let-up. After each successful bar I could hear Frodo grunt. Then, just after seven, he told us to change over. Myself and Ready-Mix were to tie steel, Tommy and Dog-Biscuits were to replace us. We lit cigarettes while Frodo drank from a flask of schnapps. I was slumped forward with relief, thinking he had proved his point. Obviously he hadn't. He told us to begin again and put Dog-Biscuits on the back of the bar.

From the outset they were in trouble. It wasn't just Dog-Biscuits. Tommy was wearing hob-nailed boots: steel on steel, he slid about like an ice-skater. They lost the first six bars. Dog-Biscuits was letting go of them too early. Colin was trying to compensate but kept getting in the way and Frodo was shouting at them. The Italians drew back from the edge on their side, sensing danger. Dog-Biscuits tried to blame them for not catching the bars. They objected. Frodo told them to shut up and start working. As the next bar came over they reached out and grabbed it, but as they did Dog-Biscuits lost control of his end and one of them had to jerk another back

from the gap by grasping the collar of his jacket. They stood
swearing across the divide. Colin swore back at them and
began to clutch his crotch. The youngest of the three Italians
bounded then across the bars we had tied in place. I was still
bent over, pretending to have some purpose, and I could see
the steel he'd crossed bouncing up and down. I straightened
myself in time to see him bring his tying nips full circle and hit
Colin on the forehead. Colin staggered back across Dog-
Biscuits. Tommy charged at the Italian but Ready-Mix blocked
him. Frodo meanwhile was already on his walkie-talkie.

'For fuck's sake,' Ready-Mix said, 'it'll be like Custer's
Last Stand.'

Tommy drew back momentarily. I had gone to pick
Colin up. Blood was streaming down the side of his face. The
other two Italians were tensed on the far side of the gap.
Already the noise of what had happened had begun to attract
attention from all over the deck. It seemed to have got bright
without us noticing: and in the morning light there were over
a hundred men — all of them Italian — spread out in a semi-
circle around us. Ready-Mix took the man who'd assaulted
Colin by the elbow and pointed him back across the gap.
Ready-Mix told Dog-Biscuits to take Colin for first-aid. We
watched them make their way up the ladder and off the deck
as the crowd began to disperse. Tommy was bent over on the
deck. He was shielding a cigarette.

'What do we do now?' I asked.

'Work,' said Ready-Mix so we hoisted the next bar up. I
took my place again on the back. It was five-to-eight in the
morning. Five minutes later I heard Frodo summon a crane
and tell the driver to drop a bundle of steel across the gap.
That was Germany.

The following week I started work on the chimney. The
chimney was the centrepiece of the job. It already dominated
the skyline over Karlsruhe. I got sent up to replace Freddy the

Frog who'd lasted two hours before one of the Albanians had
him by the throat out over the edge of the shutter, high above
the Rhine. Freddy said they were mad bastards and I was
apprehensive as I made my way up the centre of the chimney
in the bucket. There was no way of avoiding work up there.
The job was being done by a hydraulic shutter that was
pumped upwards twenty-four hours a day. Everything, steel,
concrete and men, came up the centre of the chimney and the
concrete was poured all the time. There were two twelve-hour
shifts — the day shift was Albanian and the night shift
Turkish. One began at six in the morning and the other at six
in the evening. On the top there was a small wooden hut to
shelter in, two mini-tractor drivers who moved the concrete,
a hoist driver and four steel-fixers. It was a small, crowded
platform and once you were up you stayed up for the whole
shift. We tied steel-risers, vertically, ten centimetres apart and
horizontal bars also every ten centimetres. The gauge of the
steel grew smaller as the shutter rose. There was inside work
and outside. Inside was confined within the innards of the
shutter, up against the hydraulic system. That was where I
worked, going round in ever decreasing circles as the shutter
rose and the chimney grew narrower. The work was relentless,
hunkered-down, with two fifteen-minute breaks. We shared
food in the small hut. I was working with the Turks. They
tried to place, geographically, where I was from. That night I
went along with the fiction that I had never tasted cucumber
before. I knew I was there for the duration of the job. I was
genuinely happy about that. The German tractor drivers and
the hoist driver drank beer. They weren't supposed to. Not up
there. But almost everybody steadily drank beer then on
German sites. They smuggled it up in buckets. The Turks said
even Hitler wouldn't have tried to stop the Germans
drinking. There was no shouting up there. It was a
surprisingly peaceful place with a view across Germany, into
Alsace in France and as far as Switzerland. The hydraulics

creaked and the chimney swayed slightly in the wind. I had to shift my feet slightly to keep my balance. I could see right down along the Rhine, where the river wended like a great thoroughfare through the heart of Europe. There was a period between five and six in the morning, when everything wound down. I used to go to the edge and stand there looking at the lights of the barges blinking far below, where they'd moored for the night. Memhet, one of the Turks, would point to where the sun was rising in the distance and tell me that was home. Mine, I'd say, was the other way, far over there towards the darkened edges of the world, where the earth curved. If you looked, I told him, you could see the slight curve from up there. And I'd go down in the bucket, the last man into it off the shift — they had their own hierarchy and I was at the bottom of it. Down the centre of the chimney, the bucket swaying and creaking on its guy wire, while Inver, another Turk, clamped his eyes shut and prayed, muttering invocations I had no inkling of.

It all began to become uncaulked a week before the chimney was finished, when we were coming off the night-shift and the bonds on a load of steel snapped and maybe three tonnes of it fell on two Italians. Ready-Mix was driving a tractor by then, sorting and hauling steel for the hydraulic shutters. He waited for me in the morning at the foot of the chimney. We were walking back to the changing rooms when we heard the crane groan, as if it was lifting too heavy a load. There should have been an alarm set off. We looked up. We could see the jib, bent towards the ground, straining to lift a bundle of steel. Then there was a rending sound as if it were pulling something deep rooted from the earth and the jib sprung back into position. A load of steel jerked upwards. The jib was already moving and the steel seemed to track its course in slow motion, swaying behind it. Then there was a crack as the bonds on the steel snapped and the whole load plummeted back to the ground. Everybody was looking up, including the two men who were hit. The steel seemed to tremble for an instance before it fell. It hit them full on, their heads turned upwards, their faces twisted into a rictus of terror. Freed of its burden the jib of the crane spun in a circle. The whole structure was shaking. Blood spouted into the air, splattering myself and Ready-Mix. It all went wrong from there.

At that stage we were friendly with the Italians. After the incident with Dog-Biscuits and Colin we'd hidden amongst them while we learned to tie steel. The Italians blamed the Germans. We tried to explain that there was nothing personal in it. The Germans hadn't set out to kill Italians: it could have been us or the Turks or the Albanians, Kurds, Armenians, Russians, Poles, French or Dutch or any of the other fourteen nationalities there were on that job. The Italians wanted the job closed down. The Germans argued with them. There would be an inquiry: that would take time. The Germans thought the Italians were emotional. They should get over it. All this was happening during the 1982 World Cup, when there were pictures everywhere of excited Italians gesticulating at televisions all over Germany. An effort at compromise was brokered. Nobody would have to work the day the bodies were transported back to Sicily — but for anyone who did want to work the job would remain open. The Italians weren't happy.

For three days they'd been hanging about in morose groups. They were still in shock. Even Frodo couldn't motivate them. On the day the bodies went back they placed a picket on the gates of the job. That evening they told myself and Ready-Mix that some men had gone in. They said if we all stuck together what could the Germans do? It was only one day after all. I said that one or two men weren't important. We could be got rid off. It was different for them. The Germans couldn't afford to lose over a hundred men. One of the Italians put his arm round my shoulder. He said

we would have to do what we thought was right. He asked
the men at the gate to move aside. They did so reluctantly.

I went into the changing rooms and sat down. The
Turkish foreman came in. I asked him was he going to work.
He shrugged. He said his men were changed but he didn't
know if they were going to work. They were in the canteen. I
told him I was minded not to go up the chimney. He looked
at Ready-Mix who nodded in agreement with me. We didn't
change.

In the canteen the Turks were playing backgammon. We
sat at a table opposite them, sipping two beers. We could see
the day-shift coming off the chimney. The Albanians came
into the canteen. One of them came over to me, '*Keine
Arbeit?*'

I shook my head. He looked across at the Turks and
shook his head then. It was no good, he told me. The Italians
were dead. They should be honoured with work — if they
were to be honoured at all, he added as an afterthought.
There was antagonism between the Italians and the
Albanians. Somebody told me that there were Albanian
villages on the Adriatic coast of Italy. The Italians would
mime a stabbing motion at the mention of Albania. But then
the northern Italians thought the southerners were inferior
and called them *afros* or monkeys.

Frodo came into the canteen. He joined the Turks,
gesturing towards the chimney. We could see there was
already two concrete wagons waiting at the gate. The
conversation was animated. The Turkish foreman kept
shaking his head. Frodo came over to us. He asked us if we
were going to work. Ready-Mix said we would work
tomorrow.

'*Ach Scheisse,*' he said and he got up and kicked over a
chair.

I went up to the counter and bought a crate of beer. I
brought it down and left it on the table beside the Turks. We

finished our drinks and left. That canteen was big enough to hold a thousand men. When I looked back from the door the group of Turks looked like a small detail in a painting. On our way out we saw the hoist driver coming down off the chimney. The concrete wagons had been turned away and the Italians were gone from the gate.

We went back the next evening as if nothing had happened. Nobody mentioned what had passed the day before. We met some of the Italians coming off the day shift. They saluted us silently. When we went into the changing room Freddy the Frog was waiting for us.

'You've blown it there now,' he said.

'How could we have blown it?'

'The Krauts are pissed off now,' he said. 'You don't interfere with their work you know. Oh, you'll be alright for a week or two. There won't be anything done until the chimney's finished. They'll not interfere with that. Then they'll do all of us. They'll do any man who makes a mistake now.'

We mightn't have liked what Freddy was saying but we didn't doubt it was true. Frodo had been livid when he kicked the chair over. Yet there were too many Italians and Turks for him to be able to get back at them.

The first to go were two men who weren't attached to us, Scots Bob and Sligo John. They'd been there before any of us. They worked for the same agent as we did. They were so long working on big gangs on the day-shift they'd begun to think they were invisible. Frodo found them asleep on the banks of the Rhine. Scots Bob blamed us. He said it should have been last-in, first-out. Ready-Mix had no sympathy for him. He told him he should have stuck to his Glasgow factory. Seniority counted for nothing. They were caught on a Friday and the Dutch agent told them they would have to wait two weeks to get the balance of their wages. The following week the chimney finished and I was brought back down onto the decks with everyone else. Tipperary Tommy was gone, having come to work drunk one night, waving a bottle of Jack Daniels. There was something inexorable about his departure, as if it were all preordained — like the Italians said they believed about the deaths of the two men. Tommy couldn't any longer buckle down to working long shifts, to the pulverising nature of the work. Dog-Biscuits too was long gone. Meanwhile the rest of them had been having a good time around Karlsruhe for the previous two months. They didn't welcome myself and Ready-Mix's return to the day-shift. They thought we would draw attention to them.

Whether they were right or not wasn't material. We were all told we could go. Afterwards Frodo approached myself and Ready-Mix and offered us work direct. We asked, as usual, for a couple of days to think it over.

We were standing around in the back of the cabin like a bunch of schoolboys when Scots Bob came in. We hadn't heard from the Dutchman for a week, and had been hanging round, wondering if we would get paid. Bob was paranoid: he said he'd been caught by too many Dutchmen too many times. And the paranoia had spread to the rest of us. When Bob came into the cabin there was an intake of breath. He'd been drinking since early morning. He walked up to the table in front of the Dutchman and laid a pick-axe handle across it. The wide boss of it pointing at where the Dutchman was sitting. The Dutchman lifted his brief-case onto the table. The brief-case was narrow and looked expensive — looked like it was made from aluminium. He opened it, took out a gun from it and laid it on the table. The briefcase was now between the gun and the pick-axe handle. The Dutchman didn't blink. No one said anything. You could see from where we were standing that Scots Bob was afraid. You could smell the fear off him. His skin had the bluey tinge of wet back-streets at night. Eventually the Dutchman took our wage

packets from the case and handed them to us. He said what
Bob had done hadn't been smart. He was going to pay us. He
was acting in good faith. We needed him more than he
needed us. Did we know how many phone calls he got every
day, looking for work? The Germans didn't need us anymore.
As far as he was concerned, he believed they'd have let us go
weeks ago if it weren't for the chimney. He smiled as he told
us he didn't have anything immediately. We could keep in
contact by phone. He closed his case and left the room. It was
a while before any of us moved.

Ready-Mix took the job direct. I couldn't blame him. It
had been my fault he'd turned down two such jobs. Freddy
said he'd got work landscape gardening. The money wasn't as
good but it was work anyway. I said I was going back to
London. They all said there was nothing in London. I
phoned Tommy's woman in Stuttgart and asked to speak to
him. I told him what I was going to do. He sighed. He
seemed fatigued. He had nowhere else to go, he said. He'd
have to go back and face it all. Two days later I stood outside
the Red Cross Station in the Karlsruhe Bahnhof, waiting for
him. I missed the first train and decided to try the number.
There was no reply. I got the next train by myself.

23

AFTER MY EXPERIENCE OF BEING PULLED IN AT HOLYHEAD, I developed a paranoia about points of arrival and departure. I believed it was my state in life to be viewed with suspicion. I tried to affect a nonchalance about these things but that only appeared to complicate matters.

A Sabra at Ben Gurion Airport found a flick knife when she searched my bag. She held it up to the light as if she were myopic. I'd got it from some Basques in Salonikia, a fraternal gesture, though I knew better than to say that. It was a fine piece of work, with an ornate, inlaid handle and a nine-inch blade that was difficult to miss.

'You can't exactly butter bread with it,' she said, suggesting that I leave it behind me. Embarrassed, I agreed as she slipped it into the side pocket of her army skirt. If I was feeling paranoid there, then I knew nothing about the level of security at an Israeli airport. I looked about me and saw a group of Hassidics silently suffering similar treatment. The Israelis were nothing if not egalitarian — as suspicious of their own as they were of visitors.

On the Continent I was mostly ignored. My passport was an EC one after all. My real troubles were with Her Majesty's officialdom. What I felt from the beginning was some fearsome burden of collective guilt for something I was innocent of. And there was something atavistic also about this feeling — my servant's face illuminated momentarily by a shaft of light from the Great House doorway, as I stole across the yard, a stolen *bonamh* tucked under my arm perhaps. It was a strange feeling to have, knowing also that once I passed through Customs I was generally speaking alright. Once in, I could walk through Brixton or Dalston on a Saturday night without harassment, while groups of black males of my own age were stopped under the SUS laws.

Even at Arrivals and Departures I was only a footnote, a statistic. I knew all that — yet I seemed conditioned to play my part in this historical choreography. Sometimes I faced it head-on, as if I were going for a dental appointment, and was first at the Customs point. And other times — like that day in Folkestone when I returned from Karlsruhe — I loped about towards the back of the crowd. Invariably the result was the same. As if I gave off some low-grade hum, a redolence that made the two heads behind the desk swivel in my direction, in unison, like antennae. Look, here comes another recidivist.

'Can I see your passport sir?' He didn't so much look at it as dangle it from his fingertips, as if it were radioactive. 'McBride,' he said, 'McBride.' The name giving him obvious pause for thought. 'Follow me, sir' and he led me into a room.

'You're making a mistake,' I said. He was overweight. He put his hand on my shoulder and I felt the dampness on his palm through my shirt. I shrugged it off. He looked like a policeman out of uniform, ill at ease, but his look suggested those were the very words Reggie Kray had uttered all those years ago.

'That's not for you or I to decide sir,' he replied. It was the week of the Hyde Park bombing. I knew nothing about what had happened in Hyde Park. Eleven soldiers died with two bombs, one in Hyde Park and the other in Regent's Park.

The room I was in had no windows. There was a table and four chairs in the middle of it. I was there for four hours, then the man who'd brought me there came back. He said nothing for a minute but stood and watched me. Then he told me to strip. He took all my belongings away and gave me a set of white overalls. He took me to a cell, again windowless. A harsh fluorescent light flickered on and off overhead. I began to lose all sense of time. They had taken away my watch. I knew it was serious this time. Eventually I was led back to the first room and the routine I was to become familiar with began.

There were four of them altogether. They questioned me in teams of two. Sometimes it was the same two, other times they swapped over. They told me their names, conspiratorially, as if I could believe or disbelieve them if I wanted. The first two did most of the questioning. One of them was perhaps twenty years older than the other. They had a strange relationship in which the older man deferred grudgingly to the younger one. It was like master and protégé: wherein the protégé has passed the master out in worldly wisdom, yet the master remains reluctant to acknowledge this. They argued amongst themselves as if I was a side-show. The elder of the two saw himself as avuncular, patient. He'd continue the same line of questioning, like a dog retracing its steps around a series of lampposts. Then, from time to time, he'd erupt, slam the table and abuse me. Then he'd loosen his collar or straighten his tie like he was a good bloke — and everyone knew that — things just got on top of him from time to time, like the suspect's recalcitrance for instance. The other one watched this performance, perfunctorily drumming his fingers on the table top, narrowing his eyes menacingly. His questions were direct and unconnected — they suggested their own answers. I knew this was the way I might have expected them to behave. It was classic good cop, bad cop. Yet it was difficult to believe that I was seeing them any other way than they really were.

The questions were the same as Holyhead. They called me Pat. It would go on for what felt like hours. No matter what I did I couldn't get comfortable in that chair. I was physically off-balance, tilted towards the table. They'd leave the room and I could hear them yammering beyond the door. I couldn't differentiate between their voices. I'd get a cup of bland, tepid coffee from time to time. They smoked incessantly and when I asked for a cigarette they laughed at me. You'll have to tell us something first Pat. Once, when they'd left the room, I switched my chair over to the other side of the table. They came back into the room. The elder one sat in the chair. He got up immediately then, came round the table and kicked my chair from beneath me. I fell backwards onto the floor and banged my head. He threw the chair at me. I deflected it with my arm.

'Know your counter-interrogation business then, Pat? Used to this?' he shouted.

After a while I'd say I was hungry. They would take me back to the cell where the light flickered like a strobe and later I would get a plate of cold chips and a desiccated egg. I stirred it about. They came for me again, growing by turns friendly and intimidatory. They suggested things I might know, places I might have been.

'Many IRA in Germany,' they'd say, 'you must have met some?'

Back in the cell I'd think of the time I stopped off in Düsseldorf, on the way back to the job in Bergisch Gladbach. I went to the Irish pub. That was in the last few days of the Hunger Strikes. There were three men sitting at the counter. They saw I had Irish cigarettes, 20 Major, and we began talking. We were talking about football when we were interrupted. The interference came from a crowd of drunken squaddies at the back of the bar. They were taunting us. One of them said something about hoping all those bastards die. That was when one of the men got off his stool and lifted the nearest squaddie. He hefted him through a plate-glass window into the street. We ran. They shouted at me to follow them, they had a car. Two of the squaddies after us had stopped to pick up the man who'd been thrown through the window. Some more fell across them, shouting 'Get the bastards!' The car, a Capri with Southern plates and a Tricolour sticker, was parked facing uphill. It wouldn't start. We had to push it so it faced downhill. It caught and we accelerated through the squaddies knocking two of them over. The men apologised to me. One of them pointed at Bernard, the driver, who had thrown the squaddie through the window. 'His brother is on the list to join the strike,' he said. They told me they'd travelled south through Rosslare, avoiding Britain, and journeyed across France to get to Germany. I didn't need to hear anymore. They said they were sick of it all. They had jobs on a site outside Bonn. They were working for Boma the Dutch crowd I'd worked with. I got the impression, by the time they'd dropped me off in Cologne, that they too had done time.

There was a part of me that wanted to tell my interrogators this story. It might mollify them. But what significance did it have? It was pure synchronicity, the hapless result of being in the wrong bar on the wrong afternoon. I told myself I'd forgotten the three men's names. They had nothing to do with my situation. What's more, they were attempting to leave their pasts behind. I also feared that if I told the story it would make my interrogators more aggressive. They would have achieved something. The fact was I had nothing to tell them. I told them that over and over. You have the wrong man. They said it didn't matter. I was a Paddy so I was guilty.

I couldn't sleep. The flickering light in the cell was never switched off. I asked them to repair it and they laughed, saying there was nothing wrong with the light, that I was imagining things. I began to believe I was. I could hear furtive scratching from somewhere, doors slammed open and shut, the shutter in the cell door opening and closing regularly. They said I was on suicide watch. What was I supposed to top myself with? The overalls they'd given me felt like they were made from paper. The bed in the cell was bolted to the floor. The mattress was sponge, it stank of the bodily functions of other men. There was a blanket and a bucket. I listened for sounds from way off, church bells, a clock tower, anything that might give me some purchase on the passage of time. The difference between night and day. There was nothing, only that harsh, irregular fluorescent drone.

'You fuckin' did it Pat.'

I said nothing. My head was weighed forward. My senses were dulled. His voice was like a distant ocean pounding in my eardrums. 'You fuckin' did it.' Yet when I asked, 'Did what?' he said nothing or 'You know', and added, 'Tell me about it?' Offering absolution. He walked behind me. I exhaled through my teeth.

'I know nothing.'

He exploded. He clapped his hands over my ears. The pain was excruciating. Something was about to give, to burst. Nausea rose within me, I could smell the stench of my own body. I tried to get off the chair and reeled, off-balance, across the room. Someone stuck a foot out and tripped me.

They were sophists. They argued amongst themselves. They'd suggest scenarios, go away and come back with a pad and a pencil and present things to me. All I had to do was sign. They told me about Hyde Park. One of them grew emotional.

'The fucking horses,' he roared, 'the fucking horses! They murdered the fucking horses!'

I tried to explain that I was outside this chronology.

Northern Ireland rarely made the news in Germany and I
didn't follow the news in any case. This infuriated them. They
said it was one thing Paddies killing each other — no one
gave a fuck — it was another thing when Paddies brought it
over here. I could have, they said, slipped off to the
Continent after I'd planted the bomb. How many of you were
involved? Names? Names? Names?

They had my passport, I said, they could check the
details.

Passports, they said, had no meaning. 'Are you sure you
had a passport when we arrested you?'

There was little stopping me from signing anything they
wanted in the end. I would be free of them. We could be
friends even, co-conspirators — and I would walk away from
it all. I wouldn't have to stand up in court. I knew it wouldn't
stand up in court. If it came to that I could prove where I had
been. Yet the scenario retained an aura of Hitchcockian
menace: what if I couldn't prove it? If there was no one left to
offer me an alibi back in Karlsruhe. No one knew I was in
that police station. I was living a semi-vagrant life. It would
be easy to make me disappear — legally or otherwise. I was
becoming increasingly paranoid beneath those fluorescent
lights. I like to think it was a justified paranoia that kept me
from going along with them. I had a well-enough honed
notion of what had happened to other people, in the recent
past, to know that signing something was likely to be the
beginning rather than the end of my troubles.

They seemed resigned to letting me go, the way a child
eventually accepts that a favourite toy is broken beyond
fixing. Appropriately, the first thing I got back was my watch.
Yet I had the same problem I'd had during the interrogation
when I'd sneaked glimpses at their watches. They'd seemed
aware of what I was at but it didn't appear to bother them. At
first I wondered at this — but then it became apparent: was
it half-eight in the morning or half-eight at night? What day

was it anyway? It was 9.45 when they let me go, two days later. I had to wait until I emerged from the station before I knew it was night time. I signed for what I owned. I'd like to think I went through each individual piece of my belongings, as they had done, making sure I had everything. I didn't though. I was signing the least thing I could have signed. I couldn't get away fast enough.

The older of the two followed me outside. I was literally blinking in the half-light. I expected him to say something like 'No hard feelings' — to make some sort of apology. Instead he put his arm about my shoulder and drew me to him. I could smell warm, flat beer, cheap after-shave and sweat, as he told me my time would come. My cards were marked. They knew me now.

I stumbled away from there, walking in an almost somnambulant state, in what felt like several directions at once. I had no purpose other than to walk. I was disorientated. The streetlights had the effect of a neon cosh, as I followed my feet with my eyes. Eventually I stopped in the middle of some wasteland bordered by concrete blocks of apartments. The concrete was the colour of dirty rain. Some children tried to sail bits of timber in becalmed puddles. A woman called to me from a stairwell and hiked up her skirt. She laughed as I rushed on. I felt I had reached the ends of a flat world — a place where the money had run out. Beyond me, in the distance, I could see a ship readying to sail. Groups of men with tool-bags and yellow Stabila spirit-levels walked resolutely towards it. It was the same boat I'd arrived on two days before.

I slept that night on a bench in the departure area. I could smell the fear and the Jeyes Fluid that my body seemed to be secreting. The following morning I hit north, for London.

24

I CAME OUT OF THE TUBE IN HAMMERSMITH. I'D BEEN AWAY almost three years. I'd lost weight and I was tanned. I thought I looked different but I met Fighting McHale, the RB driver I'd worked with in Bracknell, on the Broadway. He wasn't fooled.

'The hard man,' he said, then he told me Lonesome Tom was dying. 'The Big C,' he said, 'it'll take a miracle now' and he shook his head. He was selling tickets for a benefit dance for Tom. I got a bus to the haunted flat near Clapham Junction. Brian let me in. I was just in time, he said, he was thinking of moving again. We spent the afternoon in the sun, on the grass outside a pub on the Common. He told me a Royal baby had been born, and he updated me on his nocturnal visitors. '*Los Malvinas son Argentinas*,' he whispered, leaning towards me and looking about to make sure he wasn't overheard. I was welcome to the flat again. He was fed up with the Tory Government and what they stood for.

I saw what he meant immediately. The area had changed. There was a wine bar, newly opened, opposite his flat. Called

The Inebriated Newt, it was populated by a whole new class of people, young men and women who watched the windows as they sipped claret, in case their cars were stolen from outside. The place was on the rise. This new class consorted together. They were charmed by the second-hand shops and the street market on the Northcote Road. Sequestered behind their renovated facades, they were removed from what happened on the streets. It was, the old lady next door told me, the first time there'd been alarms in the area. 'People here always looked after their own,' she said balefully. 'It was a case of give a dog a bad name,' she said, 'and he'll stare through your living room window. If you didn't want him to stare why didn't you put up curtains?' They would be staring at the restored interior, its lexicon of new buzzwords: dado rails and Adams fireplaces, original plasterwork, genuine Victoriana, bookcases by Habitat. Still the remnants of the streets could bite back. There was an old man on the corner by the Newt. An old man being persecuted — rightly or wrongly — but persecuted nonetheless. A child was doing the taunting, watched by a couple who were wondering whether it was safe to get out of their car.

'You facking pervert. You're riding your facking grand-children, you ole cunt!'

'Your uncle rode your mother, you little toe-rag,' the old man rejoined. 'That's why your old man left. Who's your father then?'

And the child in tears, roaring at the silhouette of the old man as he disappeared behind the glass of the slammed door, 'You facking pervert!'

And the young professionals deciding that it wasn't perhaps the best time to sample that new Beaujolais.

From the beginning I saw in these incidents a victory of sorts, having always had an affinity with the pyrrhic myself.

I got to know the guv'nor of a pub on the other side of the Junction. I wandered in there by mistake the same night I'd

visited the pub Del and Tel drank in on the Falcon Road. I
had a woman with me. The interior of the pub hadn't
changed but the man with the pit-bull seemed to be in
complete control. He served us a drink and then, for no
discernible reason, told us to leave. 'Don't even facking finish
it,' he said, the pit-bull salivating on a short leash. The smell
of overheated feral dog was overwhelming. We backed out of
the place as the other customers laughed in our wake. We
walked about half-a-mile before our breathing came close to
regular again. Then we entered the nearest pub. Breslin was
standing behind the bar, wiping a glass with his shirt-tails. We
hit it off straight away. He was from Kinnegad or some place
like that. He had, as a man once said to me, a great welcome
for himself. He was expansive, the master of all he surveyed.
Old Paddies and Cockneys he told me were his customers. All
they wanted was continuity midst all the changes going on.
Maybe he was right or maybe he was just being ironic,
because he had, more than anyone else I'd met, an innate
sense of the changes that were coming. He was well aware
that a pub gov'nor was still a revered figure who represented
continuity. It took a few bob to put a pub behind you. A
guv'nor wasn't just a manager. He was king of his own castle.
He was landlord of all he surveyed, spigots and bottles,
furnishings and customers alike. He controlled an arcane
world. He was a master of alchemy, knowing just the right
amount of water a keg of beer might take and how to lace
spirits: and always the proportionate distance he needed to
maintain from his customers.

The problem with Breslin was that he only represented
some of this, the darker side. Oh, he was an alchemist of the
highest order — his cellar, when I saw it, represented an
approximation of a high-tech science lab; there were funnels
and tubes running everywhere. He was however the antithesis
of continuity. He was on his fourteenth pub in eighteen years
in the business. It was apparent even then — particularly

then when a publican was still expected to stand for personal rectitude and sobriety — that this was a war of attrition of sorts in which there could only be one winner. Or at least that's what it looked like at the time.

I liked him just the same, even though he was on the make. And there was nothing furtive about him in that respect: he spelled it out. He cut a dash, looked the part, with his Havana Cigars, his loud ties and his suits, the pin-stripe as subtle as a zebra-crossing. He was like an old penny caught up in a modern pub video-game. It was Breslin who fixed me up with work, just as the summer drew to an end. I had all but spent what was the price of a small house by then, meandering daily about London looking for some form of resolution to a question I couldn't quite frame.

What was I at? If I hadn't the cheap roof over my head I might have ended up on Shepherd's Bush Green. It was like I was waiting on the earth to tilt on its axis, apocalypse to pour from the skies. I went to the benefit for Lonesome Tom and was shocked at what I found there. He'd failed and what I saw frightened me: the stench of mortality, the knowledge that what he was fighting was ineluctable, gnawing its way through him like an army of termites. A white lie was what he wanted and I told him one. I told him he looked good. He had a new suit that fitted him well but the shirt he was wearing was an old one. His neck was lost in it. His face glowed, the result I guessed of whatever treatment he was getting. His big hands looked the width of my wrists. He was all angles and protruding bones, a witness to his own withdrawal from what he'd always found vital — Old Holborn, Players untipped and light & lager. For the night he was allowed to sip pints of weakened shandy, in moderation he told me ruefully. 'Come round the house,' he said, as I left the Catholic Club that night. 'Come round the house, we'll talk, have a few cans. I could do with the company. All the women,' he said. Smiling over at his wife and daughters. I spoke to his wife and promised her I would visit. She told me he always thought of me as a son.

I never did visit. I eventually consoled myself that he might have believed I'd returned to Germany. What could I have said to him, my tongue swollen in my mouth? It was an easy enough decision to make at the time. But I deluded myself. All he had wanted was some stories about tying steel on crawling shutters. That was how he realised the world, through stories, by bearing witness to things: remembering. That night he reminded me of myself and Diffley and the dumper stuck in the tunnel at the Airport. He laughed.

The oddest things can come to haunt you, a minor wrong not righted. In a work's canteen once I referred to someone as a man who would call a spade a spade. It was a casual comment, throwaway, but there was a black man sitting opposite me and I remember the look of anger, of disdain, in his eyes. He said nothing. There were three of us. No one else noticed but I still remember it. The worst things are often unintentional. So now I remember all the time how I failed as a witness, was a disloyal friend. I heard he was dead a few months later. Overheard it in a pub conversation. He was referred to as a great man, which he was because he was sympathetic and true to what he believed in. The night I heard I felt I was fumbling at things. I looked down at my hands which were stiff after a day's work, stiff and blunted and useless.

I was, through all that time, completely unsettled, riven by doubts about my own intent. Most of the people I knew were finding some focus to their lives, were in relationships. Those who weren't all said that they should be doing something other than what they were doing. They were like waiters in Los Angeles, awaiting discovery — the next audition. I walked all over London, following the canals and the river. I walked through graveyards that were bigger than the town I came from. Irrevocably, I was drawn to the places where men congregated for work, Hammersmith, Seven Sisters, Camden Town. The crowds of men had thinned out. Here and there were faces I half-remembered — but far more were missing. There were increasing numbers of young men, tyros in turned-down Wellingtons, concrete splattered, aiming kicks at thin air, vying to impress one another, cupping cigarettes against a non-existent wind in the dying days of that summer. I thought about returning to Germany. I heard nothing from the old crowd. In desperation, one Monday, I went down around the Bush Green and Furnival Gardens to see if Tipperary Tommy might have reappeared. Nobody knew anything about him, they were reluctant to talk. It was like he'd offended them.

Winter was coming slowly, unlike Germany where it galloped in after September. The day Breslin offered me work I'd walked from Hampstead Heath back to South London. I stood on the Heath and looked at the roofs below me glinting, like oil on water, in the first hoar frost. There seemed a natural dying fall about things.

Breslin wanted me behind the jump. I told him I had no notion of bar work. He didn't push the idea, but at the same time he gave me to understand that it was something he would be revisiting. I then got a start at the only type of work that was going then — renovation. The money was bad, paltry after Germany. The Irish subbie who took me on spoke about salary, about a career structure and benefits. All of this was new to me — it was the new language, the new hegemony of economic speak. I didn't ask him to elaborate. I was back where I'd started, tearing down ceilings, choking on soot and ancient horse hair, scratches like tramlines on my hands and arms. There was dope and the pub after work like a Stygean river — infinite forgetfulness.

I'd heard an Irish politician once saying there was no need for any of us to be ashamed of exile any longer. Yet exile was a political condition, I thought, the result of the failure of politics. The politician said we were exporting an educated workforce. But he wasn't sending many of them round the back of Earls Court, where I was working. He could have joined me at any time, with a plastic bag full of debris on his back and another empty skip on the street — like Dante's ninth circle — with a cadre of the most ignorant men his country had ever exported to keep him company. Self-styled muck savages. Not even intelligent enough to keep their mouths closed. But I'd known this before I started. On one of my walks I went into Biddy Mulligans in Kilburn on a Monday morning. There was one other customer in the bar. The barman was obviously hungover, blinking against the daylight that leaked through the greasy window panes. I ordered a light & lager, by then a drink that came from another age: I had to tell him what it was. I opened the paper out on the bar and heard the other customer lurch towards me. He burped and bumped into me. There was no denying he was Irish. I looked at him and he belched again, in my face. I took my drink and the paper and moved down the bar. He followed me and banged into me again.

We went up to Dalston to dig out the footings for an extension. Why use a machine, the subbie said, labour was plentiful. It was also cheap. He told me I had a future as he inspected the disconsolate bunch of men he employed. 'Take Joe with you,' he said. 'Joe's a good man.'

Joe was the subbie's brother which leavened the fact he was useless. The plumber swore he'd seen him looking at the drawings in the pub at lunchtime, holding them upside down. That bit of confusion resulted in a trench that went off in the wrong direction. Another time he'd put gloss on an antique teak door, destroying it. Primo Levi once wrote that 'Loving your work represents the best, most concrete approximation of happiness on earth.' But I wasn't that ambitious. Like everyone else of any merit I knew, work was, at best, a way to avoid life's other freight. Dalston held out the promise of new ground and the open air. The promise of heavy digging.

The problem with Joe was almost geographical. He had never left whatever part of Meath he came from — it dominated his imagination. I thought of Diffley's comment about men tethered to Hammersmith Broadway, their idea of a good read the *Donegal Democrat* or the *Western People*. Joe — weak as he might have been on geography — had a sense of priorities, and breakfast was top of that list. I thought we might as well get it out of the way. We'd go to eat so and Joe would complain about the Greeks. I'd explain that there were no Greeks around Dalston. Dalston was Turkish, Finsbury Park was Greek. He'd say like Holloway Road is Kerry and Harlsden is Mayo? That wasn't accurate either but I'd agree. I was generalising anyway. Then he'd give out about the lack of choice in the café, like he had some fundamental grip on Thatcherism, its language infecting everything. The job in Dalston continued like that. Nepotism had made Joe the boss or so he thought. He marked out the footings in the wrong place. I refused to dig and he went off to phone his brother. The brother arrived and told him to let me do the tasty work. Joe reluctantly agreed. We began digging. Then he had to go to sign on — which meant he had to cross the city. The next day he spent most of his time in the bookies. I knew I'd have to do something about him, but as it happened he landed himself in trouble.

One of the old boys who did an odd shift for Joe's brother drank in Breslin's place. He was called Hughie Jackson but everyone had forgotten that. He was always in the same spot at the top of the bar. Once, when some wit inquired if he believed in *déjà-vu*, Hughie replied, 'Did you ask me that before?' So that's what he was called — Déjà-Vu. All he wanted was a few bob to keep himself ticking over. He was an odd character, a man who knew an awful lot about contemporary music. He claimed to have seen Elvis down south when he was in America. Anyhow, he was found dead outside his flat one weekend. Everybody was shocked. We then realised that nobody knew that much about him. Joe took a proprietorial interest in Déjà-Vu's funeral. He was a Meath man after all, who came from the next parish to Joe. So I took Joe up to Breslin's to make the arrangements. McEvaddy, one of Breslin's regulars, held a collection to cover a few drinks on the day of the burial. I paid my few bob and left it at that. There was no sign of Joe over the next few days. I had to finish the footings on my own. I wouldn't say I was worried about him but I was curious as to how it took four days to arrange a funeral. On the Saturday morning after work I went up to Breslin's place. McEvaddy and another man were ensconced on bar-stools in the corner where Déjà-Vu used to sit. They looked like they'd been there all night. I asked them what had happened with the burial.

'Oh that,' McEvaddy said.

'Yeah that,' I agreed.

'Well,' he says, 'you know the way Déjà-Vu was — all he wanted was to be buried back yonder.'

This was news to me.

'Aye,' he says, 'and that boy you brought up here ... what do you call him ... Joseph wasn't it? Well it was all he could do to give Déjà-Vu what he wanted.'

'All Déjà-Vu wanted,' McEvaddy's pal said, like an echo.

'That,' says McEvaddy, 'or a pink Cadillac. He was a great Elvis fan. There weren't many men of that generation liked Elvis at all.'

'Yeah,' his friend agreed, 'Elvis. Do you mind the time Déjà-Vu got up on the stage in the Dagmar Castle and sang "Suspicious Minds"?'

I was getting impatient with their reminiscing. I wanted

to know what had happened to Joe. So I said, 'He was buried then, in the wind-up, was he?'

'God no! Sure isn't that what I'm getting at,' McEvaddy said, 'that Joseph fella you brought up here — when he heard Déjà-Vu wanted to be buried beyond, didn't he phone his brother?'

'His brother the subbie?' I interrupted.

'No, Déjà-Vu's brother back yonder. Didn't Joseph know him? Anyways, he explains to him about the death. Didn't knock a spark off your man. "So what do you want me to do?" he says. Well, your friend Joseph says that he'd like him to bring the body back. Well your man turns out to be tight. He wasn't having that. They had a row, so they did. I was here listening to them at it on the phone.'

'So Déjà-Vu got buried here then,' I said.

'Well that's what I'm trying to tell you and you keep interrupting. Your man Joseph, he convinces the brother to go some way. They agree if we could get the body back as far as Dublin — the vegetable market there — the brother'd take it over. So what did Déjà-Vu's brother do? He said he'd have him cremated so he'd be a handy size for sending back on a vegetable wagon or something … Them foreign vegetables I suppose.'

'Only Déjà-Vu didn't want to be burned,' McEvaddy's friend said.

'No — that's for sure,' McEvaddy agreed, 'he didn't want to be burned. He wanted to be buried back yonder.'

McEvaddy looked at me.

'And before you interrupt,' he said, 'he wasn't burnt either. That's where your friend Joseph comes in. For what did he do only break into the crematorium up there in Golders Green — for wasn't Déjà-Vu lined up for incineration the next day — breaks in, he does himself and a townie of his and steals the body.

I was taken aback. 'So where is it now?' I said.

'Now that's the problem,' McEvaddy's friend said. 'You see Joseph ... well he takes the body down to King's Cross, into one of them yards there where the lorries are going all over the place. He ups her and puts her onto the back of a wagon ...'

'So Déjà-Vu's in Ireland now?' I said.

'Onto the back of a wagon,' the friend continued as if I hadn't interrupted. 'So far, so good, you might think, except for that wagon was going to some place called Ankara in Turkey. That's where Déjà-Vu is now.'

There was a few seconds' silence. We all looked at our pints as if in respect.

'God knows,' said McEvaddy, 'what them Turks'll make of him?'

'What about ... ?' I began.

'Oh, the few bob's still safe. Breslin has it. We'll have a few pints one of the nights.'

'No,' I said, 'I'm not worried about the money. What happened to the Joseph fella?'

McEvaddy smiled. 'He's lying low,' he said, 'if you'll forgive the expression. The police want him to help them with their inquiries.' He took a sip of his pint. 'God, he's pure innocent that fella — it's the father I blame for sending him over here like that.'

25

THE JOB HAD FINISHED IN DALSTON BUT THERE WAS NO END of work at the back of Earls Court. Joe's brother the subbie had employed two Glaswegian brothers. They looked so alike I took them for twins, although it turned out there was a year between them. One of them was married with a hyperactive child — before there was such a diagnosis. They were called Frank and John. The names were interchangeable, a ruse to confuse any potential dole inspectors. The problem was it confused me: I could never get their names right — but they were powerhouses to work. Everybody on that job was called John or Mick, apart from Frank that is. The way the subbie was paying it was hardly surprising that they were all signing on. Cheap rent was keeping me on the straight and narrow.

I got a postcard from Brian, whose flat I had, who was by now in Paris. He said he wouldn't be back for another while. He'd met someone. He asked me to drop off a bottle of Black Bush at the landlord's house before Christmas. To keep on the right side of him. 'Let on it's from me,' he wrote. I asked around, as Black Bush was difficult to come by. Harrods Food

Hall, somebody advised, and that was how I came to be in Harrods, on Saturday, the week before Christmas that year — the year of the Harrods' bomb. Except that when the bomb went off I was already crossing Chelsea Bridge on my bicycle home. I heard it — a sound like the crunch of dry snow — and felt a brief compression of air behind me. I turned back to see the pall of grey smoke rising over Knightsbridge.

On The Northcote Road the market traders were just beginning to do business and I stopped to buy fruit from a stall-holder I vaguely knew. As he put my satsumas in a bag, I could hear the first news of casualties come through on the radio behind him. I strained towards it.

'Wot's up Pat,' he said, 'coming from 'Arrods then ?'

That afternoon I could hear the police cars and the ambulances screaming with great clarity in the frosty air. I dozed with the radio on — half-listening to the football commentary and starting awake as updated reports came through. Six people died that Saturday. It felt like it all had happened in a dream, felt distant and muffled. I started awake again late that evening. There was someone banging on the door. I went out into the hallway where I could see a shape lit from outside. It looked like a man on his own. I knew from the persistence of the knocking that he might depart but he would be back. Still, I made no move to answer. Then something dropped through the letter box and the shadow moved off. I heard footsteps retreating down the stairs. I picked up a postcard off the mat and almost laughed aloud with relief. I opened the door, went out onto the balcony and caught Diffley just as he made his way across the forecourt.

'Why didn't you answer the door?'

I made some excuse. He looked like he didn't believe it but he let the matter rest. We went for a drink. I took him down to Breslin's place, thinking he would enjoy Breslin. The bar was empty. Breslin told us that was hardly surprising,

given the night was in it. 'The bastards,' he said. It was typical
of them bringing their war over here and who suffered
anyhow but the likes of us? It was bad for business. 'Talking
about business,' he said, as an old couple came in and he went
off to serve them. When he came back to us, he grew
animated: he had some new-fangled yoke, he said, the
coming thing in pubs — karaoke. 'You have to be careful
with the material,' he said, 'judge it to suit the customers.'
This one had a few Paddy songs on it. He set it up later and
a customer got up on the stage and belted out a desultory
version of "The Fields of Athenry". Diffley and myself
argued. I said it was a bad song. He said he was minded to
agree but everybody else seemed to like it. 'They couldn't
surely all be wrong?' he said. 'That's like saying Simon Le Bon
or Wham or whoever are good because they sell records,' I
said. It was like old times. But Diffley took an immediate
dislike to Breslin. The antipathy was almost palpable and it
was shared. I could see that he wasn't sorry to see us leave.
Diffley wanted to go somewhere else, away from what he
called that maudlin, Plastic-Paddy shite. We went up to The
White Hart on Fulham Broadway.

I wanted to know what he had against Breslin. We'd
entered the public bar where the television was on. Diffley
asked them to turn it up. He said he would answer me later.
He was watching a report of a funeral in South Africa. There
was a phalanx of black people advancing up a dusty road.
They were stomping and singing, the singing rhythmic and
emotional. Out of nowhere men in uniform appeared and
loosed dogs on them. The front ranks broke. There was
confusion and screaming. The reporter was saying something
which we couldn't make out. Somebody asked the barman to
change the channel. Diffley asked him to leave it for another
minute. The barman looked at him dubiously, then nodded.
On the television the reporter had finished his piece to
camera. We could hear the singing, chanting and stomping

that had been taken up again. Now it was coming from the rear of the phalanx that was already re-forming. 'They're some people,' Diffley said, as the barman switched over, 'they'll never be beaten. People that can sing like that can't be beaten.'

The usual three Irish musicians were on the stage in the back bar. Their music seemed defiant that night. There was a notion that they were playing just for us — in a place where everyone knew each other. What they were expressing was mutual relief that they had this to turn to — some emblem of shared values. This was in the music, as it always was, the notion of home, whatever that was — and home meant a better place. There was no discussion of what had happened that afternoon, up the road from there. Nothing beyond muttered banalities, 'Terrible wasn't it?' We had all shrunk back among ourselves, hermetically — you left your politics at the door. It was not a good time to be Irish. What had happened at Harrods invoked worse times, the 1970s, the Birmingham, Woolwich and Guildford bombs, the relief many of those in the bar would have felt when the Balcombe Street gang were finally caught after they'd terrorised the West End, bombing and shooting up restaurants for the best part of four months.

Diffley had been non-committal all night. I'd pushed him on where he'd been for the past twelve months. He said he'd spent some time in a factory in the south of Germany, making boxes for pre-cast concrete. Then he'd come back to London. There wasn't an awful lot about, he said. He'd got very good at the *Guardian* crossword. I asked him why he'd taken a turn against Breslin. He sipped his pint and thought about it for a long time.

'I don't know,' he said, 'I'm not like you though. I've had enough of subbies.'

'Breslin's no subbie,' I said.

'The mentality's the same. The same blood-sucking mentality. Take it out of their own all the time. The fact he's serving drink doesn't change that. Where are you working now? The same auld thing isn't it? For less money than you should be getting. Shite work.' He was spitting the words out between his teeth.

'It's just a job,' I said, weakly. I was growing angry with him. I thought he was patronising me. 'Who gives a fuck?'

'That's just the point,' he said, 'it's what you do marks you. You're the one who's been going on about the greeshens you have to work with. Are you trying to tell me you're happy at that job now?'

'Oh for fuck's sake.'

'Look — it's not just you — it's me as well. All I'm saying is that there's other things out there.'

'What do you mean by other things? Office work is it?'

'No.'

'What then? What are you on about?'

'What I mean is who's going to remember you for the fall you're able to put on a load of concrete? Digging,' he said, 'you'd be as well-off digging your back garden in your own time.'

But that wasn't good enough. I knew he was thinking of something else so I pushed him on it. 'What other things?'

'Other things like politics I suppose. Knowing why you're doing what you're doing.'

I acted wilfully ignorant. 'Politics my arse,' I said. 'I'm doing what I'm doing for a week's wage. Do you think Garret FitzGerald or Charlie Haughey's lying awake at night worrying about me pulling down ceilings?'

'That's not what I mean and you know it. That's not real politics.'

'Oh — so what happened in Harrods today is politics is it? It's got real bodies to prove it.' I'd raised my voice. The barman was looking at me. Diffley lowered his. We were hissing at each other.

'What happened in Harrods today was wrong. But there's

more to it than that. If there was six people dead in Belfast, me and you wouldn't be sitting here talking about it.'

'Yeah,' I said, 'the likes of me could be pulled in for that. That's what it means when they bring their war over here.'

'Exactly my point. The boys who are in for Birmingham and Guildford did nothing wrong.'

This was classic Diffley. He was bending my argument to suit his own. Twisting my words. There wasn't hardly an Irishman in London who believed the Birmingham Six and Guildford Four were anything other than innocent. A cursory reading of their background made that blatantly obvious. The Irish Government showed little interest in their cases and the British were intransigent as ever.

'No,' he went on, 'they did nothing wrong but they serve a purpose. They're a warning to us. They say if we don't keep our mouths shut and watch our step, this is what will happen to us. They're like hostages to fortune for our good behaviour.'

'I'm not very good at this,' he went on, 'but look at us. Look at the likes of Breslin. He says it's bad for business. Jesus Christ — there's more to life than business.'

'I've heard all this before,' I said, 'there isn't a thing we can do. Do you think they'll listen to the likes of us?'

'That's not the point either — but do I think they'll listen? If we keep saying it they'll listen. They'll listen eventually. Those boys will be out in the next five years. I'll guarantee you that. But that's not what I'm saying. That's only one small part of it.'

'Jesus Christ, what are you saying then? Will you say what you're saying?'

'What I'm trying to say is that we have to look at what we're at, as a people I mean.'

'Oh yeah, we the people,' I snarled. He ignored me.

'The way we look at things. The way we glorify work we're not being half-paid for. The way we let the subbies get away with it. Talking about big money that's only there for a

few months. You only have to go up to the hostel in Camden
Town and see the results of that type of talk — all them old
boys up there wasted from drink and not a pension between
them.'

I thought it was typical of Diffley to get interested in
workers' rights just as unions were going out of fashion.

'Jasus Christ,' I said, 'you're the boy that used to go on
about the poetry of work.'

He nodded. 'And I was wrong,' he said. 'Do you think the
Green Murphy ever went on about the poetry of work? The
poetry of money more like.'

We were interrupted. The barman tapped me on the
shoulder and raised his fingers to his lips. The National
Anthem was playing. Everybody was standing to attention.
We stood up. Diffley dug me in the ribs and whispered, 'This
is another thing. What's the point in this?'

What he was saying was making me increasingly angry. It
was making me angry because I felt it was aimed specifically
at me. I didn't doubt his sincerity. That was part of the
problem: he was telling me things I was in the process of
working out for myself. I could understand his reasoning but
the awkward streak in me said it had nothing to do with me.
I believed that all I wanted was a few bob in my pocket. I
could hear him yammering on about FitzGerald and
Haughey and Thatcher and how they were all the same. We
were outside on the street by this time. Usually the crowd
would hang around talking after the pub closed, even in cold
weather. But given the night that was in it everybody cleared
off home straight away. We were the only two left. We were
over at the crush barriers outside the tube station. It was
obvious that his earlier invitation back to Clapham had been
rescinded. You could have told that from the way we stood
apart from each other — the distance between us. He was
going his way and I was going mine. But I was determined to
have the last word. I cut off his diatribe.

'Sure all I'm in it for is a few pints at the weekend. Fuck all this political shite, man.'

He turned on me. I'd never seen him so angry. His voice was low and even.

'Drink,' he said, 'yeah that's it. Like one of them bollockses just off the boat.'

'Now hold on,' I said.

'No, I won't hold on. You won't listen. You say you're working with a shower of idiots — what does that make you then? They're the same age as you — it's just you're over here a long time and they've only arrived. You should know better. What have you left to learn on a building site?'

I said nothing. I was shaping up to hit him, but his tirade had taken me aback. I was looking for an opening. He knew the score well enough and he recognised what I was at.

'Don't do that,' he said, 'this isn't about lamping someone. That's your answer to everything. That or you'd walk away.'

He had his car door open and the keys were in his hand. He was still talking when I swung at him. He moved and I caught him with a glancing blow. He whanged off the door and slipped onto the pavement on all fours. I drew back my boot to bury it in him. He raised his hand.

'Don't do it,' he said, 'you'll only be sorry later.'

I stopped and looked about me. I could see a copper at the door of the police station up by the Chelsea ground. He was looking in our direction.

'You're one patronising bastard,' I sneered.

He pulled himself upright and I turned away. I walked back up the road.

'That's it,' he shouted, 'walk away. Like you did with Sligo Sheila. Like you did with that German girl.' I walked faster to get away from his taunts. 'What happened with Lonesome Tom anyway?' he shouted. 'You never told me that one.'

I heard his car start up and squeal away. It was a three-mile walk home. I was seething — as much with anger at myself as anything else. I'd been sorry after I tried to hit him but I couldn't say it. I should have helped him up and apologised. The situation had been recoverable. The sheer futility of it sickened me. The way I'd been drawn in and knew it even as I balled my fist. They way he'd known. How predictable it all was.

I took the back way, cutting down from Wandsworth Bridge. The streets were cold and near-deserted that night, and the few pedestrians who were about eyed each other warily. There was genuine fear about — as if time had been transfixed and the instant in which that bomb had detonated still lingered in the air. Strange emotions were footloose — what people were still out in the freezing night were like beasts frightened down from the mountainside by lightning. It was only when I got to the Northcote Road that I realised I'd been crying.

26

WE GUTTED THE BUILDING AT THE BACK OF EARLS COURT, myself and the two Scots boys, knocking down the internal walls and subdividing the building into glorified bed-sits. I remember the shock of each blow of the sledge hammer against those walls, day after day. Holding it high, pivoting backwards, transferring weight onto the back foot, the right hand sliding down the hammer as it swung until it was fully extended, in an arc — punching holes in the walls relentlessly.

Both of the Scots boys were serious gamblers, one of them on the horses and the other on slot machines. Frank could lose his day's money at breakfast. It certainly wasn't about winning: the jackpot in the machine where we ate breakfast was £2.50. He claimed he knew how the machines worked. The Council was promising him and his wife a three-bed basement flat with a back garden for the hyperactive youngster. If he ever got that, he said, then he'd save up and go to Vegas or Atlantic City, where there were wall-to-wall machines. He grew excited when he talked about the qualities of different one-armed bandits, it was a near science for him. He had a junkie's classic vacancy when it came to the machines. I used to watch him, staring dead-eyed across the shoulder of whoever was playing. When his turn came he'd almost ride the thing, straddling it, moving in motion with it. He told me you were better not thinking about them as machines at all, you had to gift them with personalities. He'd scoop up the first 50p it paid out and put it straight back in. That was what he called the sweetner, it makes you think you're on a roll. He said you should be able to tell by listening when it was going to pay out, you had to know the sequence of bells and lemons and all the other fruits. You had to know how to use the nudges. You could see it coming. The woman behind the counter was embarrassed listening to him. The machine started clanking and lit up and paid out and he began putting the £2.50 back into it.

The foreman on the job was from Wexford. Wexford Mick he was called, naturally. He was a gifted tradesman. One day he could take no more. The sun was shining and he too heard the siren call of the Bush Green. He cleared all the money out of the payphone, went home, got his accordion and disappeared. None of us blamed him. I was wondering how much longer I could stick the job. Then the subbie told me Joe was coming back.

All of this to-ing and fro-ing reminded me of Tipperary Tommy. There was no sign of him and no word from Ready-Mix either. He could be anywhere. I met Mick Coen by accident on the Holloway Road. I had his sister's number and had phoned looking for him several times. She was suspicious though and never passed a message to him. He was foreman on a hotel conversion up the West End: he had fifty chippies working under him. He was drinking less, he said, but the night I met him he must have skulled a half-bottle of vodka in a couple of hours. He made out it was meeting me, like it was for old times he was doing it. He was off to meet a woman he was seeing. By the time he'd left his eyes had filmed over, and he was grinning. I thought to myself how well I knew him. How good he was at it. How he could fool most people, that bland exterior he projected, as if any form of extreme emotion like anger or love was beyond him. As if he'd reached a perfect state where the only thing his arteries transported was diluted blood, the only thing his nerve endings responded to was the early-morning jump-start — the initial jolt alcohol delivered to the system. I felt like pinching him to see if he was real. He was driving that night. We were sitting on our own. The barman wiped the ashtray and used the same grimy rag to clean off the tabletop.

I went to see Breslin. He said he was glad to see me. I got the impression he meant particularly without Diffley. He didn't listen to anything I had to say. He was excited and animated, wittering on about change, as if an alien species were about to land and transport us off to a distant galaxy.

I had the feeling the soot from between the floorboards in those old houses would stain my skin forever. The television was turned on behind him, Margaret Thatcher was speaking, the sound turned down. In any case I was inured to hearing the same things over and over. There were openings for them who wanted to take advantage of them. The world was hardening up. The day of the dead man was gone. The subbie was in the ascendant. Bollocks talk was everywhere.

As for the aliens I was beginning to believe they were called entrepreneurs. But the Scots boys had a handle on this lingo. They used it ironically, describing themselves as small businessmen with cash-flow difficulties, forced to diversify. They were selling drugs to the Sloans who were moving into the area. I was spending more of my nights with them. They'd pound you out of it with drink. We went to a party round the corner from where we were working one Friday night. I could feel the grit of the site on my skin. I got talking to a woman there but left after a while, unable to interest myself in anything that was going on. I went back to the flat in Clapham, where I was still living on my own. I fell asleep on the couch. I hadn't slept in a bed for weeks. I never made it that far and whether the place was haunted or not I never found out either.

The next morning I was out on the road, mixing screed by hand. The two boys hadn't shown up and I had to mix it, carry it downstairs into the basement in buckets, spread, tamp and level it by myself. I wasn't in the best of humour. I saw the woman I'd spoken to the night before coming up the road with a man I'd seen at the party. They looked like they hadn't slept. She saw me and crossed over to talk to me.

'I thought it was you,' she said, 'is this what you do?'

'More or less,' I agreed.

'I've never met anyone who did anything like this before,' she said, running a hand through her marcelled hair. Reminding me how Lonesome Tom had told me about working near Camden Town tube station when he'd come over in the Fifties. There was a group of them sinking a shaft. It was a sweltering day and some of them had removed their shirts. A man without a shirt wasn't seen much then in public. He said a child had come up to them. Its mother on the other side of the road, screaming at the child to leave the animals alone, they might be dangerous.

The subbie wanted to know what the two Jocks were up to. Could they work, should he get rid of them? I said they were great workers. He wanted to know where they were. 'Signing on,' he said, 'I knows well what them boys is at.'

'They probably are signing on,' I agreed, 'they'd need to with the money they're getting.' He stalked off. Then he thought better of it. He came back and offered me a cigarette. Manholes, he said, what did I know about them. I told him I knew a lot.

'I'm starting two brickies to do the interior brickwork but

you can do the manhole if you want.' He rubbed his chin like it was something silky. I knew there was something else.

There was, his brother Joe was back.

'And those Jocks,' he said again before he left, 'are they druggies?'

I shook my head.

'I'm going to have to get rid of them anyway,' he said, 'what'd they be at? Smoking dope and mugging grannies when good men are working. What do they want — me to bring them round the money in bed of a Friday evening?'

The Scots boys were moving out of the Bush. They got a cheap flat down at The Elephant. Frank's wife wanted rid of him. I missed it at the party, they said. God the English'd get up on anything. There were men riding each other. 'All because of drugs,' John laughed as he tipped lines of heroin onto the cover of a Billy Connolly album. It was the coming business. His customers were demanding it. Dealing it put you on another plane altogether, you were mixing with the big boys. 'Fuck the work,' he said, 'fuck that toe-rag subbie. Fuck Mondays.'

I snorted a line. I could hear John going on to Frank about how he liked watching people get high. 'Let me see him,' he was saying. Everything that happened after that was peripheral. I was thinking that John was well into it as I sank back onto the bed, a warm beneficent glow taking hold of me. All my troubles ceased to matter. Everywhere was warm and everything was warm. I was awash in a penetrating heat. My bones were powdered. I wasn't there anymore, I was part of something greater than myself, a feeling or an emotion that enveloped the world. I had no value on time until I found myself clutching the sides of a toilet bowl, retching violently.

What happened that evening changed the discourse between me and the two Scots boys — it erected a barrier of suspicion. There was no reason for that. They knew it and I

knew it. Still it happened. They went on about horses for
courses and strokes for folks. I told them it had done nothing
for me. In truth it had. It had transported me to somewhere
else, which was all it was meant to do. The difficulty was that
I didn't like that place. I didn't want to be somewhere where
nothing mattered, where the frayed and tattered edges of
things were dulled and smoothed over. I saw something
positive, kinetic even, in the continual frustration and anger
I felt. I also knew that when I had first tried drink I hadn't
liked it. For that reason I wasn't prepared to persevere
snorting heroin, and end up feeling life pass by without me.
Like lying on my back in a boat in the sun, listening to the
waves flap dolorously against the gunwales — to no purpose
— as it drifted towards a slowly moving vortex. It was a life
best avoided. I didn't have the required genetic impulse for
addiction — not that kind of addiction at any rate.

But with John and Frank I'd closed a door. I'd managed
to carry off being a shuttering carpenter, a steel fixer and any
number of other jobs on site. I'd even passed myself off as a
foreman with men who were years older than I was. But I had
to draw a line. Everybody wanted to be somebody else.
Diffley wanted to change the world, the Scots boys wanted to
be big-time drugs dealers. Joe, by comparison, had a simple
need, he just wanted to be his brother.

I continued to cover for the two boys, not that it
mattered to them. They were no longer bothered about work.
When they were there, a BMW with smoked glass windows
would call for one of them and he'd disappear for the rest of
the day. The little I gleaned from them hinted at criminal
doings. The post office round the corner from the job was
robbed. The police were looking for two Rastafarians. Frank
told me that they never passed any remarks about a white
man driving a big car. He grinned to himself. He told me this
absent-mindedly and promptly forgot about it. Much of what
he said had a hollow ring to it, sounded like bravado. But

there was something more than just vacancy in it, there was also a sense of impending danger. The bottom feeders were casting envious looks upwards through the silt and the murk at what was above them. They were looking at something they thought they had a right to.

In the end the subbie didn't have to sack them — they just stopped showing up altogether. Frank had taken up with another woman. I'd see him in the distance occasionally, coming out of one of the pubs on Sinclair Road, at the top of the Bush Green, arm in arm with her. They were a mutual-aid society in the making, herself in a dirty fur-coat and her fishnets in shreds. I could hear her voice tear and shriek as she leant against him and the two of them tottered into the distance, swaying from right to left and back again, two steps forward and one back. Going home, as we said, by rail. I only saw John once after that. I met him on the road. He was wearing stovepipe jeans and a biker's jacket. It was a scorching hot day. His hair was peroxided and he had wrap-around shades on. He was listening to a Walkman, the sound turned up so loud heads turned towards him. '*London Calling/Now don't look to us/Phoney Beatlemania's bitten the dust.*' I doubt he even saw me.

I benched the manhole on a Monday and started the brick-work. There wasn't a trowel mark in the benching. It was as smooth as finished plasterwork. It took two days to do the brickwork. Thirty-six inch at the bottom, narrowing to nine inch. It came up above my waist. It was buttressed and as solid as a medieval castle. The sand and cement mix I made up for mortar was two and one, as strong as possible. It dried dark and the joints looked black against the deep red of the heavy engineering bricks. It looked like it would last forever. It was a monument of sorts, to myself and various other things that were on my mind, a monument like one of those big ones you'd see in a cemetery, up in Highgate or Stoke

Newington, all verdigris, weathered and overgrown, existing only for themselves, the names long worn off them. And those who were buried there forgotten. I knew what its tolerance was. There wasn't a pinhole in it from which water could leak. The bricklayers from upstairs heard about it and came down to inspect it.

'You're in the wrong game, mate,' one of them said.

The Clerk of Works, when he came, admired it. He walked in a circle round it before we backfilled it. 'Don't see many like this,' he said. 'In fact I've never seen one like this. Seems a shame to cover it up.' Still he lit his cigarette and flicked a match into the water we'd filled it with. He looked at me and grinned. The grin making it feel like an old game being played out between equal adversaries, the game of less significance than the fact that both sides had taken the field.

'I'll see you later no doubt,' he said.

I went out onto the street in front of the house. There was nothing left to do. The two brickies who were closing off doorways and knocking out new openings for windows had stopped for lunch. They had the jobs section of the *Evening Standard* spread out in front of them on the wall in the sunlight that had begun to warm the world. The Havelock was round the corner, it was near enough lunchtime and I had nothing else to do so I decided to go for a pint. Joe followed me. I was in such good humour I didn't even mind him. He'd tended me for the two days building the manhole. He'd hardly spoken a word. As we walked up the road he was telling me about the significance of what the Clerk of Works had done with the match. Telling me what I had explained to him months before. I was thinking to myself that if you were around long enough, every story you told would surely rebound to you. I was thinking too of Breslin.

I'd met him the previous Saturday. He'd taken me to see his latest acquisition, a pub called The Adversity at the far side of Islington, up near Chapel Market. He was as full of himself as ever. The pub in Clapham was changing, he said, there were Masons and Tories holding meetings in the room he had done up upstairs. They were a new type of customer altogether and they'd asked him to join.

'Which asked you to join?' I asked.

He laughed. 'Is there any difference?' he said.

Breslin was what the Cockneys called a bit of a spiv. He was the makings of a relic of the post-war era he'd never seen. He was in demand again, almost despite himself. He understood innately what he could get away with. He'd been all but washed up and he'd been handed a second chance, a better chance than all those other times. He had three pubs, The Adversity was going to be the fourth. The Adversity where several Cockney landlords had failed in the recent past was a landmark. If a covert tide had flooded somewhere and made Breslin newly buoyant, then he had his flagship and she was an architectural wonder, dating from the days when pubs had served as roadside inns. It had become a gin palace then and still retained the vaulted ceilings, engraved glass work and intricate plaster mouldings of its glory days. It had a turret topped off by a copper, onion-shaped dome. Inside, Breslin moved through the bar like a cologne-scented whirlwind, loudly dismissing the customers, a group of old-age pensioners and rag-bag anarchists, trying to make cheap beer last. They were to be pushed down towards King's Cross, he said. There were plenty of dodgy establishments on the Essex Road. 'Look at all the hoardings on Liverpool Road,' he said. 'Look at all the skips on the streets.'

He was an imperialist bestride his several worlds. The pub up in Kilburn was changing cheques for Paddies, withholding five per cent, thousands in it, he said. His other pub was out past the end of the Picadilly Line. There wasn't an Irishman near the place and what his English customers needed was distraction — there was nothing happening out there. He organised themed nights: Mexican nights where they all wore glue-on moustaches and drank watered-down tequila, or Spanish nights where the beer garden was transformed into a *playa* with the help of a load of knocked-off builder's sand. The locals loved it. In the end I agreed to have a look for myself and went up for the Fourth of July celebration, unaware that this was how Breslin inveigled you into his realm. He'd hit on a perfect plan. For £10 they could eat as many burgers and drink as much as they wanted. He sold two hundred tickets. It began to rain early that afternoon. He'd annexed the green opposite the pub, set up arc lights and early in the evening a group of majorettes plodded over and back in the mud to a tape of Philip Sousa's "Stars and Stripes Forever". There was a rock 'n' roll band who reprised a string of Fifties hits and he'd managed to get his hands on a load of cheap fireworks. The fireworks display was to be the highlight of the evening's entertainment. Everybody had been drinking steadily since the afternoon, drinking and masticating the tasteless burgers — I knew better than to ask where they'd come from — when Breslin put a tape of the soundtrack to *Apocalypse Now* on the stereo. It was all Wagner and the whop of helicopters. By that time the heavy rain had begun to gust across the green, each drop highlighted like a separate particle in the arc lights. There was an air of anticipation and a drum roll as the first of the fireworks was lit. Nothing happened for a few seconds and then there was a fizzle as a rocket took off, weakly skywards. It wasn't far above our heads when it began to stutter. We all watched as, caught by the wind and rain, it appeared to travel sideways for a bit before it was wholly extinguished and plunged back to earth. Nobody said anything as rocket after rocket followed the same course. Then Breslin began to laugh uproariously — his laughter drowning out whatever other pyrotechnics were going on. The crowd then began nervously to join with him. Within half-an-hour the whole debacle had been forgotten. The band ploughed manfully through Jerry Lee's "Great Balls of Fire" with no sense of irony and the customers were back at the bar again. They couldn't get enough of him. Breslin clapped me on the back. 'I love the English,' he said, 'they love a man who makes an effort.'

That Saturday in The Adversity he walked me through fully equipped catering kitchens, two function rooms, a cellar big enough to play football in, shaded space for a beer garden, family and staff quarters and, finally, the turret. I had never been in The Adversity although I'd often passed it and the turret had always interested me. He stopped on the stairway and searched a great key-ring for the required key, a big iron one with lugs like the handles of a tea cup on it. The lock groaned as he turned it and he stopped before pushing it open.

'Oh, I have things to tell you alright,' he said. He leant close to me. I could smell his expensive cologne. Something vaguely lemony. He had two Montecristo cigars in his top pocket and one in his sovereigned hand.

'You know,' he said, 'things are changing faster than we can keep up. They're talking about tills that are linked straight to head office like a telephone. When I started in this game it was every man for himself and no one came near you. Now they think they own you. They think the till roll is the best thing since they put gas in beer. They know fuck-all. They come and check the till rolls. What I does is put the till in the deep freeze. They never figured that one out. Five hours in the deep freeze and it lights up but it registers fuck-all. On a Friday night, in Kilburn, I have Benny upstairs in the kitchen with the Company's till. He's ringing away steady, but not as fast as the lads downstairs are ringing on my own till. They're smart. They can read a till roll but still the fuckers have no imagination.'

He stopped in the middle of his diatribe. There was, as I'd known since he asked me up there, something on his mind.

'Anyways,' he says, 'I'm not going to beat about the bush

here. You know I like you. I think you have a good head on your shoulders. I'm going to lay it on the line here — make you an offer. What I'm saying to you is I'll back you in this place. I'll put up the money. I'll front it — you pay me rent. We'll work something out.'

At this stage we were in the room in the turret. It had windows that went from floor to ceiling. It was empty apart from a table and a couple of battered chairs. He was talking about the potential to rent alone. Then he was going on about a former footballer who'd been done because he'd been got with a fortune in krugerrands behind a radiator in a pub somewhere else. I didn't know what to say. I could be as cynical as I liked but it was an incredibly generous offer. He threw open a window. The view from the turret in The Adversity was impressive — the way London is when you're young. It's a feeling that never wholly recedes. I could see from Hampstead Heath on one side way down to the Docklands, where they would eventually build Canary Wharf — like a great soul-less admonition, a monument to Breslin's world view.

'This,' he said, 'is the big time though. Biblical, you might say.'

The wind was tugging at the curtains as we stepped over towards the open window. We were standing almost on the ledge, staring down transfixed at the market traders setting up far below us.

'If you think of the time Your Man was tempted the three times,' he added. 'Except that this time there'll be no angel to pull you back if you stumble.'

I was on the roof at the back of Earls Court two days later, having finished that morning the perfect manhole nobody would ever see. I was thinking of Breslin's offer — thinking of the manhole as a valediction. I'd been thinking about it in the Havelock earlier, listening to Joe waffling on about the

Clerk of Works and the match and how much work his brother had and the way we could be doing this together for years to come. That was when the woman I'd met at the party came in. She stared at me as if she wasn't sure she knew me. Then she took her drink and her paper and came over and sat beside me.

'It's you,' she said.

'It's me,' I agreed. Then I noticed she was shaking like she was coming down from something. She was a good-looking girl in a very English, waifish way. I suppose she was older than me but I thought of most people round my own age as somehow younger. I thought the way she was going she'd end up very old before long. She looked like she was tired or had been badly scared. I asked her if she was alright. She thought about it and nodded. That was when she knew she knew something I didn't. She told me the two Scots boys had gone home the previous Friday. There'd been some sort of a fire in the flat at the Elephant. They were both dead. She said the police thought at first it had to do with gas. The place had been blown apart. 'If you could believe that,' she added.

'What do you mean, "if you could believe that"?' I asked

She said the police had questioned her twice and they wanted to talk to her again.

'It appears,' she said, 'that there was a petrol bomb in the microwave. Someone must have set the timer and got out a window. They were waiting for them. At least that's what the police believe now.'

'Who was waiting for them?'

'Well, look at who they were mixed up with?'

'Who were they mixed up with?'

'Geezers,' she said.

'Geezers?'

'Some bad geezers.' You'd think the way she said "geezers" it was something distasteful she'd picked up off the streets —

which, in her case, indeed it was. She said it like she had dirt
in her mouth.

'What geezers?'

'What does it matter?' she said. 'Dealers, West Indians,
Yardies. They were dealing and using. It was a fireball. They
hadn't a chance.' She said their mother had to come down
from Glasgow. 'The police couldn't tell them apart.'

That last, I could have told her, was a problem I'd always
had. I said nothing. She was shaking. She had taken on the
same bluish colour as the blood I could see in the veins
through her translucent skin. I put my arm round her
shoulder and she collapsed against me, sobbing. Her body
was wracked and she wheezed like a bellows. There was little
enough of her in it and what comfort she got crying against
my shoulder was of no earthly use to her. It was like she'd had
some deathly premonition. I could see that even Joe was at a
loss for words. He made his excuses and left me with her.
Drinking was doing her no good. Eventually I got her to leave
in a cab. She said she would go round to her daddy's house.
Her stepmother would be there. She said I was a good man.
I went back to work.

I was wondering where Diffley was and Ready-Mix and
Paddy Carn and Tipperary Tommy and Road-Kill — even
then. I could see that one world was becoming another. That
the world I'd walked into when I got in the van with Dunne
five years before was all but gone now. I glanced up and saw
that the two brickies were outside a phonebox across the
road. They were jumping up and down and clapping each
other on the back. I had their *Evening Standard.* They'd torn
the Jobs section out but I found the piece I wanted, about the
deaths of the two boys. MYSTERY EXPLOSION AT ELEPHANT
AND CASTLE. It was a short piece. They weren't named,
though the fact they were believed to be brothers was
mentioned. It said the Metropolitan Police hadn't ruled out
foul play. The men who died were known to them. It also said

the coroner had difficulty in identifying the bodies. I could hear the two brickies asking for me. Someone said 'McBride's above on the roof.' That was when they joined me. One of them was holding the jobs section.

'You've been in Germany. You can lay a brick mate,' he said. 'Fancy a trip to over there? Just heard there's a big long wall starting near Hamburg or Munich, somewhere over there, mate. Years of work in it, mate, and all on a price, a good price too and you know your way around, mate.' He stopped and looked at me. I must have been standing with my mouth open.

'Say what you want mate,' he said, 'it's the future.'

What was it Lonesome Tom used to say?

It came back to me then.

'There's no future in history.'

And definitely no indemnity in it either.